GLENCOE LANGUAGE

Teacher's Annotated Edition

PONCA CITY SENIOR HIGH SCHOOL

Grammar and Language Workbook

GRADE 9

Glencoe McGraw-Hill

New York, New York   Columbus, Ohio   Woodland Hills, California   Peoria, Illinois

Glencoe/McGraw-Hill

A Division of The **McGraw·Hill** *Companies*

Send all inquiries to:
Glencoe/McGraw-Hill
8787 Orion Place
Columbus, Ohio 43240-4027

ISBN 0-02-818295-2

Printed in the United States of America

7 8 9 10 024 08 07 06

Contents

Handbook of Definitions and Rules

PARTS OF SPEECH

Nouns

1. A **singular noun** is a word that names one person, place, thing, or idea: brother, classroom, piglet, and joy. A **plural noun** names more than one person, place, thing, or idea: brothers, classrooms, piglets, and joys.

2. To help you determine whether a word in a sentence is a noun, try adding it to the following sentences. Nouns will fit in at least one of these sentences:
   I know something about _____.   I know something about a(n) _____.
   I know something about **brothers**.   I know something about a **classroom**.

3. A **collective noun** names a group. When the collective noun refers to the group as a whole, it is singular. When it refers to the individual group members, the collective noun is plural.
   The class meets two days a week. (singular)
   The board of trustees come from all walks of life. (plural)

4. A **common noun** names a general class of people, places, things, or ideas: soldier, country, month, or theory. A **proper noun** specifies a particular person, place, thing, event, or idea. Proper nouns are always capitalized: **G**eneral **S**chwartzkopf, **A**merica, **J**uly, or **B**ig **B**ang.

5. A **concrete noun** names an object that occupies space or that can be recognized by any of the senses: tuba, music, potato, and aroma. An **abstract noun** names an idea, a quality, or a characteristic: courage, sanity, power, and memory.

6. A **possessive noun** shows possession, ownership, or the relationship between two nouns: Raul's house, the cat's fur, and the girls' soccer ball.

Pronouns

1. A **pronoun** takes the place of a noun, a group of words acting as a noun, or another pronoun.

2. A **personal pronoun** refers to a specific person or thing. **First person** personal pronouns refer to the speaker, **second person** pronouns refer to the one spoken to, and **third person** pronouns refer to the one spoken about.

	Nominative Case	Possessive Case	Objective Case
First Person, Singular	I	my, mine	me
First Person, Plural	we	our, ours	us
Second Person, Singular	you	your, yours	you
Second Person, Plural	you	your, yours	you
Third Person, Singular	he, she, it	his, her, hers, its	him, her, it
Third Person, Plural	they	their, theirs	them

3. A **reflexive pronoun** refers to the subject of the sentence. An **intensive pronoun** adds emphasis to a noun or another pronoun. A **demonstrative pronoun** points out specific persons, places, things, or ideas.
   Reflexive: **They** psyched **themselves** up for the football game.
   Intensive: **Freddie himself** asked Julie out.
   Demonstrative: **That** is a good idea! **Those** are my friends.

4. An **interrogative pronoun** is used to form questions. A **relative pronoun** is used to introduce a subordinate clause. An **indefinite pronoun** refers to persons, places, or things in a more general way than a noun does.
   Interrogative: **Which** is your choice?   With **whom** were you playing video games?

Relative: The cake **that** we baked was delicious.
Indefinite: **Everyone** has already voted.   **No one** should enter without knocking.

5. The antecedent of a pronoun is the word or group of words referred to by the pronoun.
   Ben rode **his** bike to school. (*Ben* is the antecedent of *his.*)

Verbs

1. A verb is a word that expresses action or a state of being and is necessary to make a statement. Most verbs will fit one or more of these sentences:
   We _____.   We _____ loyal.   We _____ it.   It _____.
   We **sleep.**   We **remain** loyal.   We **love** it!   It **snowed.**

2. An action verb tells what someone or something does. The two types of action verbs are transitive and intransitive. A transitive verb is followed by a word or words that answer the question *what?* or *whom?* An intransitive verb is not followed by a word that answers *what?* or *whom?*
   Transitive: Children **trust** their parents.   The puppy **carried** the bone away.
   Intransitive: The team **played** poorly.   The light **burned** brightly.

3. A linking verb links, or joins, the subject of a sentence with an adjective, a noun, or a pronoun.
   The concert **was** loud. (adjective)   I **am** a good card player. (noun)

4. A verb phrase consists of a main verb and all its auxiliary, or helping, verbs.
   My stomach **has been growling** all morning.   I **am waiting** for a letter.

5. Verbs have four principal parts or forms: base, past, present participle, and past participle.
   Base: I **eat.**   Present Participle: I am **eating.**
   Past: I **ate.**   Past Participle: I have **eaten.**

6. The principal parts are used to form six verb tenses. The tense of a verb expresses time.

Simple Tenses

Present Tense: She **eats.** (present or habitual action)
Past Tense: She **ate.** (action completed in the past)
Future Tense: She **will eat.** (action to be done in the future)

Perfect Tenses

Present Perfect Tense: She **has eaten.** (action done at some indefinite time or still in effect)
Past Perfect Tense: She **had eaten.** (action completed before some other past action)
Future Perfect Tense: She **will have eaten.** (action to be completed before some future time)

7. Irregular verbs form their past and past participle without adding *-ed* to the base form.

PRINCIPAL PARTS OF IRREGULAR VERBS

Base Form	Past Form	Past Participle	Base Form	Past Form	Past Participle
be	was, were	been	catch	caught	caught
beat	beat	beaten	choose	chose	chosen
become	became	become	come	came	come
begin	began	begun	do	did	done
bite	bit	bitten *or* bit	draw	drew	drawn
blow	blew	blown	drink	drank	drunk
break	broke	broken	drive	drove	driven
bring	brought	brought	eat	ate	eaten

Base Form	Past Form	Past Participle	Base Form	Past Form	Past Participle
fall	fell	fallen	run	ran	run
feel	felt	felt	say	said	said
find	found	found	see	saw	seen
fly	flew	flown	set	set	set
freeze	froze	frozen	shrink	shrank *or* shrunk	shrunk *or* shrunken
get	got	got *or* gotten			
give	gave	given	sing	sang	sung
go	went	gone	sit	sat	sat
grow	grew	grown	speak	spoke	spoken
hang	hung *or* hanged	hung *or* hanged	spring	sprang *or* sprung	sprung
have	had	had	steal	stole	stolen
know	knew	known	swim	swam	swum
lay	laid	laid	take	took	taken
lead	led	led	tear	tore	torn
lend	lent	lent	tell	told	told
lie	lay	lain	think	thought	thought
lose	lost	lost	throw	threw	thrown
put	put	put	wear	wore	worn
ride	rode	ridden	win	won	won
ring	rang	rung	write	wrote	written
rise	rose	risen			

8. **Progressive forms** of verbs, combined with a form of *be,* express a continuing action. **Emphatic forms**, combined with a form of *do,* add emphasis or form questions.
   Kari **is scratching** the cat.   Loni **has been washing** the walls.
   We **do support** our hometown heroes. (present)   He **did want** that dinner. (past)

9. The **voice** of a verb shows whether the subject performs the action or receives the action of the verb. The **active voice** occurs when the subject performs the action. The **passive voice** occurs when the action of the verb is performed on the subject.
   The owl **swooped** upon its prey. (active)   The ice cream **was scooped** by the cashier. (passive)

10. A verb can express one of three moods. The **indicative mood** makes a statement or asks a question. The **imperative mood** expresses a command or request. The **subjunctive mood** indirectly expresses a demand, recommendation, suggestion, statement of necessity, or a condition contrary to fact.
    I **am** overjoyed. (indicative)   **Stop** the car. (imperative)
    If I **were** angry, I would not have let you in. (subjunctive)

Adjectives

1. An **adjective** modifies a noun or pronoun by giving a descriptive or specific detail. Adjectives can usually show comparisons. (See Using Modifiers Correctly on pages 9 and 10.)
   cold winter   **colder** winter   **coldest** winter

2. Most adjectives will fit this sentence:
   The _____ one looks very _____.
   The **dusty** one looks very **old**.

3. Articles are the adjectives *a, an,* and *the.* Articles do not meet the above test for adjectives.

4. A **proper adjective** is formed from a proper noun and begins with a capital letter.
   Marijka wore a **Ukrainian** costume.   He was a **Danish** prince.

5. An adjective used as an **object complement** follows and describes a direct object.
   My aunt considers me **funny**.

Adverbs

1. An **adverb** modifies a verb, an adjective, or another adverb. Most adverbs can show comparisons. (See Using Modifiers Correctly on pages 9 and 10.)

   a. Adverbs that tell *how, where, when,* or *to what degree* modify verbs or verbals.
      The band stepped **lively**. (how)   Maria writes **frequently**. (when)
      Put the piano **here**. (where)   We were **thoroughly** entertained. (to what degree)

   b. Adverbs of degree strengthen or weaken the adjectives or other adverbs that they modify.
      A **very** happy fan cheered. (modifies adjective)   She spoke **too** fast. (modifies adverb)

2. Many adverbs fit these sentences:
   She thinks _____.   She thinks _____ fast.   She _____ thinks fast.
   She thinks **quickly**.   She thinks **unusually** fast.   She **seldom** thinks fast.

Prepositions, Conjunctions, and Interjections

1. A **preposition** shows the relationship of a noun or a pronoun to some other word. A **compound preposition** is made up of more than one word.
   The first group **of** students arrived.   They skated **in spite of** the cold weather.

2. Some common prepositions include these: *about, above, across, after, against, along, among, around, at, before, behind, below, beneath, beside, besides, between, beyond, but, by, concerning, down, during, except, for, from, into, like, near, of, off, on, out, outside, over, past, round, since, through, till, to, toward, under, underneath, until, up, upon, with, within, without.*

3. A **conjunction** is a word that joins single words or groups of words. A **coordinating conjunction** joins words or groups of words that have equal grammatical weight. **Correlative conjunctions** work in pairs to join words and groups of words of equal weight. A **subordinating conjunction** joins two clauses in such a way as to make one grammatically dependent on the other.
   Coordinating conjunction: He **and** I talked for hours.
   Correlative conjunctions: Russ wants **either** a cat **or** a dog.
   Subordinating conjunction: We ate lunch **when** it was ready.

4. A **conjunctive adverb** clarifies a relationship.
   He did not like cold weather; **nevertheless,** he shoveled the snow.

5. An **interjection** is an unrelated word or phrase that expresses emotion or exclamation.
   Wow, that was cool!   **Aha!** You fell right into my trap!

PARTS OF THE SENTENCE

Subjects and Predicates

1. The **simple subject** is the key noun or pronoun that tells what the sentence is about or who is performing the action. A **compound subject** is made up of two or more simple subjects that are joined by a conjunction and have the same verb.
   My **father** snores.   My **mother** and **I** can't sleep.

2. The **simple predicate** is the verb or verb phrase that expresses the action or the essential thought about the subject of the sentence. A **compound predicate** is made up of two or more verbs or verb phrases that are joined by a conjunction and have the same subject.

   The night **was** cold.   The guests **sang** and **danced** in the flower garden.

3. The **complete subject** consists of the simple subject and all the words that modify it.

   The bright lights of the city burned intensely.   **The cheerful, soothing fire** kept us warm.

4. The **complete predicate** consists of the simple predicate and all the words that modify it or complete its meaning.

   Dinosaurs **died out 65 million years ago.**   The sun **provides heat for the earth.**

5. Usually the subject comes before the predicate in a sentence. In inverted sentences, all or part of the predicate precedes the subject.

   There **are** two **muffins** on the plate.   Over the field **soared** the **glider.**

Complements

1. A **complement** is a word or a group of words that complete the meaning of the verb. There are four kinds of complements: direct objects, indirect objects, object complements, and subject complements.

2. A **direct object** answers *what?* or *whom?* after an action verb.

   Sammi ate the **turkey.** (Sammi ate what?)

   Carlos watched his **sister** in the school play. (Carlos watched whom?)

3. An **indirect object** receives what the direct object names.

   Marie wrote **June** a letter.   George Washington gave his **troops** orders.

4. A **subject complement** follows a subject and a linking verb and identifies or describes the subject. A **predicate nominative** is a noun or pronoun that follows a linking verb and further identifies the subject. A **predicate adjective** follows a linking verb and further describes the subject.

   Predicate Nominative: The best football player is **Jacob.**

   Predicate Adjective: The people have been very **patient.**

5. An **object complement** describes or renames a direct object.

   Object Complement: Ami found the man **handsome.**

   Object Complement: Carlo thought the woman a **genius.**

PHRASES

1. A **phrase** is a group of words that acts in a sentence as a single part of speech.

2. A **prepositional phrase** is a group of words that begins with a preposition and usually ends with a noun or a pronoun called the **object of the preposition**. A prepositional phrase can modify a noun or a pronoun, a verb, an adjective, or an adverb.

   One of my favorite meals is pigs **in a blanket.** (modifies the noun *pigs*)

   The supersonic jet soared **into the sky.** (modifies the verb *soared*)

   The love of a household pet can be valuable **for a family.** (modifies the adjective *valuable*)

   The child reads well **for a six-year-old.** (modifies the adverb *well*)

3. An **appositive** is a noun or a pronoun that is placed next to another noun or pronoun to identify it or give more information about it. An **appositive phrase** is an appositive plus its modifiers.

   My grandfather **Géza** takes me fishing.   C.S. Lewis, **my favorite author,** lived in England.

4. A **verbal** is a verb form that functions in a sentence as a noun, an adjective, or an adverb. A **verbal phrase** is a verbal plus any modifiers.

   a. A **participle** is a verbal that functions as an adjective: Gary comforted the **crying** baby.

   b. A **participial phrase** contains a participle plus any modifiers: **Thanking everyone,** my uncle began to carve the turkey.

   c. A **gerund** is a verbal that ends with -*ing*. It is used in the same way a noun is used: **Skiing** is a popular sport.

   d. A **gerund phrase** is a gerund plus any modifiers: **Singing the national anthem** is traditional at many sports events.

   e. An **infinitive** is a verbal that is usually preceded by the word *to*. It is used as a noun, an adjective, or an adverb: I never learned **to dance**. (noun) She has an errand **to run**. (adjective) I will be happy **to help**. (adverb)

   f. An **infinitive phrase** contains an infinitive plus any modifiers: My father woke up **to watch the news on television.**

5. An **absolute phrase** consists of a noun or a pronoun that is modified by a participle or a participial phrase but has no grammatical relation to the sentence.
His legs terribly tired, Honori sat down.

CLAUSES AND SENTENCE STRUCTURE

1. A **clause** is a group of words that has a subject and a predicate and is used as a sentence or part of a sentence. There are two types of clauses: main and subordinate. A **main clause** has a subject and a predicate and can stand alone as a sentence. A **subordinate clause** has a subject and a predicate, but it cannot stand alone as a sentence.

      main   sub.
The book bored me until I read Chapter 5.

2. There are three types of subordinate clauses: adjective, adverb, and noun.

   a. An **adjective clause** is a subordinate clause that modifies a noun or a pronoun.
   The students **who stayed after school for help** did well on the test.

   b. An **adverb clause** is a subordinate clause that modifies a verb, an adjective, or an adverb. It tells *when, where, how, why, to what extent,* or *under what conditions.*
   When the sun set, everyone watched from the window. (modifies a verb)
   Today is warmer **than yesterday was.** (modifies an adjective)

   c. A **noun clause** is a subordinate clause used as a noun.
   Who will become president has been declared.   I now remember **what I need to buy.**

3. Main and subordinate clauses can form four types of sentences. A **simple sentence** has only one main clause and no subordinate clauses. A **compound sentence** has two or more main clauses. A **complex sentence** has one main clause and one or more subordinate clauses. A **compound-complex sentence** has more than one main clause and at least one subordinate clause.

Simple: The stars fill the sky.
Compound: The plane landed, and the passengers left.
Complex: Although the children found the letter, they couldn't read it.
Compound-Complex: The earth is bountiful; we may destroy it if we abuse it.

4. A sentence that makes a statement is classified as a **declarative sentence**: The Cleveland Browns are my favorite team. An **imperative sentence** gives a command or makes a request: Please go to the dance with me. An **interrogative sentence** asks a question: Who would abandon a family pet? An **exclamatory sentence** expresses strong emotion: Look out!

SUBJECT-VERB AGREEMENT

1. A verb must agree with its subject in person and number.
Doli **runs.** (singular)   Doli and Abay **run.** (plural)
He **is** singing. (singular) They **are** singing. (plural)

2. In **inverted sentences** the subject follows the verb. The sentence may begin with a prepositional phrase, the words *there* or *here,* or the verb form of *do.*
Out of the bushes **sprang** the *leopard.*   There **is** never enough *time.*
Do those *pigs* **eat** leftover food?

3. Do not mistake a word in a prepositional phrase for the subject.
The **boss** of the employees **works** very hard. (The verb *works* tells the action of the boss.)

4. Make the verb in a sentence agree with the subject, not with the predicate nominative.
Her problem **was** the twins.   The twins **were** her problem.

5. A title is always singular, even if nouns in the title are plural.
***The War of the Worlds* was** a radio broadcast that caused widespread panic.

6. Subjects combined with *and* or *both* use plural verbs unless the parts are of a whole unit. When compound subjects are joined with *or* or *nor,* the verb agrees with the subject listed last.
Chocolate, strawberry, and vanilla are common ice cream flavors.
Peanut butter and jelly is a good snack.   Neither **books nor a briefcase is** needed.

7. Use a singular verb if the compound subject is preceded by the words *many a, every,* or *each.*
Every **dog and cat** needs to be cared for.   Many a **young man** has stood here.

8. A subject remains singular or plural regardless of any intervening expressions.
Gloria, as well as the rest of her family, **was** late.
The **players,** accompanied by the coach, **enter** the field.

9. A verb must agree in number with an indefinite pronoun subject.
Always singular: *each, either, neither, one, everyone, everybody, everything, no one, nobody, nothing, anyone, anybody, anything, someone, somebody,* and *something.*
Always plural: *several, few, both,* and *many.*
Either singular or plural: *some, all, any, most,* and *none.*
Is any of the **lemonade** left?   **Are** any of the **biscuits** burnt?

10. When the subject of an adjective clause is a relative pronoun, the verb in the clause must agree with the antecedent of the relative pronoun.
He is one of the singers who dance. (The antecedent of *who* is *singers,* plural: singers dance.)

USING PRONOUNS CORRECTLY

1. Use the **nominative case** when the pronoun is a subject or a predicate nominative.
She eats cake.   Is **he** here?   That is **I.** (predicate nominative)

2. Use the objective case when the pronoun is an object.
   Clarence invited **us**. (direct object)   Chapa gave **me** a gift. (indirect object)
   Spot! Don't run around **me!** (object of preposition)

3. Use the possessive case to replace possessive nouns and precede gerunds. Never use an apostrophe in a possessive pronoun.
   That new car is **hers**.   They were thrilled at **his** playing the violin.

4. Use the nominative case when the pronoun is a subject or a predicate nominative.
   We three—Marijian, his sister, and I—went to camp.

5. Use the objective case to rename an object.
   The teacher acknowledged **us**, Burny and **me**.

6. When a pronoun is followed by an appositive, choose the case of the pronoun that would be correct if the appositive were omitted.
   We the jury find the defendant guilty.   That building was erected by **us** workers.

7. In elliptical adverb clauses using *than* and *as*, choose the case of the pronoun that you would use if the missing words were fully expressed.
   Kareem is a better sprinter than **I**. (I am)   It helped you more than **me**. (it helped me)

8. Use a reflexive pronoun when it refers to the person who is the subject of the sentence. Avoid using *hisself* or *theirselves*.
   Jerry found **himself** in a mess.   The candidates questioned **themselves** about their tactics.

9. In questions, use *who* for subjects and *whom* for objects. Use *who* and *whoever* for subjects and predicate nominatives in subordinate clauses. Use the objective pronouns *whom* and *whomever* for objects of subordinate clauses.
   Who roasted these marshmallows?   **Whom** will you hire next?
   This medal is for **whoever** finishes first.
   The newspaper will interview **whomever** the editor chooses.

10. An antecedent is the word or group of words to which a pronoun refers or that a pronoun replaces. All pronouns must agree with their antecedents in number, gender, and person.
    Colleen's **friends** gave up **their** free time to help.   The **Senate** passed **its** first bill of the year.

11. Make sure that the antecedent of a pronoun is clearly stated.
    VAGUE: The people who lost their dogs stayed in their yards, hoping **they** would return.
    CLEAR: The people who lost their dogs stayed in their yards, hoping **the dogs** would
              return.

    INDEFINITE: If you park the car under the sign **it** will be towed away.
    CLEAR: If you park the car under the sign **the car** will be towed away.

USING MODIFIERS CORRECTLY

1. Most adjectives and adverbs have three degrees of form. The positive form of a modifier cannot be used to make a comparison. The comparative form of a modifier shows two things being compared. The superlative form of a modifier shows three or more things being compared.
   The year went by **fast**.   This year went by **faster** than last year.
   I expect next year to go by the **fastest** of all.

2. One- and two-syllable adjectives add *-er* to form comparative and *-est* to form superlative.

POSITIVE:	bold	happy	strong
COMPARATIVE:	bolder	happier	stronger
SUPERLATIVE:	boldest	happiest	strongest

3. For adverbs ending in *-ly* and modifiers with three or more syllables, use *more* and *most* or *less* and *least* to form the comparative and superlative degrees.

He was the **least** exhausted of the group.   She spoke **more** caringly than some others.

4. Some modifiers have irregular forms.

POSITIVE:	good, well	badly, ill	far	many, much	little
COMPARATIVE:	better	worse	farther	more	less
SUPERLATIVE:	best	worst	farthest	most	least

5. Do not make a double comparison using both *-er* or *-est* and *more* or *most*.

INCORRECT: That musical was the **most funniest** I have ever seen.
CORRECT: That musical was the **funniest** I have ever seen.

6. Do not make an incomplete or unclear comparison by omitting *other* or *else* when you compare one member of a group with another.

UNCLEAR: Joey has missed more school than any kid in the ninth grade.
CLEAR: Joey has missed more school than any **other** kid in the ninth grade.

7. Avoid double negatives, which are two negative words in the same clause.

INCORRECT: I have **not** seen **no** stray cats.
CORRECT: I have **not** seen **any** stray cats.

8. For clarity, place modifiers as close as possible to the words they modify.

MISPLACED: The fire was snuffed out by the storm **that we accidentally started**.

CLEAR: The fire **that we accidentally started** was snuffed out by the storm.

DANGLING: **To avoid the long walk,** a friend drove us.

CLEAR: **To avoid the long walk,** we were driven by a friend.

9. Place the adverb *only* immediately before the word or group of words it modifies.

Only Afi wants choir rehearsal next week. (No one but Afi wants rehearsal.)
Afi wants **only** choir rehearsal next week. (She wants no other rehearsal.)
Afi wants choir rehearsal **only** next week. (She does not want rehearsal any other week.)

USAGE GLOSSARY

a, an Use the article *a* when the following word begins with a consonant sound. Use *an* when the following word begins with a vowel sound.

a house   **an** understudy   **an** hour   **a** united front

a lot, alot Always write this expression, meaning "a large amount," as two words.

With his help, we will learn **a lot** about photography.

a while, awhile *In* or *for* often precedes *a while,* forming a prepositional phrase. *Awhile* is used only as an adverb.

Let us listen to the forest for **a while.**   The students listened **awhile.**

accept, except *Accept,* a verb, means "to receive" or "to agree to." *Except* may be a preposition or a verb. As a preposition it means "but." As a verb it means "to leave out."
I will **accept** all of your terms **except** the last one.

adapt, adopt *Adapt* means "to adjust." *Adopt* means "to take something for one's own."
Species survive because they **adapt** to new situations. My church will **adopt** a needy family.

advice, advise *Advice,* a noun, means "helpful opinion." *Advise,* a verb, means "to give advice."
I must **advise** you to never take Jakel's **advice.**

affect, effect *Affect,* a verb, means "to cause a change in, to influence." *Effect* may be a noun or a verb. As a noun it means "result." As a verb it means "to bring about."
Is it true that the observer can **affect** the results? (verb)
I have no idea what **effect** that may have. (noun)
How can the president **effect** a good approval rating? (verb)

ain't *Ain't* is unacceptable in speaking and writing. Use only in exact quotations.

all ready, already *All ready* means "completely ready." *Already* means "before or by this time."
We had **already** purchased our plane tickets, and we were **all ready** to board.

all right, alright Always write this expression as two words. *Alright* is unacceptable.
Because she is your friend, she is **all right** with me.

all together, altogether The two words *all together* mean "in a group." The single word *altogether* is an adverb meaning "completely" or "on the whole."
The hikers gathered **all together** for lunch, and they were **altogether** exhausted.

allusion, illusion *Allusion* means "an indirect reference." *Illusion* refers to something false.
Mr. Lee made an **allusion** to *The Grapes of Wrath.*   The magician performed **illusions.**

anyways, anywheres, everywheres, somewheres Write these words and others like them without a final *-s: anyway, anywhere, everywhere, somewhere.*

bad, badly Use *bad* as an adjective and *badly* as an adverb.
We watched a **bad** movie.   He sang the national anthem quite **badly.**

being as, being that Use these only informally. In formal writing and speech, use *because* or *since.*

beside, besides *Beside* means "next to." *Besides* means "moreover" or "in addition to."
Who, **besides** Antonio, will offer to sit **beside** the window?

between, among Use *between* to refer to or to compare two separate nouns. Use *among* to show a relationship in a group.
I could not choose **between** Harvard and Princeton.   Who **among** the class knows me?

borrow, lend, loan *Borrow* is a verb meaning "to take something that must be returned." *Lend* is a verb meaning "to give something that must be returned." *Loan* is a noun.
People **borrow** money from banks.   Banks will **lend** money to approved customers.
People always must apply for a **loan.**

bring, take Use *bring* to show movement from a distant place to a closer one. Use *take* to show movement from a nearby place to a more distant one.
Bring in the paper, and **take** out the trash.

can, may *Can* indicates the ability to do something. *May* indicates permission to do something.
Anyone **can** use a credit card, but only the cardholder **may** authorize it.

can't hardly, can't scarcely These terms are considered double negatives. Do not use them. Use *can hardly* and *can scarcely.*

continual, continuous *Continual* describes repetitive action with pauses between occurrences. *Continuous* describes an action that continues with no interruption in space or time.
We make **continual** trips to the grocery.   **Continuous** energy from our sun lights the sky.

could of, might of, must of, should of, would of Do not use *of* after *could, might, must, should,* or *would.* Instead, use the helping verb *have.*
That **must have been** the longest play ever!

different from, different than The expression *different from* is preferred to *different than.*
Baseball is **different from** the English sport of cricket.

doesn't, don't *Doesn't* is the contraction of *does not* and should be used with all singular nouns. *Don't* is the contraction of *do not* and should be used with *I, you,* and all plural nouns.
My dog **doesn't** like the mail carrier.   Bobsled riders **don't** take their job lightly.

emigrate, immigrate Use *emigrate* to mean "to move from one country to another." Use *immigrate* to mean "to enter a country to settle there." Use *from* with *emigrate* and *to* with *immigrate.*
Refugees **emigrate** from war-torn countries.   My great-grandfather **immigrated** to America.

farther, further *Farther* refers to physical distance. *Further* refers to time or degree.
Traveling **farther** from your home may **further** your understanding of different places.

fewer, less Use *fewer* to refer to nouns that can be counted. Use *less* to refer to nouns that cannot be counted. Also use *less* to refer to figures used as a single amount or quantity.
If **fewer** crimes were committed, there would be **less** misery in the world.
The box measured **less** than 100 cm².

good, well *Good* is an adjective, and *well* is an adverb.
That spot is a **good** place for a picnic.   We dined **well** that day.

had of Do not use *of* between *had* and a past participle.
I wish I **had eaten** my sundae when I had the chance.

hanged, hung Use *hanged* to mean "put to death by hanging." Use *hung* in all other cases.
In the Old West, many were convicted and **hanged**.   I **hung** my coat on the hook.

in, into, in to Use *in* to mean "inside" or "within" and *into* to indicate movement or direction from outside to a point within. *In to* is made up of an adverb *(in)* followed by a preposition *(to).*
The fish swim **in** the sea.   We moved **into** a new house last year.
The student walked **in to** see the principal for a meeting.

irregardless, regardless Always use *regardless. Irregardless* is a double negative.
Root beer tastes great **regardless** of the brand.

this kind, these kinds Because *kind* is singular, it is modified by the singular form *this* or *that.* Because *kinds* is plural, it is modified by the plural form *these* or *those.*
I love **these kinds** of desserts!   I do not feel comfortable with **this kind** of situation.

lay, lie *Lay* means "to put" or "to place," and it takes a direct object. *Lie* means "to recline" or "to be positioned," and it never takes an object.
I taught my dog to **lay** the paper at my feet and then **lie** on the ground.

learn, teach *Learn* means "to receive knowledge." *Teach* means "to impart knowledge."
I want to **learn** a new language and later **teach** it to others.

leave, let *Leave* means "to go away." *Let* means "to allow" or "to permit."
My guest had to **leave** because his parents do not **let** him stay up too late.

like, as *Like* is a preposition and introduces a prepositional phrase. *As* and *as if* are subordinating conjunctions and introduce subordinate clauses. Never use *like* before a clause.

I felt **like** a stuffed crab after the feast.   The pigeons flew away, **as** they always do when scared.

loose, lose Use *loose* to mean "not firmly attached" and *lose* to mean "to misplace" or "to fail to win."

You don't want to **lose** your nice pair of **loose** jeans.

passed, past *Passed* is the past tense and the past participle of the verb *to pass. Past* can be an adjective, a preposition, an adverb, or a noun.

He **passed** the exit ramp because he could not see the sign **past** the bushes.

precede, proceed *Precede* means "to go or come before." *Proceed* means "to continue."

We can **proceed** with the plans.   From a distance, lightning appears to **precede** thunder.

raise, rise *Raise* means "to cause to move upward," and it always takes an object. *Rise* means "to get up"; it is intransitive and never takes an object.

Raise the drawbridge!   For some, it is difficult to **rise** in the morning.

reason is because Use either *reason is that* or *because.*

The **reason** he left **is that** he was bored.   He left **because** he was bored.

respectfully, respectively *Respectfully* means "with respect." *Respectively* means "in the order named."

We **respectfully** bowed to the audience.

Abla, Héctor, and Shelly, **respectively,** play first, second, and third base.

says, said *Says* is the third-person singular of *say. Said* is the past tense of *say.*

Listen carefully to what she **says**.   I love what the keynote speaker **said**.

sit, set *Sit* means "to place oneself in a sitting position." It rarely takes an object. *Set* means "to place" or "to put" and usually takes an object. *Set* can also refer to the sun's going down.

Sit anywhere you would like.   Set the nozzle back in its slot before paying for the gas.

                                    Today the sun will **set** at seven o'clock.

than, then *Than* is a conjunction that is used to introduce the second element in a comparison; it also shows exception. *Then* is an adverb.

Julio hit more home runs **than** Jacob this year.   Call for help first, and **then** start CPR.

this here, that there Avoid using *here* and *there* after *this* and *that.*

This bunk is yours.

who, whom *Who* is a subject, and *whom* is an object.

Who first sang the song "Memories"?   To **whom** should I throw the ball now?

CAPITALIZATION

1. Capitalize the first word in a sentence, including direct quotes and sentences in parentheses unless they are contained within another sentence.

Shakespeare asked, "**W**hat's in a name?" (**T**his is from *Romeo and Juliet.*)

2. Always capitalize the pronoun *I* no matter where it appears in a sentence.

Because **I** woke up late, **I** had to race to school.

3. Capitalize the following proper nouns.

   a. Names of individuals, titles used in direct address or preceding a name, and titles describing a family relationship used with a name or in place of a name

   President Nixon   **George B**urns   **S**is   **S**ir **A**nthony **H**opkins   **U**ncle **J**ay

b. Names of ethnic groups, national groups, political parties and their members, and languages

African Americans   Mexicans   Republican party   Hebrew

c. Names of organizations, institutions, firms, monuments, bridges, buildings, and other structures

National Honor Society   Vietnam War Memorial   Brooklyn Bridge   Parliament

d. Trade names and names of documents, awards, and laws

Kleenex tissues   Declaration of Independence   Academy Award   Bill of Rights

e. Geographical terms and regions or localities

North Carolina   Arctic Ocean   Nile River   West Street   the South   Central Park

f. Names of planets and other heavenly bodies

Jupiter   Horsehead Nebula   the Milky Way

g. Names of ships, planes, trains, and spacecraft

Challenger   *Spirit of St. Louis*   USS *George Washington*

h. Names of most historical events, eras, calendar items, and religious terms

Fourth of July   Jurassic   Gulf War   Friday   Yom Kippur   Protestant

i. Titles of literary works, works of art, and musical compositions

"The Road Less Traveled" (poem)   *The Old Man and the Sea* (book)
Venus de Milo (statue)   *The Magic Flute* (opera)

4. Capitalize proper adjectives (adjectives formed from proper nouns).

Socratic method   Jungian theory   Chinese food   Georgia clay   Colombian coffee

PUNCTUATION, ABBREVIATIONS, AND NUMBERS

1. Use a period at the end of a declarative sentence and at the end of a polite command.

Robin Hood was a medieval hero.   Pass the papers to the front.

2. Use an exclamation point to show strong feeling or to give a forceful command.

What a surprise that is!   Watch out!   That's just what I need!

3. Use a question mark to indicate a direct question. Use a period to indicate an indirect question.

DIRECT: Who ruled France in 1821?
INDIRECT: Gamal wanted to know how much time was left before lunch.

4. Use a colon to introduce a list or to illustrate or restate previous material.

For my team, I choose the following people: Zina, Ming, and Sue.
In light of the data, the conclusion was not hard to obtain: Earth is not flat.

5. Use a colon for precise time measurements, biblical chapter and verse references, and business letter salutations.

10:02 A.M.   John 3:16   Dear Ms. Delgado:

6. Use a semicolon in the following situations:

a. To separate main clauses not joined by a coordinating conjunction

My computer isn't working; perhaps I need to call a technician.

b. To separate main clauses joined by a conjunctive adverb or by *for example* or *that is*

Cancer is a serious disease; however, heart disease kills more people.

c. To separate items in a series when those items contain commas

I have done oral reports on Maya Angelou, a poet; Billy Joel, a singer; and Mario van Peebles, a director and actor.

    d. To separate two main clauses joined by a coordinating conjunction when such clauses already contain several commas
According to Bruce, he spent his vacation in Naples, Florida; but he said it was a business, not a pleasure, trip.

7. Use a comma in the following situations:

    a. To separate the main clauses of compound sentences
She was a slow eater, but she always finished her meal first.

    b. To separate three or more words, phrases, or clauses in a series
Apples, oranges, grapefruit, and cherries are delicious.

    c. To separate coordinate modifiers
The prom was a happy, exciting occasion.

    d. To set off parenthetical expressions
He will, of course, stay for dinner.   Mary, on the other hand, is very pleasant.

    e. To set off nonessential clauses and phrases; to set off introductory adverbial clauses, participial phrases, and long prepositional phrases
Adjective clause: The bride, who is a chemist, looked lovely.
Appositive phrase: The parade, the longest I've ever seen, featured twelve bands.
Adverbial clause: After we had eaten, I realized my wallet was still in the car.
Participial phrase: Laughing heartily, Milan quickly left the room.
Prepositional phrase: At the sound of the final buzzer, the ball slid through the hoop.

    f. To separate parts of an address, a geographical term, or a date
1640 Chartwell Avenue, Edina, Minnesota   September 11, 1982

    g. To set off parts of a reference
Read *Slaughterhouse-Five*, pages 15–20.   Perform a scene from *Hamlet*, Act II.

    h. To set off words or phrases of direct address and tag questions
Sherri, please pass the butter.   How are you, my friend?   We try hard, don't we?

    i. After the salutation and close of a friendly letter and after the close of a business letter
Dear Richard,   Sincerely,   Yours,   Dear Mother,

8. Use dashes to signal a change in thought or to emphasize parenthetical matter.
"Remember to turn off the alarm—oh, don't touch that!"

9. Use parentheses to set off supplemental material. Punctuate within the parentheses only if the punctuation is part of the parenthetical expression.
I saw Bill Cosby (he is my favorite comedian) last night.

10. Use brackets to enclose information inserted by someone besides the original writer.
The paper continues, "The company knows he [Watson] is impressed."

11. Ellipsis points, a series of three spaced points, indicate an omission of material.
The film critic said, "The show was great . . . a must see!"

12. Use quotation marks to enclose a direct quotation. When a quotation is interrupted, use two sets of quotation marks. Use single quotation marks for a quotation within a quotation.
"This day," the general said, "will live on in infamy."
"Yes," the commander replied. "The headlines today read, 'Allies Retreat.'"

13. Use quotation marks to indicate titles of short works, unusual expressions, and definitions.
"The Gift of the Magi" (short story)   "Ave Maria" (song)
Large speakers are called "woofers," and small speakers are called "tweeters."

14. Always place commas and periods *inside* closing quotations marks. Place colons and semicolons *outside* closing quotation marks. Place question marks and exclamation points *inside* closing quotation marks only when those marks are part of the quotation.
"Rafi told me," John said, "that he could not go."
Let me tell you about "Piano Man": it is a narrative song.
He yelled, "Who are you?"
Did she say "Wait for me"?

15. Italicize (underline) titles of books, lengthy poems, plays, films, television series, paintings and sculptures, long musical compositions, court cases, names of newspapers and magazines, ships, trains, airplanes, and spacecraft.
The Last Supper (painting)   *Bang the Drum Slowly* (film)   *Roe v. Wade* (court case)
Titanic (ship)   *Time* (magazine)   *Boston Globe* (newspaper)

16. Italicize (underline) foreign words and expressions that are not used frequently in English and words, letters, and numerals used to represent themselves.
Please discuss the phrase *caveat emptor.*
Today, *Sesame Street* was sponsored by the letters *t* and *m* and the number *6.*

17. Add an apostrophe and *-s* to all singular indefinite pronouns, singular nouns, plural nouns not ending in *-s,* and compound nouns to make them possessive. Add only an apostrophe to plural nouns ending in *-s* to make them possessive.
anyone**'s** guess   the dog**'s** leash   the women**'s** club
student**s'** teacher   singer**s'** microphones   runner**s'** shoes

18. If two or more people possess something jointly, use the possessive form for the last person's name. If they possess things individually, use the possessive form for both names.
mom and dad**'s** checkbook   Carmen**'s** and Sumil**'s** projects

19. Use a possessive form to express amounts of money or time that modify a noun.
a day**'s** pay   fifty dollar**s'** worth   a block**'s** walk

20. Use an apostrophe in place of omitted letters or numerals. Use an apostrophe and *-s* to form the plural of letters, numerals, and symbols.
cannot is *can't*   *do not* is *don't*   1978 is *'78*
Mind your **p's** and **q's**.

21. Use a hyphen after any prefix joined to a proper noun or a proper adjective. Use a hyphen after the prefixes *all-, ex-,* and *self-* joined to a noun or an adjective, the prefix *anti-* joined to a word beginning with *i-,* the prefix *vice-* (except in *vice president*), and the prefix *re-* to avoid confusion between words that are spelled the same but have different meanings.
all-inclusive   ex-wife   self-reliance
anti-immigrant   vice-principal   re-call *instead of* recall

22. Use a hyphen in a compound adjective that precedes a noun. Use a hyphen in compound numbers and in fractions used as adjectives.
a green-yellow jersey   a red-hot poker   jet-black hair
ninety-nine   one-fifth cup of sugar

23. Use a hyphen to divide words at the end of a line.
daz-zle   terri-tory   Mediter-ranean

24. Use one period at the end of an abbreviation. If punctuation other than a period ends the sentence, use both the period and the other punctuation.
Bring me the books, papers, pencils, etc.   Could you be ready at 2:00 P.M.?

25. Capitalize the abbreviations of proper nouns and some personal titles.
U.K.   C.E.O.   R. F. Kennedy   B.C.   A.D.   Ph.D.

26. Abbreviate numerical measurements in scientific writing but not in ordinary prose.
Measure 89 g into the crucible.   Jim ran ten yards when he heard that dog barking!

27. Spell out cardinal and ordinal numbers that can be written in one or two words and those that appear at the beginning of a sentence.
Five hundred people attended.   I look forward to my **eighteenth** birthday.

28. Use numerals for date; for decimals; for house, apartment, and room numbers; for street and avenue numbers greater than ten; for sums of money involving both dollars and cents; and to emphasize the exact time of day and with A.M. and P.M.
Aptil **1, 1996**   Room **251**   **$2.51**   **2:51** P.M.

29. Express all related numbers in a sentence as numerals if any one should be a numeral.
The subscriptions gradually rose from **10 to 116**.

30. Spell out numbers that express decades, amounts of money that can be written in one or two words, streets and avenues less than ten, and the approximate time of day.
the **seventies**   **fifty** cents   **Fifth** Avenue   half past **five**

VOCABULARY AND SPELLING

1. Clues to the meaning of an unfamiliar word can be found in its context. Context clues include definition, the meaning stated; example, the meaning explained through one familiar case; comparison, similarity to a familiar word; contrast, opposite of a familiar word; and cause and effect, a cause described by its effects.

2. Clues to the meaning of a word can be obtained from its base word, its prefix, or its suffix
telegram **gram** = writing   psychology **psych** = soul, mind
antibacterial **anti** = against   biology **-logy** = study

3. The *i* comes before the *e*, except when both letters follow a *c* or when both letters are pronounced together as an $\bar{a}$ sound. However, many exceptions exist to this rule.
f**ie**ld (*i* before *e*)   dec**ei**ve (*ei* after *c*)   r**ei**gn ($\bar{a}$ sound)   w**ei**rd (exception)

4. Most word endings pronounced *sēd* are spelled *-cede.* In one word, *supersede,* the ending is spelled *-sede.* In, *proceed, exceed,* and *succeed,* the ending is spelled *-ceed.*
pre**cede**   re**cede**   con**cede**

5. An unstressed vowel sound is not emphasized when a word is pronounced. Determine the spelling of this sound by comparing it to a known word.
hesitant (Compare to *hesitate.*)   *fantasy* (Compare to *fantastic.*)

6. When adding a suffix that begins with a consonant to a word that ends in silent *e,* generally keep the *e.* If the suffix begins with a vowel or *y,* generally drop the *e.* If the suffix begins with *a* or *o* and the word ends in *ce* or *ge,* keep the *e.* If the suffix begins with a vowel and the word ends in *ee,* or *oe,* keep the *e.*
encourag**ement**   scar**y**   chang**eable**   flee**ing**

7. When adding a suffix to a word ending in a consonant +*y,* change the *y* to *i* unless the suffix begins with *i.* If the word ends in a vowel +*y,* keep the *y.*
heart**iness**   read**iness**   sp**ying**   stra**ying**

8. Double the final consonant before adding a suffix that begins with a vowel to a word that ends in a single consonant preceded by a single vowel if the accent is on the root's last syllable.
   plan**ned**   fin**ned**   misfit**ted**

9. When adding -*ly* to a word that ends in a single *l,* keep the *l.* If it ends in a double *l,* drop one *l.* If it ends in a consonant +*le,* drop the *le.*
   real becomes real**ly**   dull becomes dul**ly**   inexplicable becomes inexplica**bly**

10. When adding -*ness* to a word that ends in *n,* keep the *n.*
    lean**ness**   mean**ness**   green**ness**

11. When joining a word or prefix that ends in a consonant to a suffix or word that begins with a consonant, keep both consonants.
    quiet**ness**   great**ly**   red**ness**

12. Most nouns form their plurals by adding -*s.* However, nouns that end in -*ch, -s, -sh, -x,* or -*z* form plurals by adding -*es.* If the noun ends in a consonant +*y,* change *y* to *i* and add -*es.* If the noun ends in -*lf,* change *f* to *v* and add -*es.* If the noun ends in -*fe,* change *f* to *v* and add -*s.*
    can**s**   chur**ches**   fa**xes**   spi**es**   hal**ves**   loa**ves**

13. To form the plural of proper names and one-word compound nouns, follow the general rules for plurals. To form the plural of hyphenated compound nouns or compound nouns of more than one word, make the most important word plural.
    Shatner**s**   Stockholder**s**   brother**s**-in-law   Master Sergeant**s**

14. Some nouns have the same singular and plural forms.
    sheep   species

COMPOSITION

Writing Themes and Paragraphs

1. Use **prewriting** to find ideas to write about. One form of prewriting, **freewriting**, starts with a subject or topic and branches off into related ideas. Another way to find a topic is to ask and answer questions about your starting subject, helping you to gain a deeper understanding of your chosen topic. Also part of the prewriting stage is determining who your readers or **audience** will be and deciding your **purpose** for writing. Your purpose—as varied as writing to persuade, to explain, to describe something, or to narrate—is partially shaped by who your audience will be, and vice versa.

2. To complete your first **draft**, organize your prewriting into an introduction, body, and conclusion. Concentrate on unity and coherence of the overall piece. Experiment with different paragraph orders: **chronological order** places events in the order in which they happened; **spatial order** places objects in the order in which they appear; and **compare/contrast order** shows similarities and differences in objects or events.

3. **Revise** your composition if necessary. Read through your draft, looking for places to improve content and structure. Remember that varying your sentence patterns and lengths will make your writing easier and more enjoyable to read.

4. In the **editing** stage, check your grammar, spelling, and punctuation. Focus on expressing your ideas clearly and concisely.

5. Finally, prepare your writing for **presentation**. Sharing your composition, or ideas, with others may take many forms: printed, oral, or graphic.

Outlining

1. The two common forms of outlines are sentence outlines and topic outlines. Choose one type of outline and keep it uniform throughout.

2. A period follows the number or letter of each division. Each point in a sentence outline ends with a period; the points in a topic outline do not.

3. Each point begins with a roman numeral.

4. A point may have no fewer than two subpoints.

SENTENCE OUTLINE
I.   This is the main point.
   A. This is a subpoint of I.
      1. This is a detail of A.
         a. This is a detail of 1.
         b. This is a detail of 1.
      2. This is a detail of A.
   B. This is a subpoint of I.
II. This is another main point.

TOPIC OUTLINE
I.   Main point
   A. Subpoint of I
      1. Detail of A
         a. Detail of 1
         b. Detail of 1
      2. Detail of A
   B. Subpoint of I
II. Main point

Writing letters

1. Personal letters are usually handwritten in indented form (the first line of paragraphs, each line of the heading, the complimentary close, and the signature are indented). Business letters are usually typewritten in block or semiblock form. Block form contains no indents; semiblock form indents the heading, the complimentary close, and the signature.

2. The five parts of a personal letter are the heading (the writer's address and the date), the salutation (greeting), the body (message), the complimentary close (such as "Yours truly"), and the signature (the writer's name). The business letter has the same parts and also includes an inside address (the recipient's address).

PERSONAL LETTER

Heading
Salutation
Body
Complimentary Close
Signature

BUSINESS LETTER

Heading
Inside Address
Salutation
Body
Complimentary Close
Signature

3. Reveal your personality and imagination in colorful personal letters. Keep business letters brief, clear, and courteous.

4. **Personal letters** include letters to friends and family members. **Thank-you notes** and **invitations** are personal letters that may be either formal or informal in style.

5. Use a **letter of complaint** to convey a concern. Begin the letter by telling what happened. Then use supporting details as evidence. Complete the letter by explaining what you want done. Avoid insults and threats, and make reasonable requests. Use a **letter of request** to ask for information or to place an order of purchase. Be concise, yet give all the details necessary for your request to be fulfilled. Keep the tone of your letter courteous and be generous in allotting time for a response.

6. Use an **opinion letter** to take a firm stand on an issue. Make the letter clear, firm, rational, and purposeful. Be aware of your audience, their attitude, how informed they are, and their possible reactions to your opinion. Support your statements of opinion with facts.

7. Use a **résumé** to summarize your work experience, school experience, talents, and interests. Be clear, concise, and expressive. Use a consistent form. You do not need to write in complete sentences, but use as many action verbs as possible.

8. Use a **cover letter** as a brief introduction accompanying your résumé.

Troubleshooter

Sentence Fragments

Troubleshooter

PROBLEM 1

Fragment that lacks a subject

| frag | Ali baked a chocolate cake. (Took it to the party.) |
| frag | Maria thought the comedian was funny. (Laughed at his jokes.) |

SOLUTION

Ali baked a chocolate cake. He took it to the party.
Maria thought the comedian was funny. She laughed at his jokes.

Make a complete sentence by adding a subject to the fragment.

PROBLEM 2

Fragment that lacks a complete verb

| frag | Helen is a photographer. (She becoming well-known for her work.) |
| frag | Alicia has a new computer. (It very powerful.) |

SOLUTION A

Helen is a photographer. She is becoming well-known for her work.
Alicia has a new computer. It is very powerful.

Make a complete sentence by adding a complete verb or a helping verb.

SOLUTION B

Helen is a photographer and is becoming well-known for her work.
Alicia has a new computer, which is very powerful.

Combine the fragment with another sentence.

PROBLEM 3

Fragment that is a subordinate clause

frag   Akira repaired the old boat. Because it was beautiful.

frag   Jennifer has two race car magazines. Which she bought at the store.

SOLUTION A

Akira repaired the old boat because it was beautiful.

Jennifer has two race car magazines, which she bought at the store.

Combine the fragment with another sentence.

SOLUTION B

Akira repaired the old boat. It was beautiful.

Jennifer has two race car magazines. She bought them at the store.

Make the fragment a complete sentence by removing the subordinating conjunction or the relative pronoun and adding a subject or other words necessary to make a complete thought.

PROBLEM 4

Fragment that lacks both subject and verb

frag   The soft rustle of the trees makes me sleepy. In the afternoon.

frag   The next morning. We talked about our adventure.

SOLUTION

The soft rustle of the trees makes me sleepy in the afternoon.

The next morning, we talked about our adventure.

Make the fragment part of a sentence.

More help in avoiding sentence fragments is available in Lesson 31.

Run-on Sentences

PROBLEM 1

Comma splice—two main clauses separated only by a comma

run-on (I don't know where the oil paints are, they were over by the easel.)

SOLUTION A

I don't know where the oil paints are. They were over by the easel.

Make two sentences by separating the first clause from the second with end punctuation, such as a period or a question mark, and start the second sentence with a capital letter.

SOLUTION B

I don't know where the oil paints are; they were over by the easel.

Place a semicolon between the main clauses of the sentence.

SOLUTION C

I don't know where the oil paints are, but they were over by the easel.

Add a coordinating conjunction after the comma.

PROBLEM 2

No punctuation between two main clauses

run-on (Deelra ran the hurdles in record time Shawna placed second.)

SOLUTION A

Deelra ran the hurdles in record time. Shawna placed second.

Make two sentences out of the run-on sentence.

SOLUTION B

Deelra ran the hurdles in record time; Shawna placed second.

Separate the main clauses with a semicolon.

SOLUTION C

Deelra ran the hurdles in record time, but Shawna placed second.

Add a comma and a coordinating conjunction between the main clauses.

PROBLEM 3

Two main clauses without a comma before the coordinating conjunction

run-on   The robins usually arrive in the spring and they start building nests at once.

run-on   Emily won the scholarship last year but she decided not to accept it.

SOLUTION

The robins usually arrive in the spring, and they start building nests at once.

Emily won the scholarship last year, but she decided not to accept it.

Separate the main clauses by adding a comma before the coordinating conjunction.

More help in avoiding run-on sentences is available in Lesson 32.

Lack of Subject-Verb Agreement

PROBLEM 1

A prepositional phrase between a subject and its verb

agr   The arrangement of those colorful pictures (make) a vivid, exciting combination.

agr   One of those big, gray sea gulls (have perched) on the roof.

SOLUTION

The arrangement of those colorful pictures makes a vivid, exciting combination.

One of those big, gray sea gulls has perched on the roof.

Make the verb agree with the subject, not with the object of the preposition.

PROBLEM 2

A predicate nominative differing in number from the subject

agr   Fast-paced adventure movies (was) always Jenny's choice.

SOLUTION

Fast-paced adventure movies were always Jenny's choice.

Make the verb agree with the subject, not with the predicate nominative.

PROBLEM 3

A subject following the verb

agr   On the sun deck there (was) several chairs and a table.

agr   Here (comes) the rain clouds and the heavy, slanting rain.

SOLUTION

On the sun deck there were several chairs and a table.
Here come the rain clouds and the heavy, slanting rain.

Look for the subject after the verb in an inverted sentence. Make sure that the verb agrees with the subject.

PROBLEM 4

Collective nouns as subjects

agr   The crowd really like the music, doesn't it?

agr   Margaret's company arrives tomorrow by bus and by train.

SOLUTION A

The crowd really likes the music, doesn't it?

Use a singular verb if the collective noun refers to a group as a whole.

SOLUTION B

Margaret's company arrive tomorrow by bus and by train.

Use a plural verb if the collective noun refers to each member of a group individually.

PROBLEM 5

A noun of amount as the subject

agr   The past two days seems like a week.

agr   One thousand millimeters equal a meter.

SOLUTION

The past two days seem like a week.
One thousand millimeters equals a meter.

A noun of amount that refers to one unit is singular. A noun of amount that refers to a number of individual units is plural.

PROBLEM 6

Compound subject joined by and

agr   A clear day and a light breeze (brightens) a summer afternoon.

agr   Pop and pizza (are) a common meal.

SOLUTION A

A clear day and a light breeze brighten a summer afternoon.

Use a plural verb if the parts of the compound subject do not belong to one unit or if they refer to different people or things.

SOLUTION B

Pop and pizza is a common meal.

Use a singular verb if the parts of the compound subject belong to one unit or if they refer to the same person or thing.

PROBLEM 7

Compound subject joined by or *or* nor

agr   Neither Yuri nor Sarah (like) the menu.

SOLUTION

Neither Yuri nor Sarah likes the menu.

Make your verb agree with the subject closer to it.

PROBLEM 8

Compound subject preceded by many a, every, *or* each

agr   Many a brush and tube of paint (were scattered) around the studio.

SOLUTION

Many a brush and tube of paint was scattered across the studio.

The subject is considered singular when *many a, each,* or *every* precedes a compound subject.

PROBLEM 9

Subjects separated from the verb by an intervening expression

agr   Jamal's new sculpture, in addition to his other recent works, (reflect) his abiding love of nature.

SOLUTION

Jamal's new sculpture, in addition to his other recent works, reflects his abiding love of nature.

Expressions that begin with *as well as, in addition to,* and *together with* do not change the number of the subject. Make the verb agree with its subject, not with the intervening expression.

PROBLEM 10

Indefinite pronouns as subjects

agr   Each of the trees along the old canal (have) different colors in the fall.

SOLUTION

Each of the trees along the old canal has different colors in the fall.

Some indefinite pronouns are singular, some are plural, and some can be either singular or plural depending on the noun to which they refer. (A list of indefinite pronouns is on page 53.)

More help with subject-verb agreement is available in Lessons 44–51.

Lack of Agreement Between Pronoun and Antecedent

PROBLEM 1

A singular antecedent that can be either male or female

> ant   A great coach inspires (his) athletes to be their best on or off the field.

Traditionally, masculine pronouns referred to antecedents that might have been either male or female.

SOLUTION A

A great coach inspires his or her athletes to be their best on or off the field.

Use *he* or *she, him* or *her,* and so on, to reword the sentence.

SOLUTION B

Great coaches inspire their athletes to be their best on or off the field.

Make both the antecedent and the pronoun plural.

SOLUTION C

Great coaches inspire athletes to be their best on or off the field.

Eliminate the pronoun.

PROBLEM 2

A second-person pronoun that refers to a third-person antecedent

> ant   Mary and Jodi prefer the new bridle trail because (you) get long stretches for galloping.

Troubleshooter

Do not use the second-person pronoun *you* to refer to an antecedent in the third person.

SOLUTION A

Mary and Jodi prefer the new bridle trail because they get long stretches for galloping.

Replace *you* with the appropriate third-person pronoun.

SOLUTION B

Mary and Jodi prefer the new bridle trail because the horses have long stretches for galloping.

Replace *you* with an appropriate noun.

PROBLEM 3

Singular indefinite pronouns as antecedents

ant   Each of the women in the boat received a rowing medal for (their) victory.

SOLUTION

Each of the women in the boat received a rowing medal for her victory.

Determine whether the antecedent is singular or plural, and make the personal pronoun agree with it.

More help with pronoun-antecedent agreement is available in Lessons 55–57.

Unclear Pronoun References

PROBLEM 1

Unclear antecedent

> ref   The wind was fair and the water calm, and (that) made sailing across the bay an absolute pleasure.
>
> ref   The traffic was snarled, (which) was caused by an accident.

SOLUTION A

The wind was fair and the water calm, and those conditions made sailing across the bay an absolute pleasure.

Substitute a noun for the pronoun.

SOLUTION B

The traffic was snarled in a massive tie-up, which was caused by an accident.

Rewrite the sentence, adding a clear antecedent for the pronoun.

PROBLEM 2

A pronoun that refers to more than one antecedent

> ref   The team captain told Karen to take (her) guard position.
>
> ref   The buses came early for the students, but (they) were not ready.

SOLUTION A

The team captain told Karen to take the captain's guard position.

Substitute a noun for the pronoun.

SOLUTION B

Because the buses came early, the students were not ready.

Rewrite the sentence, eliminating the pronoun.

PROBLEM 3

Indefinite uses of you *or* they

> ref   In those hills (you) rarely see mountain lions.
>
> ref   In some movies (they) have too much violence.

SOLUTION A

In those hills hikers rarely see mountain lions.

Substitute a noun for the pronoun.

SOLUTION B

Some movies have too much violence.

Eliminate the pronoun entirely.

*More help in making clear
pronoun references is available
in Lesson 58.*

Shifts in Pronouns

PROBLEM 1

Incorrect shift in person between two pronouns

pro	They went to the stadium for the game, but you could not find a place to park.
pro	One needs to keep their study time free from other commitments.
pro	We were on the hill at dawn, and you could see the most wondrous sunrise.

Incorrect pronoun shifts occur when a writer or a speaker uses a pronoun in one person and then illogically shifts to a pronoun in another person.

SOLUTION A

They went to the stadium for the game, but they could not find a place to park.

One needs to keep one's study time free from other commitments.

Replace the incorrect pronoun with a pronoun that agrees with its antecedent.

SOLUTION B

We were on the hill at dawn, and Mary and I could see the most wondrous sunrise.

Replace the incorrect pronoun with an appropriate noun.

Shift in Verb Tenses

PROBLEM 1

Unnecessary shifts in tense

shift t Akira waits for the bus and (worked) on the computer.

shift t Jenny hit the home run and (runs) around the bases.

Two or more events occurring at the same time must have the same verb tense.

SOLUTION

Akira waits for the bus and works on the computer.

Jenny hit the home run and ran around the bases.

Use the same tense for both verbs.

PROBLEM 2

Tenses do not indicate that one event precedes or succeeds another

shift t By the time the movie finally started, we (waited) impatiently through ten minutes of commercials.

If events being described occurred at different times, shift tenses to show that one event precedes or follows another.

SOLUTION

By the time the movie finally started, we had waited impatiently through ten minutes of commercials.

Use the past perfect tense for the earlier of two actions to indicate that one action began and ended before another action began.

More help with shifts in verb tenses is available in Lesson 42.

Incorrect Verb Tenses or Forms

PROBLEM 1

Incorrect or missing verb endings

tense	Ricardo said it (snow) last night.
tense	Karen and her family (travel) to Costa Rica last year.

SOLUTION

Ricardo said it snowed last night.

Karen and her family traveled to Costa Rica last year.

Regular verbs form the past tense and the past participle by adding *-ed*.

PROBLEM 2

Improper formation of irregular verbs

tense	The sun (rised) out of scarlet clouds into a clear, blue sky.

SOLUTION

The sun rose out of scarlet clouds into a clear, blue sky.

An irregular verb forms its past tense and past participle in some way other than by adding *-ed*.

PROBLEM 3

Confusion between the past form of the verb and the past participle

tense	The horses (have ate) their feed already.
tense	The coach (has wore) the old team jacket to every graduation.

SOLUTION

The horses have eaten their feed already.

The coach has worn the old team jacket to every graduation.

When you use the auxiliary verb *have,* use the past participle form of an irregular verb, not its simple past form.

PROBLEM 4

Improper use of the past participle

tense	Deemee ⟨drawn⟩ the winning ticket for the door prize at the dance.
tense	The old rowboat ⟨sunk⟩ just below the surface of the lake.

Past participles of irregular verbs cannot stand alone as verbs. They must be used in conjunction with a form of the auxiliary verb *have.*

SOLUTION A

Deemee had drawn the winning ticket for the door prize at the dance.

The old rowboat had sunk just below the surface of the lake.

Form a complete verb by adding a form of the auxiliary verb *have* to the past participle.

SOLUTION B

Deemee drew the winning ticket for the door prize at the dance.

The old rowboat sank just below the surface of the lake.

Use the simple past form of the verb instead of the past participle.

More help with correct verb forms is available in Lessons 36, 37, and 41.

Misplaced or Dangling Modifiers

PROBLEM 1

Misplaced modifier

> mod   (Untended and overgrown since last summer,) Marlene helped Keshia in her garden.
>
> mod   Sarah won the jumping contest with her mother's horse, (wearing western riding gear.)

A misplaced modifier appears to modify the wrong word or group of words.

> **SOLUTION**
>
> **Marlene helped Keshia in her garden, untended and overgrown since last summer.**
>
> **Wearing western riding gear, Sarah won the jumping contest with her mother's horse.**
>
> Place the modifying phrase as close as possible to the word or words it modifies.

PROBLEM 2

Misplacing the adverb only

> mod   Akiko (only) runs hurdles in track.

> **SOLUTION**
>
> **Only Akiko runs hurdles in track.**
>
> **Akiko runs only hurdles in track.**
>
> **Akiko runs hurdles only in track.**
>
> Each time *only* is moved in the sentence, the meaning of the sentence changes. Place the adverb immediately before the word or group of words it is to modify.

PROBLEM 3

Dangling modifiers

mod	(Branches swaying in the breeze,) we rested in the shade.
mod	(Trying out the new exercise equipment,) the new gym is a great improvement over the old one.

A dangling modifier does not modify any word in the sentence.

SOLUTION

Branches swaying in the breeze, the tree provided us with shade.

Trying out the new exercise equipment, Mary said the new gym is a great improvement over the old one.

Add a noun to which the dangling phrase clearly refers. You might have to add or change other words, as well.

More help with misplaced or dangling modifiers is available in Lesson 64.

Misplaced or Missing Possessive Apostrophes

PROBLEM 1

Singular nouns

> poss   (Charles) car is the white one, but (Jamals) is the red convertible.

SOLUTION

Charles's car is the white one, but Jamal's is the red convertible.

To form the possessive of a singular noun, even one that ends in -*s*, use an apostrophe and an -*s* at the end of the word.

PROBLEM 2

Plural nouns that end in -s

> poss   The seven maple (trees) cool, delicious shade is the best in the park.

SOLUTION

The seven maple trees' cool, delicious shade is the best in the park.

To form the possessive of a plural noun that ends in -*s*, use an apostrophe by itself after the final -*s*.

PROBLEM 3

Plural nouns that do not end in -s

> poss   The (childrens) movies are on that rack next to the nature films.

SOLUTION

The children's movies are on that rack next to the nature films.

Form the possessive of a plural noun that does not end in -*s* by using an apostrophe and -*s* at the end of the word.

PROBLEM 4

Pronouns

poss	That painting cannot be just (anybodys) work.
poss	(Their's) is the trophy in the center of the display case.

SOLUTION A

That painting cannot be just anybody's work.

Form the possessive of a singular indefinite pronoun by adding an apostrophe and *-s* to it.

SOLUTION B

Theirs is the trophy in the center of the display case.

With any of the possessive personal pronouns, do not use an apostrophe.

PROBLEM 5

Confusing its *with* it's

poss	The computer is booting up; I see (it's) power light blinking.
poss	(Its) going to be a great victory party.

SOLUTION

The computer is booting up; I see its power light blinking.
It's going to be a great victory party.

It's is the contraction of *it is,* not the possessive of *it.*

More help with apostrophes and possessives is available in Lesson 89.

Missing Commas with Nonessential Elements

PROBLEM 1

Missing commas with nonessential participles, infinitives, and their phrases

com	Lois scowling fiercely turned her back on Clark.
com	The detective mystified by the fresh clue scratched his head in bewilderment.
com	Television to tell the truth just doesn't interest me.

SOLUTION

Lois, scowling fiercely, turned her back on Clark.

The detective, mystified by the fresh clue, scratched his head in bewilderment.

Television, to tell the truth, just doesn't interest me.

If the participle, infinitive, or phrase is not essential to the meaning of the sentence, set off the phrase with commas.

PROBLEM 2

Missing commas with nonessential adjective clauses

com	The sailboat which looked like a toy in the storm rounded the point into the breakwater.

SOLUTION

The sailboat, which looked like a toy in the storm, rounded the point into the breakwater.

If the clause is not essential to the meaning of the sentence, set it off with commas.

PROBLEM 3

Missing commas with nonessential appositives

com	The palomino a beautiful horse with almost golden hair is often seen in parades.

SOLUTION

The palomino, a beautiful horse with almost golden hair, is often seen in parades.

If the appositive is not essential to the meaning of the sentence, set it off with commas.

PROBLEM 4

Missing commas with interjections and parenthetical expressions

com	Wow did you see that falling star?
com	I would have told you by the way but you weren't home.

SOLUTION

Wow, did you see that falling star?
I would have told you, by the way, but you weren't home.

Set off the interjection or parenthetical expression with commas.

More help with commas and nonessential elements is available in Lesson 78.

PROBLEM 1

Commas missing in a series of words, phrases, or clauses

s com   Mona said that Amy Tan James Baldwin and Charles Dickens were her favorite authors.

s com   Sailing on the Great Lakes can be as challenging adventurous and rewarding as sailing on the ocean.

s com   Our forensics team practiced hard did their research and used all their wit and intelligence to win the championship.

s com   The wind shifted the clouds parted and the sunlight streamed down.

SOLUTION

Mona said that Amy Tan, James Baldwin, and Charles Dickens were her favorite authors.

Sailing on the Great Lakes can be as challenging, adventurous, and rewarding as sailing on the ocean.

Our forensics team practiced hard, did their research, and used all their wit and intelligence to win the championship.

The wind shifted, the clouds parted, and the sunlight streamed down.

Use a comma after each item in a series except the last.

More help with commas is available in Lessons 76–83.

Grammar

Unit 1: Parts of Speech

Lesson 1
Nouns: Singular, Plural, and Collective

A **noun** is a word that names a person, place, thing, or idea. A **singular noun** names one person, place, thing, or idea, and a **plural noun** names more than one. Most plural nouns are formed by adding -s to the singular form. Words that end in *ch, sh, s, x,* or *z* form the plural by adding -es. Words that end in a consonant and *y* form the plural by changing *y* to *i* and adding -es. Some plurals are formed irregularly, for example, *child, children; foot, feet; mouse, mice.* Some singular and plural forms are the same, for example, *sheep, deer, series.*

	SINGULAR	PLURAL		SINGULAR	PLURAL
Person:	child	children	**Thing:**	piano	pianos
Place:	corner	corners	**Idea:**	religion	religions

A **collective noun** names a group. A collective noun is singular when it refers to the group as a whole. It is plural when it refers to the individual members of a group.

The **jury** is still deliberating. (singular)   The **jury** are arguing loudly. (plural)

▶ **Exercise 1** Write *S* above each singular noun and *P* above each plural noun.

      S   S   S   P
Congress debated the issue and approved the bill defining consumer rights.

1. My parents expect us children to help with the housework. *(P, P, S)*

2. The film followed a herd of cows through a typical day. *(S, S, P, S)*

3. She probably has more self-confidence than any of my other friends. *(S, P)*

4. The returning astronauts waved to the cheering crowd. *(P, S)*

5. The principal congratulated the class on its performance. *(S, S, S)*

6. The dodo is an extinct bird. *(S, S)*

7. Her favorite team lost in the playoffs. *(S, P)*

8. My grandmother always used to say that pride went before a fall. *(S, S, S)*

9. The paintings were in the new section of the museum. *(P, S, S)*

10. This particular book contains both stories and poems. *(S, P, P)*

11. Before we could paint the house, we had to scrape off the old paint. *(S, S)*

              S   S

12. Frankly, your dog is not the smartest creature I've ever seen.

          S   S   S   S

13. The eerie music during the play added to the atmosphere of mystery.

         S   S   S   P

14. Every time he went to the mall he saw the same group of kids.

         S   S   S

15. The awful smell from the laboratory reached to the gym.

         S   S   S

16. When the chain fell off her bicycle, she heard a terrible grating sound.

         S   S   S

17. One panel gave a presentation about democracy.

                     S

18. I usually don't like spicy food.

         S   S   S

19. That girl works at the store on the corner.

         S   S   P

20. The audience gasped in disbelief when the senators appeared.

▶ **Exercise 2** **Choose 30 singular nouns you identified above. On the lines below, write the plural form for each of those nouns.**

congresses	issues	bills

Answers should include thirty of the following: films, herds, days, crowds, principals, classes, performances, dodoes *or* dodos, birds, teams, grandmothers, falls, sections, museums, books, houses, paints, dogs, creatures, plays, atmospheres, mysteries, times, malls, groups, smells, laboratories, gyms, chains, bicycles, sounds, panels, presentations, democracies, foods, girls, stores, corners, audiences.

▶ **Writing Link** **Write three sentences about a concert or other performance you have seen. Use at least three collective nouns in your sentences.**

Grammar

Lesson 2
Nouns: Proper and Common; Concrete and Abstract

A **proper noun** is a noun that names a particular person, place, thing, or idea. A proper noun begins with a capital letter. A **common noun** is the general name of a person, place, thing, or idea.

	PROPER	COMMON
Person:	Uncle Al	uncle
Place:	Dominican Republic	country
Thing:	*Schindler's List*	movie
Idea:	(the) Renaissance	era

▶ **Exercise 1** Write *P* above each proper noun and *C* above each common noun.

   P   C   P   C
Pedro is taking his little brother to Wrigley Field to see a baseball game.

1. The World Cup is the most popular sporting event in the world.

2. Every four years, soccer teams from continents such as Europe, Africa, and South America battle for first place.

3. In 1994, the tournament was held in the United States.

4. Teams from twenty-four nations took part in the 1994 World Cup.

5. In every city where a game was played, fans of each country cheered their players.

6. Thousands of soccer fans from Italy and Ireland invaded New Jersey.

7. Soldier Field in Chicago rocked to the cheers of Germans and Bolivians.

8. Brazilians backed their team by singing samba songs in Portuguese.

9. Fans of Nigeria, champions of Africa, pounded drums to spur their team to victory.

10. Supporters of the home team enthusiastically waved the Stars and Stripes.

11. Only 16 teams advanced to the second round of the World Cup.

12. These teams then met to decide who would become world champion.

13. Several games were decided by a "shoot-out," in which a single player challenges the goalkeeper.

14. One of the best games in the second round was Holland against Brazil.

15. The United States put up a good fight against Brazil but lost by a score of 1–0.

              C   C

16. When the smoke had cleared, only four teams were left.

     P   C   P   P   C   P

17. Brazil, led by goalscorers Romario and Bebeto, advanced to the final by edging Sweden.

            C   P   C   P   P

18. In the other semifinal, Italy and its star Roberto Baggio crushed Bulgaria.

                   C   C   C   C

19. More than two billion soccer fans around the world watched the final game on television.

        P   C   C

20. They saw the Brazilians edge a tough Italian team to become world champions.

A **concrete noun** names an object that occupies space or can be recognized by any of the senses. An **abstract noun** names an idea, quality, or characteristic.

Concrete: sneeze, star, explosion, hedgehog, chimney
Abstract: politeness, ability, honesty, love, beauty

▶ **Exercise 2** Write *con.* above each concrete noun and *abs.* above each abstract noun.

   con.   con.   abs.
Bob admires people who practice modesty.

   con.   con.
1. Sheila likes to plant and care for flowers.

        abs.
2. Daniel's integrity cannot be questioned.

   con.   con.   abs.   con.
3. Ruth and Joe have shown their devotion to this company.

   abs.   abs.   con.   abs.
4. Kindness and sincerity dominate my list of important qualities.

        con.   con.
5. Claire's new bicycle impressed her neighbors.

    con.   con.
6. Uncle Rico will give you the recipe.

    con.   con.   abs.   abs.
7. The coach reminded his players of the necessity for good sportsmanship.

    con.   con.   con.
8. The bakery on the corner sells the best chocolate chip cookies.

   abs.
9. Thoughtfulness is always appreciated.

   con.   abs.   abs.
10. Rashida wants us to make compassion a priority.

   con.   con.
11. Mr. Fernandez is teaching us about great world leaders.

   abs.
12. Jealousy can be extremely destructive.

   con.   abs.   con.   abs.
13. Sunee has empathy for Roger because she has gone through a similar experience.

   con.   con.   con.   con.
14. Brad and Caroline hosted a reception for the new exchange student.

        con.   con.   abs.
15. I always enjoy visiting Mexico and Canada, although they have few similarities.

Lesson 3
Pronouns: Personal and Possessive; Reflexive and Intensive

A **pronoun** is a word that takes the place of a noun, a group of words acting as a noun, or another pronoun. A **personal pronoun** refers to a specific person or thing and can be either singular or plural. The **first person** indicates the person speaking. The **second person** indicates the person being addressed. The **third person** indicates the person or thing being discussed.

	SINGULAR	PLURAL
First Person	I, me	we, us
Second Person	you	you
Third Person	he, him	they, them
	she, her, it	

We are aware that **you** will be bringing **them** to the party.

A **possessive pronoun** indicates possession or ownership. It takes the place of the possessive form of a noun.

	SINGULAR	PLURAL
First Person	my, mine	our, ours
Second Person	your, yours	your, yours
Third Person	his	their, theirs
	her, hers, its	

My coat and **your** bookbag are in **her** locker.

A **reflexive pronoun** refers to a noun or another pronoun and indicates that the same person or thing is involved. An **intensive pronoun** adds emphasis to a noun or another pronoun.

	SINGULAR	PLURAL
First Person	myself	ourselves
Second Person	yourself	yourselves
Third Person	himself, herself, itself	themselves

Reflexive: I bought **myself** a pair of jeans.   Intensive: I **myself** bought a pair of jeans.

▶ **Exercise 1** Underline each pronoun.

She glanced in the mirror and saw him behind her.

1. I could tell it made no sense at all to her.

2. His father runs the cafe by himself.

3. Can you imagine how they felt when they saw them?

4. Their burrito is a meal in itself!

5. <u>We</u> told <u>her</u> <u>we</u> wanted to do <u>it</u> <u>ourselves</u>.

6. The telephone was ringing off <u>its</u> hook.

7. Randall couldn't tell <u>theirs</u> from <u>yours</u>.

8. <u>She</u> told <u>him</u> skipping breakfast was a bad idea.

9. Did <u>you</u> double-check <u>your</u> answers as <u>they</u> did?

10. Give <u>them</u> enough time, and <u>they</u> will reveal <u>their</u> secret.

11. <u>I</u> <u>myself</u> will perform the leading role in the play.

12. <u>You</u> have only <u>yourselves</u> to blame.

13. <u>Its</u> shine and softness make the material very popular.

14. <u>Their</u> crowd spends a lot of time at the swimming pool.

15. <u>They</u> still had one difficult task in front of <u>them</u>.

16. <u>She</u> had been studying to become a lawyer.

17. Jason forgot to bring <u>his</u> volleyball, so <u>we</u> had to use <u>hers</u>.

18. <u>You</u> mean <u>you</u> found <u>your</u> report in the recycling bin?

19. Cars are a lot smaller than <u>they</u> used to be.

20. He was shocked when <u>he</u> learned the congresswoman <u>herself</u> would be attending.

▶ **Exercise 2** **Identify what type of pronoun is in italics. Write *per.*—personal, *pos.*—possessive, *ref.*—reflexive, and *int.*—intensive. Then write *S* if the pronoun is singular and *Pl.* if it is plural.**

___per., S___   I'm not sure *she* understands how important it is.

___pos., S___   1. The large book about Alaska is *hers.*

___per., S___   2. *I* had never seen anything so amazing!

___int., S___   3. The coach gave the speech *herself.*

___per., S *or* Pl.___   4. Did that girl ask *you* to dance?

___int., Pl.___   5. We planned to build it *ourselves.*

___pos., S___   6. She took *his* order after the song stopped.

___per., Pl.___   7. What did he think *they* were doing?

___ref., S___   8. She watched *herself* in the mirror as she practiced.

___pos., Pl.___   9. Nikki and I agreed *their* project was the best.

___int., Pl.___   10. You *yourselves* will have to decide.

___per., Pl.___   11. That silly dog followed *them* all the way home.

___ref., Pl.___   12. Customers serve *themselves* from the smorgasbord.

Lesson 4
Pronouns: Interrogative, Relative, Demonstrative, Indefinite

Grammar

A **pronoun** is a word that takes the place of a noun, a group of words acting as a noun, or another pronoun. An **interrogative pronoun** is used to form a question.

who   whom   whose   what   which

Which is the correct answer?

A **relative pronoun** is used to begin some subject-verb word groups called subordinate clauses.

who	whom	whose	whoever	whomever	which
whichever	that	what	whosoever	whatever	

Maya is the student **who** wrote the article.

A **demonstrative pronoun** points out specific persons, places, things, or ideas.

this   these   that   those

These are the most interesting videodiscs.

An **indefinite pronoun** refers to persons, places, or things in a more general way than a noun does.

all	both	everything	none	several
another	each	few	no one	some
any	either	many	nothing	somebody
anybody	enough	most	one	someone
anyone	everybody	neither	other	something
anything	everyone	nobody	others	

Few are ever found again.

▶ **Exercise 1** **Underline each pronoun. In the blank, write** *int.* **if the pronoun is interrogative,** *rel.* **if it is relative,** *dem.* **if it is demonstrative, and** *ind.* **if it is indefinite.**

__int.__   Who can answer this question?

__int.__   **1.** What is the longest river in the United States?

__rel.__   **2.** The Missouri, which flows 2,540 miles, is the longest river.

__ind.__   **3.** In fact, the Missouri is one of the longest rivers in the world.

__ind.__   **4.** How many of the world's rivers are longer than the Missouri?

Grammar

__rel.__   **5.** The Ohio River and the Missouri River, <u>which</u> are tributaries of the Mississippi River, flow into the Mississippi at Cairo, Illinois, and St. Louis, Missouri.

__ind.__   **6.** <u>Both</u> are vital transportation routes.

__dem.__   **7.** <u>These</u>, along with other smaller rivers, help make up the Mississippi River Basin.

__rel.__   **8.** Statistics show <u>that</u> the Mississippi River carries almost two thirds of the country's inland freight.

__ind.__   **9.** St. Louis, Memphis, and New Orleans are <u>several</u> of the cities on the river.

__int.__   **10.** <u>Which</u> is the largest state bordering the Mississippi River?

__rel.__   **11.** A famous writer <u>who</u> is associated with the Mississippi is Mark Twain.

__rel.__   **12.** Twain wrote about <u>whatever</u> was around his hometown of Hannibal, Missouri.

__ind.__   **13.** The bustling life of the river was <u>something</u> Twain described in book after book.

__ind.__   **14.** <u>Nothing</u> was closer to the writer's heart.

__rel.__   **15.** Three books <u>that</u> are set on the river are *Life on the Mississippi, Tom Sawyer,* and *Pudd'nhead Wilson.*

__ind.__   **16.** Twain's most famous book is <u>one</u> many people love.

__rel.__   **17.** Many literary critics believe <u>that</u> *Huckleberry Finn* is the finest American novel.

__int.__   **18.** <u>What</u> makes the story so popular?

__ind.__   **19.** Perhaps there is a little bit of Huck Finn in <u>everybody</u>.

__ind.__   **20.** <u>Anybody</u> interested in America's greatest river should read Mark Twain's books.

▶ **Exercise 2 Complete each sentence by filling in an appropriate pronoun of the type indicated.** Answers may vary.

_____ This *or* That _____ is a subject open for discussion. (demonstrative)

1. The Zaire River, _____ which _____ was known as the Congo River until 1971, flows through west-central Africa. (relative)

2. _____ This *or* That _____ is the river that drains an area of the African continent known as the Congo Basin. (demonstrative)

3. The area, _____ which _____ is fed annually by as much as 100 inches of rainfall, covers 1.5 million square miles. (relative)

4. The Zaire River, _____ which _____ is 2,900 miles long, is of great importance to the people of the area. (relative)

5. _____ Which _____ of the rivers in Africa is the longest? (interrogative)

Lesson 5
Verbs: Action (Transitive/Intransitive)

A **verb** is a word that expresses action or a state of being and is necessary to make a statement. An **action verb** tells what someone or something does. Some action verbs express physical action. Other action verbs express mental action. A **transitive verb** is an action verb that is followed by a word or words that answer the question *what?* or *whom?*

The dancer **performed** the most difficult movements. (The action verb *performed* is followed by the noun *movements,* which answers the question *what?*)

An **intransitive verb** is an action verb that is not followed by words that answer the question *what?* or *whom?*

The dancer **performed** gracefully. (The action verb *performed* is followed by a word that tells how.)

▶ **Exercise 1** Underline the verb in each sentence. In the blank, write *T* if the verb is transitive. Write *I* if the verb is intransitive.

_____T_____   Jaelyn followed the recipe carefully.

_____I_____   **1.** Kathleen Battle, the opera star, sings amazingly well.

_____T_____   **2.** The red ants fought the black ants.

_____T_____   **3.** My aunt plays rugby every Sunday.

_____I_____   **4.** The hawk flew slowly over the forest.

_____T_____   **5.** Everyone saw the horse with the beautiful saddle.

_____I_____   **6.** Twenty-thousand people watched in amazement.

_____T_____   **7.** Beth finally heard that new song by the Ooglies.

_____T_____   **8.** The members of the chess club elected Janelle president.

_____T_____   **9.** The sound engineer recorded the bass and guitars first.

_____I_____   **10.** Dogs hear much better than humans.

_____T_____   **11.** I never watch game shows on television.

_____I_____   **12.** Robin finished early.

_____I_____   **13.** The dolphin turned quickly and smoothly.

_____T_____   **14.** I finished my homework during study hall.

_____T_____   **15.** I turned the pages of the old book with care.

_____I_____   **16.** Hummingbirds eat almost constantly.

___I___ **17.** Salmon actually <u>swim</u> up rivers.

___I___ **18.** The plan <u>succeeded</u> in spite of his strong opposition.

___T___ **19.** Carson's dog <u>eats</u> almost anything.

___T___ **20.** Raeanne <u>tasted</u> my bagel.

___T___ **21.** My dad never <u>drinks</u> coffee with his meals.

___T___ **22.** The beavers <u>built</u> the dam in less than a day.

___I___ **23.** Luis <u>stayed</u> at his grandmother's house for three weeks in the spring.

___I___ **24.** The parakeet <u>died</u> of pneumonia.

___T___ **25.** The outfielder <u>caught</u> the ball near the wall.

___I___ **26.** The crow <u>looked</u> at the scarecrow without the slightest trace of fear.

___I___ **27.** Aleksandr Solzhenitsyn <u>returned</u> to Russia in 1994.

___T___ **28.** Quentin <u>conducted</u> the school jazz band during one number.

___I___ **29.** Chen <u>ran</u> faster than anyone in the entire school.

___T___ **30.** He <u>returned</u> her calculator with a big scratch on it.

___T___ **31.** Good detectives never <u>reveal</u> their theories.

___T___ **32.** The tour director <u>made</u> all the reservations.

___T___ **33.** The bloodhound <u>smelled</u> something on the old, dirty jacket.

___I___ **34.** The bell <u>rang</u> at exactly midnight.

___T___ **35.** Mr. Rossi <u>ran</u> the shop with an iron hand.

___T___ **36.** She <u>opened</u> the window in the kitchen.

___I___ **37.** People <u>called</u> often during the holidays.

___I___ **38.** In *Casablanca* Bogart and Bergman <u>meet</u> for the last time at an airport.

___I___ **39.** The mayor <u>called</u> just before dinner.

___T___ **40.** Uncle Roscoe <u>met</u> me at the bus station.

▶ **Writing Link** **Write three sentences describing your favorite movie. Use both transitive and intransitive verbs in your description.**

_____

_____

_____

_____

Lesson 6
Verbs: Linking

A **linking verb** links, or joins, the subject of a sentence (often a noun or pronoun) with a word or expression that identifies or describes the subject. *Be* in all its forms (*am, is, are, was, were, been, being*) is the most common linking verb. Other linking verbs include *look, sound, feel, grow, remain, stay, seem, appear, become,* and *taste*.

| I **am** a soldier. | Bananas **were** plentiful. |
| The opera **sounded** wonderful. | She **felt** sad. |

▶ **Exercise 1** **Place a check in the blank next to each sentence whose main verb is a linking verb.**

___✔___   Fiona is Irish.

___✔___ **1.** Irish Americans are one of this country's largest immigrant groups.

_____ **2.** About 40 million Americans claim Irish ancestry.

___✔___ **3.** This total is almost ten times the number of people in the country of Ireland today.

___✔___ **4.** Among the states with the largest number of Irish Americans are Massachusetts, Delaware, New Hampshire, and Rhode Island.

_____ **5.** Irish immigrants came to this country very early in its history.

___✔___ **6.** Ireland was a country with a large population.

_____ **7.** The large number of people caused a rise in the poverty level.

___✔___ **8.** Many Irish felt hopeful about the endless job opportunities in America.

_____ **9.** In 1845 a terrible potato famine struck Ireland.

_____ **10.** The first big wave of Irish immigrants started in the 1840s.

_____ **11.** Most Irish immigrants settled in the large cities of the Northeast.

___✔___ **12.** Irish immigrants were important in building the famous Erie Canal and many highways, railroads, and cities.

_____ **13.** The Irish had an advantage over other immigrants because they could speak English.

_____ **14.** In spite of this, however, many Irish suffered discrimination.

_____ **15.** Irish Americans have made important contributions in many areas of American life and society.

___✔___ **16.** One well-known Irish American was President John F. Kennedy.

_____ **17.** Irish American Eugene O'Neill, an outstanding dramatist, won the Nobel Prize in literature for his plays.

_____ **18.** John L. Sullivan, America's first sports superstar, reigned as world heavyweight boxing champion in the late 1800s.

__✔__ **19.** Other famous Irish Americans are actor John Wayne, singer Bing Crosby, and Ronald Reagan, the former president.

__✔__ **20.** March 17, St. Patrick's Day, is the day when Irish Americans celebrate their heritage.

▶ **Exercise 2** **Underline the linking verb (or verbs) in each sentence. Then circle the word or words after the linking verb that identify or describe the subject.**

This is the (story) of an American hero.

1. John Fitzgerald Kennedy was the thirty-fifth (president) of the United States.

2. When he was a (child), his life seemed (easy.)

3. Joseph and Rose Kennedy appeared (eager) to give their children every opportunity to succeed.

4. John became an (author) when an expanded version of his senior thesis was published as a book.

5. *Why England Slept* is an (account) of Great Britain's difficulty in trying to react to military events.

6. Events grew (bleaker) in Europe as World War II advanced.

7. The United States stayed (neutral) for a time but eventually sent troops to Europe and Asia.

8. John Kennedy felt (confident) that he could command a Navy motor torpedo boat.

9. His mission grew (dangerous) when a Japanese destroyer sank his boat.

10. He became a (hero) when he led his men back to safety.

11. After the war ended, Kennedy became a (politician.)

12. He was first a (congressman) and then a (senator.)

13. In Congress, he was (responsive) to his constituents' concerns.

14. Though often ill, he looked (vigorous) and (strong.)

15. He became a strong (supporter) of civil rights legislation.

16. In 1960, Kennedy was the Democratic party's (candidate) for president.

17. He remains the youngest (person) ever elected President of the United States.

18. His inaugural address sounded (eloquent) to the citizens.

19. His ideas were (new) and (exciting.)

20. His influence on young people was (great.)

Lesson 7
Verb Phrases

The **verb** in a sentence may consist of more than one word. The words that accompany the main verb are called **auxiliary**, or helping, **verbs**. A **verb phrase** consists of a main verb and all its auxiliary verbs.

forms of *be*	am, is, are, was, were, being, been
forms of *have*	has, have, had
other auxiliaries	can, could, may, might, shall, will, do, does, did, must, should, would

The most common auxiliary verbs are the forms of *be* and *have.*

They **are going.**   They **have gone.**   They **had been going.**

The other auxiliary verbs are not used primarily to express time.

She **should be arriving.**   **Could** she **have arrived?**
She **could** already **be sitting** there.

▶ **Exercise 1 Place a check next to each sentence that contains an auxiliary verb. In the sentences that contain an auxiliary verb, underline the verb phrase. Then circle the auxiliary verb.**

✔ _____   Stock car racing (has) been popular for years.

✔ _____ **1.** No one (has) been more successful in auto races than Richard Petty.

✔ _____ **2.** The stock car race driver (was) known to millions of fans as "King Richard."

_____ **3.** Stock cars are quite different from the sleek cars in the Indianapolis 500.

✔ _____ **4.** On the outside, stock cars (may) appear normal.

✔ _____ **5.** But under the hood, stock cars (have) always had special, powerful engines.

_____ **6.** The cars also have additional safety features.

✔ _____ **7.** From 1960 to 1984, Richard Petty (was) winning in his trademark blue car.

✔ _____ **8.** He (had) crossed the finish line first more than two hundred times.

✔ _____ **9.** (Did) Richard Petty ever crash his race car?

✔ _____ **10.** The King (was) involved in many crashes, including a nasty one at the 1976 Daytona 500.

_____ **11.** Richard Petty won his last race on July 4, 1984.

✔ _____ **12.** (Did) Richard Petty's great success go to his head?

_____ **13.** No, he remained a favorite with fans because of his friendliness.

Grammar

_____✔_____ **14.** Thousands of fans (have) visited his headquarters in Level Cross, North Carolina.

_____ **15.** For many fans, stock car racing is a family affair.

_____ **16.** Men and women, boys and girls, and people of all ages enjoy watching the races.

_____✔_____ **17.** For drivers, racing (can) also be a family affair.

_____✔_____ **18.** Richard Petty's father, Lee, (had) been one of the first great stock car drivers.

_____✔_____ **19.** Not surprisingly, Richard's son (is) following in his father's footsteps.

_____✔_____ **20.** Any interested people (should) attend a stock car race.

▶ **Exercise 2** **Complete each sentence by writing a verb phrase (main verb and auxiliary verbs) using the verb indicated.** Answers will vary. Suggestions are given.

Myra _____ was reading _____ about race car drivers. (read)

1. Janet Guthrie _____ had been racing _____ cars for thirteen years before she first competed in the Indianapolis 500. (race)

2. Many famous auto racing drivers _____ were thinking _____ about the sport at a young age. (think)

3. However, Janet Guthrie _____ was interested _____ in flying airplanes. (interest)

4. She _____ could have been _____ a famous pilot. (be)

5. In fact, by age nineteen she _____ had obtained _____ a commercial pilot's license. (obtain)

6. Five years later, she _____ was taking _____ tests for a competition license in auto racing. (take)

7. She _____ would finish _____ third in her Sports Car Club of America class the following year. (finish)

8. Racing _____ was becoming _____ her primary interest. (become)

9. When she _____ should have been studying _____ for her graduate school finals in physics, she was racing somewhere instead. (study)

10. That is when she decided she _____ would be _____ a professional race car driver. (be)

11. She used all the money she _____ had saved _____ to pursue her dream. (save)

12. She _____ would stop _____ race car owners and ask them to hire her. (stop)

13. Finally, Janet decided she _____ should try _____ to build her own car. (try)

14. After building a good record, she _____ was offered _____ an opportunity to qualify for the Indianapolis 500. (offer)

15. In 1978, Janet Guthrie _____ would make _____ history by finishing in ninth place. (make)

Lesson 8
Adjectives

An adjective is a word that modifies a noun or pronoun by limiting its meaning.

shiny toaster   **friendly** neighbor   **horrible** accident   **green** bird   **that** book

Articles are the adjectives *a, an,* and *the. A* and *an* are indefinite articles. *The* is the definite article.

Possessive pronouns, such as *my* and *our,* can be considered adjectives because they modify nouns. Similarly, possessive forms of nouns, such as *Roger's* and *the captain's,* can also be considered adjectives.

A proper adjective is formed from a proper noun and begins with a capital letter.

Cervantes was a **Spanish** writer.   The **Korean** restaurant is very popular.

▶ **Exercise 1** Underline the adjectives, including articles, possessive pronouns, possessive forms of nouns, and proper adjectives in each sentence.

The weary rebels climbed the hill to the fort.

1. The weight lifter grunted and groaned trying to lift the heavy barbell.

2. The hungry boy ate a juicy hamburger and a tossed salad.

3. My little brother loves Chinese food.

4. Where did you get that beautiful coat?

5. The designers changed the basic design of the popular model.

6. A good hiking boot needs a sturdy sole.

7. We watched the little silvery fish jump completely out of the water.

8. His mother watched the new sitcom on Monday night.

9. This music is putting me in a relaxed mood.

10. Wooden tent stakes have been replaced by plastic or metal ones.

11. Whose car is parked in front of your apartment?

12. Because of the dense fog, the nervous detective could see only a dim outline of the figure.

13. Michael's new puppy loves to chew on things.

14. Probably the hottest new sport in town is in-line skating.

15. All the excited fans cheered on their favorite tennis star.

16. Kristin brought some Norwegian cookies her grandmother made to the club's last party.

Grammar

17. Trevor really wanted <u>the lead</u> role in <u>the</u> play, but <u>his</u> tryout was <u>a</u> disaster.

18. <u>Juwan's</u> sister donated <u>her old</u> computer to <u>the new</u> club.

19. Please take off <u>that awful</u> mask!

20. <u>The international</u> student in <u>our</u> class is <u>a</u> Brazilian.

▶ **Exercise 2** **Complete each sentence by adding an appropriate adjective in the space provided.**
Answers will vary. Some suggestions are given.

That was the most _____<u>interesting</u>_____ book I've ever read.

1. Sylvia unpacked her _____<u>denim</u>_____ jacket.

2. The actor gave a _____<u>realistic</u>_____ portrayal of the downtrodden farmer.

3. The _____<u>thirsty</u>_____ traveler stared at the icy glass of water.

4. The women entered the _____<u>grocery</u>_____ store.

5. We gave the _____<u>polite</u>_____ server a generous tip.

6. Samantha bit into the ripe, _____<u>juicy</u>_____ peach.

7. The _____<u>sharp</u>_____ knife cut the roast easily.

8. People consider Lucas a very _____<u>friendly</u>_____ boy.

9. The teacher seems to like _____<u>modern</u>_____ paintings.

10. My brother's _____<u>Japanese</u>_____ motorcycle is in the garage.

11. _____<u>Greek</u>_____ food can be really tasty.

12. The _____<u>tall</u>_____ girl is the captain of the volleyball team.

13. The inspector confiscated the _____<u>fake</u>_____ diamonds.

14. My aunt and uncle's vacation in Colorado was a _____<u>memorable</u>_____ experience.

15. Her best friend moved to a town in the _____<u>western</u>_____ part of the state.

16. Tracy's favorite class was the one on _____<u>Victorian</u>_____ literature.

17. It's _____<u>foolish</u>_____ to climb on the bridge.

18. I like any kind of _____<u>lively</u>_____ music.

19. The _____<u>first</u>_____ person who came around the corner was a police officer.

20. The _____<u>critical</u>_____ article about the school's dress code was written by the assistant
editor.

Lesson 9
Adverbs

An **adverb** is a word that modifies a verb, an adjective, or another adverb by making its meaning more specific. Adverbs modify by answering the questions *when? where? how?* and *to what degree?*

We left **early** for the soccer game. (The adverb *early* modifies the verb *left* by answering the question *when?)*

Janine waited **there** for the bus. (The adverb *there* modifies the verb *waited* by answering the question *where?)*

The nurse **quietly** shut the door of the hospital room. (The adverb *quietly* modifies the verb *shut* by answering the question *how?)*

Very few things in life are **completely** perfect. (The adverb *completely* modifies the adjective *perfect* by answering the question *to what degree?*)

Negative words, such as *not* and its contraction *-n't,* are also considered adverbs. Other negative words such as *nowhere, hardly,* and *never* can also function as adverbs.

The boat has **not** arrived.   I have **never** eaten squid.

▶ **Exercise 1 Circle the word or words modified by the adverb in italics. On the blank, write *v* if the adverb modifies a verb. Write *adj.* if the adverb modifies an adjective. Write *adv.* if the adverb modifies another adverb.**

___v___   Whitney *almost* cleared the hurdle.

___adv.___ **1.** I've seen Alison at the nursing home *very* often.

___v___ **2.** Ben *easily* made the cross-country team.

___adj.___ **3.** Our class had a *really* fantastic time on the field trip to the science museum.

___v___ **4.** Two hundred people had *already* ordered tickets.

___v___ **5.** *Sometimes* nice guys do finish first.

___adj.___ **6.** Shannon had a *very* difficult time after the accident.

___v___ **7.** Late in the afternoon storm clouds gathered *overhead.*

___v___ **8.** Farrah's purse was *nowhere* in the room.

___v___ **9.** *Now* and *then,* I wish for something impossible.

___v___ **10.** England had not *yet* prepared for war.

___v___ **11.** Don't stay out in the sun too *long.*

___v___ **12.** Zach would *never* understand his sister and her friends.

For item 10 also accept as correct *not* modifying *yet*, an adverb.

adj. **13.** *Almost* (every) person at the meeting was angry about the decision.

_v_ **14.** I (ll talk) to you *later.*

adj. **15.** Tuyen was *completely* (calm) when we jumped out and yelled "Happy Birthday!"

adv. **16.** Birds migrate alone *very* (infrequently).

_v_ **17.** (Hand) in your paper *today.*

adj. **18.** I don't think she was *entirely* (sure) what she had said.

adv. **19.** *Only* (rarely) can gorillas breed in captivity.

_v_ **20.** We (haven't succeeded) yet, but we'll keep on trying.

▶ **Exercise 2 Underline the adverb or adverbs in each sentence.**

Slowly, Marcus made his way to the front of the train.

1. Nicholas timidly thanked me for the birthday gift.

2. Your business with Carol is altogether private.

3. We had scarcely arrived at the park when the storm began.

4. The visiting team arrived late for the big game.

5. Kwan came here looking for you.

6. Louis had not considered that alternative.

7. Mr. Wilson usually hires students during the summer.

8. Gillian is the player who most frequently scores.

9. The votes cast in the third precinct were counted early.

10. Surprisingly, the plane was nearly empty.

11. Janice often runs through the field to the track.

12. The frightened rabbit never knew I only wanted to take its picture.

13. The rink will soon be filled with skaters.

14. Mr. Hernandez caught some bass and perch today in Silver Lake.

15. The referee blew his whistle loudly.

16. The runaway colt has not been seen lately.

17. I really must leave now.

18. We went back to the very dark cave.

19. Cooper was startled enough to scream.

20. Next, our class wholeheartedly applauded the speaker.

▶ **Exercise 3** **Underline the adverb or adverbs in each sentence. Then draw an arrow from each adverb to the word or words it modifies.**

The results of the experiment were clearly shown.

1. Fry these Chinese vegetables quickly.

2. The woman in the movie seemed truly sorry for her behavior.

3. I'll probably never get this chance again.

4. Aunt Polly was quite surprised by the thoughtful gift.

5. We heard the foghorn twice.

6. There was a yellow ribbon on almost every tree.

7. I have not seen that show yet.

8. Reluctantly, the old man closed the gate.

9. Ms. Rustagi seemed very glad about the results of the election.

10. Mortimer always talks foolishly at these editorial meetings.

11. Put your coats and hats here.

12. They asked us so politely.

13. The rank of Eagle Scout is not easily achieved.

14. The last contestant finally raised her hand.

15. Somewhat unhappily, the basketball team left the court.

16. That package should arrive tomorrow.

17. The baby looked everywhere for the rattle.

18. My mother recently got a job in an insurance office.

19. LaShon hasn't called lately.

20. Very often, the best team doesn't win the tournament.

For item 3, accept as correct *probably* modifying *never*, *never* modifying *again*, and *again* modifying *will get*.

Grammar

▶ **Exercise 4** **Complete each sentence by adding an adverb that answers the question indicated.**
Answers will vary. Suggestions are given.

The Beatles became _____extremely_____ popular in America. (to what degree?)

1. You can read your book _____later_____. (when?)

2. Put the soccer ball _____there_____, where no one will trip over it. (where?)

3. The woodpecker _____carefully_____ plucked the insect out of the hole. (how?)

4. James understood _____perfectly_____ well what he needed to do. (to what degree?)

5. In spite of the sandbag wall, the river _____easily_____ flooded its banks. (how?)

6. I saw prairie dogs _____everywhere_____ I looked. (where?)

7. Darcie's campaign for student council wasn't going _____well_____. (how?)

8. We were _____partially_____ paid back out of the club treasury. (to what degree?)

9. The children behaved _____disgracefully_____ when the teacher left the room. (how?)

10. Mr. Li promised we would work on the algebra _____tomorrow_____. (when?)

11. I've never seen anyone eat so _____fast_____. (how?)

12. The butler looked _____rather_____ nervous as the detective asked questions. (to what degree?)

13. Lisa's family moved into their new apartment _____yesterday_____. (when?)

14. They had been staying _____temporarily_____ at a motel on Broad Street. (how?)

15. If you enter this contest, you are _____automatically_____ registered for all others. (how?)

16. Lea was _____very_____ lucky to win the contest. (to what degree?)

17. The veterinarian said there was nothing _____medically_____ wrong with their hamster. (how?)

18. The woman at the desk asked us to wait _____here_____ for the mayor. (where?)

19. Hawks and eagles fly _____higher_____ than almost any other birds. (how?)

20. If the patient doesn't receive the medicine _____soon_____, he will be in great danger. (when?)

▶ **Writing Link** **Write three or four sentences about sledding. Use adverbs in your sentences.**

_____

_____

_____

_____

_____

Some adverbs have different forms to indicate degree of comparison.

POSITIVE	COMPARATIVE	SUPERLATIVE
walks **fast**	walks **faster**	walks **fastest**
writes **neatly**	writes **more neatly**	writes **most neatly**
hears **well**	hears **better**	hears **best**
behaves **badly**	behaves **worse**	behaves **worst**

▶ **Exercise 5** **Complete each sentence by adding the adverb in the form indicated.**

Kayla swam _____*more frequently*_____ than her sister. (frequently, comparative)

1. Stephanie seemed _____*truly*_____ grateful for all the gifts she received. (truly, positive)

2. I've never seen anyone walk _____*slower or more slowly*_____ than my younger brother. (slow *or* slowly, comparative)

3. The liquid in the third beaker bubbled _____*most rapidly*_____ of all. (rapidly, superlative)

4. He will probably sing _____*well*_____ in a rock band. (well, positive)

5. It was obvious that Josh had copied the drawing _____*more accurately*_____ than Reese did. (accurately, comparative)

6. The A group performed badly, but the E group did _____*worst*_____ of all. (badly, superlative)

7. If you trained harder, you could ride _____*faster*_____. (fast, comparative)

8. She changed from subject to subject _____*more quickly*_____ than I could follow. (quickly, comparative)

9. He knew the material in the chapter _____*better*_____ than anyone else. (well, comparative)

10. The green car was moving _____*slowest or most slowly*_____. (slow *or* slowly, superlative)

11. The black and white kitten behaved _____*more shyly*_____ than the ginger-colored one. (shyly, comparative)

12. Tony wore his letter jacket _____*most proudly*_____ of all the team members. (proudly, superlative)

13. All the students handed in their reports _____*earlier*_____ than I did. (early, comparative)

14. Your brother Chris did really _____*well*_____ on his college entrance tests, didn't he? (well, positive)

15. The young woman in the melodrama sat _____*forlornly*_____ by the riverbank and sang a melancholy tune. (forlornly, positive)

Grammar

16. The bells seemed to peal _____ more joyfully _____ than ever before. (joyfully, comparative)

17. Jessica handled the difficult situation _____ most tactfully _____. (tactfully, superlative)

18. The doctor said she will see you as _____ soon _____ as possible. (soon, positive)

19. Our school's team played badly, but luckily for us, Lincoln County played _____ worse _____. (badly, comparative)

20. Unfortunately, the team from Vernon played _____ best _____. (well, superlative)

When an adverb modifies a *verb,* it may be placed in various positions in relation to the verb. When an adverb modifies an *adjective* or *another adverb,* it comes immediately before the modified word.

Modifying a verb	Danielle is **probably** eating lunch.
	Danielle **probably** is eating lunch.
	Probably Danielle is eating lunch.
Modifying an adjective	The ground was **very** dry.
Modifying an adverb	We **almost** always take our dog.

▶ **Exercise 6** **Place a check next to each sentence in which the adverb is positioned correctly.**

___✔___ Owning a bike probably requires some knowledge of repair.

___✔___ **1.** Bikes work much more efficiently when all their systems are adjusted properly.

_____ **2.** If you learn to repair your own bike, you'll never have to take it to a bike shop almost.

___✔___ **3.** Generally, a person who is handy can repair most things on a bike.

_____ **4.** There are, however, quite some difficult jobs that are best left to a professional.

___✔___ **5.** Probably the most important safety feature on a bicycle is the brakes.

___✔___ **6.** You can adjust the brakes more easily with a simple tool called a third hand.

___✔___ **7.** A third hand simply holds the yokes apart so that you can adjust the rubber brake pads.

_____ **8.** It's time to adjust the brake pads when they start making an unpleasant screeching sound somewhat.

___✔___ **9.** The brake pads should press smoothly against the metal wheel rims.

_____ **10.** Another occasionally repair that bike owners attempt is cleaning or replacing an old chain.

___✔___ **11.** Scrubbing a dirty chain with kerosene and an old toothbrush will usually do the trick.

_____ **12.** Rarely only does a chain or other part need to be completely replaced.

Grammar

Lesson 10
Prepositions

A **preposition** is a word that shows the relationship of a noun or a pronoun to some other word in a sentence.

The cat food is inside the cupboard.   **We'll go to the movie after lunch.**

These are some commonly used prepositions:

aboard	as	but (except)	in	out	toward
about	at	by	inside	outside	under
above	before	concerning	into	over	underneath
across	behind	despite	like	past	until
after	below	down	near	pending	unto
against	beneath	during	of	regarding	up
along	beside	except	off	since	upon
amid	besides	excepting	on	through	with
among	between	for	onto	throughout	within
around	beyond	from	opposite	to	without

A **compound preposition** is a preposition made up of more than one word.

according to	apart from	because of	in front of	next to	out of
ahead of	aside from	by means of	in spite of	on account of	owing to
along with	as to	in addition to	instead of	on top of	

Prepositions begin phrases that generally end with a noun or a pronoun called the **object of the preposition**.

The horses jumped over the fence.   **They showered the king with gifts.**

▶ **Exercise 1** Circle the prepositions in each sentence. Sentences can have more than one preposition. If the sentence has no prepositions, circle nothing.

Keith visited the island (during) the rainy season.

1. Roberto Clemente was one (of) the greatest baseball players (of) all time.

2. Roberto Walker Clemente was born (on) August 18, 1934, (in) Carolina, Puerto Rico.

3. He is a member (of) the Baseball Hall (of) Fame (in) Cooperstown, New York.

4. Clemente began his career playing softball (for) the Santruce Cangrejeros.

5. He played (with) them (until) 1953, when he signed (with) the Brooklyn Dodgers.

6. Clemente played his entire major league career (as) an outfielder (with) the Pittsburgh Pirates.

7. He batted and threw right-handed (throughout) his career.

8. Although he weighed only 175 pounds, Clemente used one (of) the heaviest bats (in) the big leagues.

9. Clemente could hit (with) power, averaging seventeen home runs (in) a season.

10. (In) 1967 Clemente achieved his highest batting average (of) .357.

11. He batted .362 (in) the 1960 and the 1971 World Series.

12. He was named Most Valuable Player (at) the end (of) the 1966 season.

13. Roberto Clemente was also the most feared defensive outfielder (of) his time.

14. His powerful throwing arm was legendary.

15. He led the league (in) throwing out base runners five times.

16. His acrobatic fielding often took fans' breath away.

17. Sandy Koufax's advice (for) pitching (to) Clemente was "Roll the ball."

18. The manager (of) the New York Yankees called Clemente the best rightfielder he had ever seen.

19. Clemente played (on) twelve National League All-Star teams (during) his career.

20. (On) the last day (of) the regular 1972 season, Roberto got his three-thousandth hit.

21. Clemente was a superstar (on) the baseball field, but he is also remembered (for) other things.

22. When the Puerto Rican-born Clemente played his first game (in) 1955, fewer than twenty-five Hispanic players were (on) the rosters.

23. Hispanic players faced prejudice (from) both teammates and fans.

24. (In) fact Roberto Clemente was called "Bob" (in) his first few seasons because many Americans were still uncomfortable (with) foreign-sounding names.

25. Major league baseball had been allowing African American players (for) less than ten years.

26. (Like) Jackie Robinson, the first African American (in) the major leagues, Roberto Clemente changed the attitudes (of) baseball fans (across) the country.

27. When the Pirates won the 1960 World Series, Clemente skipped the team party.

28. Instead, he walked (around) the neighborhoods (of) Pittsburgh thanking fans (for) their support.

29. Clemente often helped people (in) trouble.

30. Clemente's concern (for) others cost him his life.

31. When an airplane carrying supplies (for) earthquake victims (in) Nicaragua crashed (into) the Caribbean Sea (on) December 31, 1972, Roberto Clemente was (aboard) that plane.

32. His loss was felt (by) Puerto Rico, the city (of) Pittsburgh, and baseball fans everywhere.

33. Roberto Clemente helped make a difference (in) the lives (of) many people.

Lesson 11
Conjunctions: Coordinating, Correlative, and Subordinating; Interjections

Grammar

A **conjunction** is a word that joins single words or groups of words. A **coordinating conjunction** joins words or groups of words that have equal grammatical weight in a sentence. *And, but, or, nor, for, so,* and *yet* are coordinating conjunctions.

Germaine washed the dishes **and** dried them.
The squirrel buried the nut, **but** the dog dug it up.

Correlative conjunctions work in pairs to join words and groups of words of equal weight in a sentence.

both...and   just as...so   not only...but also
either...or   neither...nor   whether...or

Both whales **and** dolphins are mammals.
Whether I fail **or** succeed, my parents will still support me.

A **subordinating conjunction** joins two ideas, or clauses, so that one is grammatically dependent on the other.

after	as long as	if	than	whenever
although	as soon as	in order that	though	where
as	as though	since	unless	whereas
as far as	because	so	until	wherever
as if	before	so that	when	while

He listened to music **until** he fell asleep.
Whenever I see a mountain, I want to climb it.

▶ **Exercise 1** Circle the conjunctions. In the blank write *coord.* if the conjunction is coordinating. Write *corr.* if the conjunction is correlative. Write *sub.* if the conjunction is subordinating.

sub. We will leave for vacation (as soon as) the tickets arrive.

sub. **1.** (While) many people have watched a marathon race, few have ever competed in one.

coord. **2.** It's Friday night, (and) I have to stay home to clean my room.

corr. **3.** (Neither) Sasha (nor) her brother could locate the car.

coord. **4.** We will visit Washington, D.C., (or) Williamsburg, Virginia, in June.

sub. **5.** (Although) I prefer apples, I also like strawberries.

corr. **6.** (Both) Jason (and) Eric made the basketball team.

sub. **7.** (Whenever) the parents leave for work, the children throw a temper tantrum.

sub. **8.** The fans were quiet (until) the golfer putted.

coord. **9.** The deadline for our science project is in two weeks,(so)you still have time.

corr. **10.** (Not only)did Maria win,(but)she(also)broke her record.

coord. **11.** Patrick overslept(and)missed the bus.

sub. **12.** In soccer,(as long as)you head the ball properly, it will not hurt you.

corr. **13.** Coach Ramirez debated(whether)to kick(or)to run.

sub. **14.** (When)the verdict came in, the defendant sobbed.

coord. **15.** Is Dad cooking dinner tonight(or)ordering pizza?

sub. **16.** (Wherever)the divers went, they found a treasure.

corr. **17.** (Either)your assignments are in on time(or)you fail the course.

sub. **18.** The Jacksons lock their doors every night(because)thefts occur frequently in their town.

coord. **19.** The storm intensified,(but)the hikers continued their journey.

corr. **20.** (Just as)radar works by sending out signals,(so)does sonar.

An **interjection** is a word that expresses emotion or exclamation. An interjection has no grammatical connection to other words.

oh	wow	oops	ouch	well	whew	ah	yipes	uh-oh
gee	ow	hey	hooray	alas	why	man	my	uh-huh

Why, I didn't realize that.   **Oops,** sorry about that.   **Uh-oh,** she'd better watch out.

▶ **Exercise 2 Complete each sentence by choosing an interjection from the list above. Answers will vary. Suggestions are given.**

_____**Uh-oh**_____ , I forgot my jacket.

1. _____**Ow**_____ ! That hurt!

2. _____**Hooray**_____ ! We won!

3. _____**Uh-huh**_____ , I'm going. Will I see you there?

4. _____**Whew**_____ , that was a close call.

5. _____**Oh**_____ , I didn't know you wanted to come.

6. _____**Ah**_____ , that tastes great!

7. _____**Well**_____ , if you don't want to play, don't play.

8. _____**Ouch**_____ ! You stepped on my foot.

9. _____**Why**_____ , what did you think it meant?

10. _____**My**_____ , how you've grown.

Unit 1 **Review**

▶ **Exercise 1** In the blank, identify the part of speech of the words in italics. Write *n* for a noun and *p* for a pronoun. Write *adj.* for an adjective and *adv.* for an adverb. Write *v* for a verb, *prep.* for a preposition, *c* for a conjunction, and *i* for an interjection.

adj.   **1.** The United States has hundreds of important *historical* sites, many of which have been designated national monuments.

c   **2.** Our national monuments include *both* natural wonders *and* structures built by people.

v   **3.** Millions of tourists *visit* these monuments every year.

prep.   **4.** Some of the monuments, such as the Statue of Liberty, are located *in* urban areas.

p   **5.** *Others,* including Yellowstone, the first national park, are located far from big cities.

adv.   **6.** One of the *most* popular national monuments is the Vietnam Veterans Memorial.

n   **7.** On the wall are the *names* of more than fifty-eight thousand Americans who died in the Vietnam War from 1960 to 1975.

v   **8.** The nation's capital *is* also the site of memorials to many outstanding Americans.

prep.   **9.** High points *of* a visit to Washington, D.C., are the Washington Monument, the Lincoln Memorial, and the Jefferson Memorial.

n   **10.** Massive *images* of these three presidents, along with one of Theodore Roosevelt, are included in the Mount Rushmore National Monument in South Dakota.

v   **11.** Not all of our national monuments *honor* famous people.

adv.   **12.** If you visited southwestern Colorado, you would find *there* Mesa Verde National Park.

n   **13.** *Mesa Verde* is a collection of Native American cliff dwellings.

p   **14.** Here is an ancient apartment building with 217 rooms—*all* under one roof!

adj.   **15.** The country's *highest* mountain, Mount McKinley, is in Denali National Park in Alaska.

adv.   **16.** *Surprisingly,* the lowest point in the United States is also a national monument.

n   **17.** In fact California's Death Valley is the lowest *point* in the Western Hemisphere.

prep.   **18.** Other national monuments honor groups of Americans, *among* them the Women's Rights National Historic Park and the Civil Rights Memorial.

adj.   **19.** Seneca Falls, New York, is the site of the first large meeting held in 1848 to plan a campaign to bring *equal* rights to women.

adj.   **20.** The Civil Rights Memorial was built in Montgomery, Alabama, where Martin Luther King Jr. led a boycott of the city bus system to protest *racial* discrimination.

Cumulative Review: Unit 1

▶ **Exercise 1** In the blank write *n* if the italicized word is used a noun. Write *p* if it is used as a pronoun. Write *v* if it is used as a verb. Write *adj.* if it is used as an adjective. Write *adv.* if it is used as an adverb. Write *c* if it is used as a conjunction. Write *prep.* if it is used as a preposition. Write *i* if it is used as an interjection.

___v___ **1.** He *cut* six slices of bread and put them on the plate.

___adv.___ **2.** Her letter came *back* stamped "Return to Sender."

___n___ **3.** In all fairness, I haven't heard his *side* of the story yet.

___adj.___ **4.** The freight train pulled off onto a *side* track to let the passenger train pass.

___adv.___ **5.** The hero rode off into the sunset, and the townspeople haven't seen him *since.*

___c___ **6.** *Since* you're so sure you're right, why don't you raise your hand?

___prep.___ **7.** You probably drove *past* the school building on your way here.

___adj.___ **8.** A person who can't dance very well is sometimes said to have two *left* feet.

___adv.___ **9.** The problem is they turned right when they should have turned *left.*

___prep.___ **10.** Whenever she insists on going *up* the down staircase, it causes a massive traffic jam.

___i___ **11.** *Why,* you're the news anchor for the Channel 10 news!

___adv.___ **12.** I do *not* want that rusty old bicycle.

___v___ **13.** It was fascinating to watch the border collies *corner* the runaway sheep.

___n___ **14.** If you ask me, the best thing about winter is that it's always followed by *spring.*

___c___ **15.** *Before* you go, be sure to turn off all the lights and close the curtains.

___prep.___ **16.** I told her I would call her *before* next Monday.

___n___ **17.** The fans cheered wildly when the American women won the *shot put* at the track meet.

___adj.___ **18.** The sales clerk at the department store said I could choose *either* blouse.

___p___ **19.** Richard said he didn't really care for *either.*

___i___ **20.** *Well,* don't say I didn't warn you.

___v___ **21.** If you don't *clean* your car's carburetor, the engine won't run smoothly.

___c___ **22.** *When* I found out about the concert, I was really upset.

Unit 2: Parts of the Sentence

Lesson 12
Simple Subjects and Simple Predicates

Every sentence has two main parts, a subject and a predicate. The **simple subject** is the main noun or pronoun that tells what the sentence is about.

The **batter** swung at the third ball. (main noun as simple subject)
She hit a high pop foul. (main pronoun as simple subject)

A **simple predicate** is the verb or verb phrase that expresses action or being about the subject.

The crowd **cheered** after the touchdown. (main verb as simple predicate)
The team **will practice** on Saturday. (main verb phrase as simple predicate)

You can find a simple subject by asking *Who?* or *What?* about the verb.

My **grandmother** lived in Poland as a girl. (Who lived in Poland?)
Her **quilts** have won many prizes at state fairs. (What won many prizes?)

▶ **Exercise 1 Draw one line under the simple subject and two lines under the simple predicate of each sentence below.**

I am ready for a vacation.

1. Our family traveled through Africa last summer.

2. At the airport we joined a sightseeing tour.

3. The guide loaded us into a huge old van.

4. He drove the van to a nearby game preserve.

5. Unfortunately, the ancient vehicle lacked good shock absorbers.

6. Our bodies were jolted with every turn of the wheels.

7. Clouds of dust around the van obscured our vision.

8. The driver slowed the van to a stop.

9. Mom started loading her camera in anticipation.

10. Suddenly, several passengers spotted a giraffe and several lions.

11. Soundlessly, we crept from the van for a closer look.

12. The lions were snoozing in the sun.

13. Two small cubs batted each other with padded paws.

14. A zebra <u>herd</u> cautiously <u>passed</u> the sleeping lions.

15. The <u>driver</u> <u>pointed</u> at a hyena on the lookout for its meal.

16. In the distance an <u>elephant</u> was <u>eating</u> the bark off a tree.

17. <u>I</u> could hardly <u>believe</u> the nearness of so many wild creatures.

18. <u>Mom</u> <u>shot</u> a whole roll of film at just that one location.

19. The <u>day</u> <u>ended</u> too soon with a journey back to the town.

20. Maybe <u>we</u> can <u>return</u> to this serene spot next year.

▶ **Exercise 2 Supply a simple subject for each of the sentences below by writing a noun or a pronoun in the blank. Draw two lines under each simple predicate.** Answers may vary.

My _____pets_____ <u>are</u> safe.

1. Earlier today, the weather _____reporter_____ <u>announced</u> an approaching snowstorm.

2. _____Father_____ <u>filled</u> several plastic bottles with fresh water.

3. _____Mom_____ <u>hung</u> extra tarpaulins over the windows in the family room.

4. My _____brother_____ <u>rushed</u> outside to find the animals.

5. My _____sister_____ <u>gathered</u> flashlights and candles.

6. Soon the _____sky_____ <u>darkened</u>.

7. The _____wind_____ in the trees <u>was moaning</u> eerily.

8. _____We_____ <u>heard</u> the sounds of the storm distinctly.

9. After a particularly loud crash _____Jerry_____ <u>told</u> a joke for relief.

10. The _____dogs_____ <u>were crouching</u> unhappily at our feet.

11. The _____cat_____, however, <u>strolled</u> through the house serenely.

12. Shortly after a lightning strike, the _____lights_____ <u>flickered</u> out.

13. Luckily _____Dad_____ <u>had bought</u> a battery-powered radio after the last storm.

14. _____We_____ <u>sat</u> in the dark with the radio as a friendly voice.

15. A _____bridge_____ <u>had been smashed</u> by high water on the Little River.

16. Thankfully, the _____police_____ <u>had closed</u> it just minutes before.

17. Civil defense _____squads_____ <u>were providing</u> shelter in the schools.

18. My _____parents_____ <u>worried</u> about their families a few miles upstate.

19. The long _____night_____ <u>passed</u> slowly into daylight.

20. _____I_____ <u>will</u> not <u>forget</u> the storm of July 1994.

Lesson 13
Complete Subjects and Complete Predicates

Grammar

Most sentences have additional words that tell more about the simple subject and the simple predicate.

The complete subject is made up of the simple subject and all the words that tell about it.

The members of the team voted to buy new uniforms.

The complete predicate is made up of all the words that tell what the subject is or does, including the simple predicate.

The principal of the school **invited us to a board meeting.**

A good way to find the complete subject and complete predicate in a sentence is to find the simple subject and simple predicate first.

The **president** of our class **won** the election by a landslide.

Once you have located the simple subject and predicate, then you can divide the entire sentence into complete subject and complete predicate.

The **president** of our class | **won** the election by a landslide.

▶ **Exercise 1** Draw one line under the simple subject. Draw two lines under the simple predicate. Draw a vertical line (I) between the complete subject and the complete predicate.

A box of old letters | was found in the trunk.

1. Several photos of the fire | were in the paper.

2. Gabriella | will take her science project to the fair.

3. The nature documentary | showed the life of a coral reef.

4. Miguel's bicycle | was stolen from the school bike rack.

5. Many people on our block | have dogs and cats.

6. We | are learning about the Arctic tundra in geography.

7. Rita | kicked four goals in her soccer game yesterday.

8. Three of the high-school classes | planned a community project.

9. A new video | will be my present to my brother.

10. Our local scout troop | has hiked up Mount Baldy three times.

11. Jena | spoke to me about her birthplace in Bosnia-Herzegovina.

12. The new encyclopedia | contains much updated material.

13. A <u>number</u> of farmers|<u>formed</u> a credit union.

14. The <u>rescuers</u>|<u>chopped</u> through the door.

15. Carla's <u>grandfather</u>|<u>writes</u> often to his family in Italy.

16. The beautiful <u>stone</u> in her ring|<u>is</u> an opal.

17. That television <u>drama</u>|<u>was</u> very unrealistic.

18. A high <u>wall</u>|<u>surrounded</u> the large mansion.

19. <u>We</u>|<u>will study</u> for the exam next week.

20. The <u>airport</u>|<u>is</u> just off Exit 14.

21. The <u>fans</u> in the grandstand|<u>cheered</u> the home team.

22. My <u>uncle</u>|<u>knows</u> a lot about solar energy.

23. The frisky <u>squirrel</u>|<u>leaped</u> for the birdfeeder.

24. Forty Canada <u>geese</u>|<u>landed</u> on the lawn.

25. Our <u>families</u>|<u>were invited</u> to the school picnic.

26. <u>They</u>|<u>dived</u> into the pool.

27. The lovely old <u>oak</u>|<u>came</u> down in the storm.

28. <u>Suellen</u>|<u>was practicing</u> for the skating contest.

29. My <u>cousin</u>|<u>called</u> me long distance last night.

30. The angry <u>drivers</u>|<u>were stalled</u> at the accident site.

31. The heavy <u>rain</u>|<u>brought</u> many worms to the surface.

32. The <u>pilot</u>|<u>landed</u> the stricken jet in a field.

33. My favorite <u>dessert</u>|<u>is</u> lemon sherbet.

34. The <u>cooks</u> at school|<u>baked</u> a cake for the principal's birthday.

35. Our <u>visitors</u> from the city|<u>were listening</u> to the croaking frogs.

36. Hillary's <u>cousins</u> from Seattle|<u>will be</u> at the wedding tomorrow.

37. <u>Jan</u>|<u>performed</u> the chemistry experiment successfully.

38. <u>You</u>|<u>will enjoy</u> the seventh-grade play.

39. The simmering <u>volcano</u>|<u>erupted</u> suddenly.

40. <u>Roger</u>|<u>slid</u> into third base safely.

Lesson 14
Compound Subjects and Compound Predicates

Grammar

A **compound subject** consists of two or more simple subjects that share the same verb. The two subjects are joined by a conjunction. (For a list of conjunctions, see Lesson 11, page 71.) The conjunctions in the following sentences are *and, neither … nor,* and *either … or.*

Andrea and **Rick** entered the relay race.
Neither the **teachers** nor the **students** favor the new schedule.
Either **cinnamon** or **nutmeg** is used in this recipe.

▶ **Exercise 1** Draw one line under each compound subject and two lines under the simple predicate they share. Circle the conjunction or conjunctions.

Misha and I saw Lani at the mall.

1. Clubs and sports are two of Lani's favorite hobbies.

2. Neither Chris nor Juan shares her interest.

3. Lani and her other friends belong to the drama club.

4. Either Tuesday or Wednesday is the day of their next meeting.

5. Sets, costumes, and props will be discussed.

6. Scripts and audition forms will be passed out.

7. Lani and Susan will audition for the fall play.

8. Either *Our Town* or *Romeo and Juliet* will be the first production.

9. Neither the drama teacher nor the club president can decide.

10. Either March or April will be the month of the second production.

11. Tessa and Mr. Tanaka will choose a musical for the spring play.

12. *Oklahoma!* and *The Sound of Music* are Lani's favorite shows.

13. Lights and sound could be a problem, though.

14. Neither time nor money is available for the improvement of the auditorium.

15. Mr. Tanaka and the drama club are meeting with the school board this afternoon.

16. Either Ms. Jenkins or Mr. Rodriguez will preside at the meeting.

17. Drama and other extracurricular activities are on the agenda.

18. Mr. Tanaka, Tessa, and Lani will make short speeches.

19. Interest and enthusiasm for drama clubs are their topics.

20. Either Lani or Tessa will speak first.

A **compound predicate** consists of two simple predicates that share the same subject. The two simple predicates are connected by a conjunction.

Harold **picked** the flowers and **arranged** them.
The well-trained dogs **will** neither **bark** nor **bite**.
The angry customer has either **called** or **written** five times.
A flock of birds **swooped** behind the hill but **reappeared** above the trees.

The conjunctions in the sentences above are *and, neither … nor, either … or,* and *but.*

▶ **Exercise 2** **Draw one line under each simple subject and two lines under each compound predicate in the following sentences.**

Audiences admire and enjoy the writer's work.

1. Plays entertain and inform audiences.

2. New plays often open the mind and spark new ideas.

3. Regional theaters either commission new works or read submissions.

4. Playwrights improve and refine their dialogue during rehearsal.

5. Directors can add elements but cannot save a weak script.

6. Actors often try different approaches and choose the most effective one for the character.

7. Set designers create and develop the proper atmosphere for the play.

8. The playwright neither describes nor limits every element of production.

9. Each artist contributes ideas and enhances the show.

10. After the first performance, the playwright will evaluate the script and make improvements.

11. Sometimes audience members complete surveys or offer comments to the writer.

12. The writer can either accept or reject their suggestions.

13. A single play may be produced and revised several times.

14. Broadway producers seek new plays and acquire rights to the best ones.

15. Audiences appreciate new shows but often buy more tickets for familiar works.

16. Producers neither desire nor support unpopular plays.

17. However, interesting new plays excite producers and draw large audiences.

18. The best plays win awards and sometimes become movies.

19. Movies are neither produced nor directed like stage shows.

20. Live theater heightens drama and adds a third dimension for the audience.

Lesson 15
Order of Subject and Predicate

In most sentences that you read and write, the subject comes before the predicate.

    SUBJECT   PREDICATE
The red-tailed **hawk** | **soared** high overhead.

For variety or special emphasis, some sentences are written in inverted order. In such cases the predicate comes before the subject.

    PREDICATE   SUBJECT
High overhead **soared** | the red-tailed **hawk.**

The subject also follows the verb in any sentence that begins with *there* or *here.*

PREDICATE   SUBJECT

There **sit** | the missing **books**!
Here **is** | your birthday **present**.

▶ **Exercise 1 Draw a vertical line (|) between the complete subject and the complete predicate.**

Here is | a summary of the plot.

1. Behind the hills sank | the setting sun.

2. Here are | the photographs of the eclipse.

3. Across the lawn crept | the stalking cat.

4. Myra | watched the baby.

5. Rich | took the pie to the Bayers next door.

6. The rainbow | appeared after the storm.

7. Over the bridge rumbled | the ancient truck.

8. From the broken dam tumbled | the floodwaters.

9. Here are | several of Grandma's quilts.

10. My friend Helen | wants to be a teacher.

11. Here are | the corrected test papers.

12. Over the intercom came | the principal's announcement.

13. Inside the car sat | my baby sister.

14. Behind the bookcase was | the entrance to a secret tunnel.

15. There is | no excuse for your behavior.

16. Through the storm flew|the brave seagull.

17. The weary travelers|camped by the river.

18. Beyond the planet Mars lie|the asteroids.

19. Here is|your baseball glove.

20. Beside the desk was|the missing picture.

▶ **Exercise 2** **Rewrite the sentences below by inverting the order of the subjects and predicates.**

Players from both teams were at the meeting. _At the meeting were players from both teams._

1. Up the falls swam the salmon. _The salmon swam up the falls._

2. Past the crowd sped the wheelchair racers. _The wheelchair racers sped past the crowd._

3. Across the range flew the fighter plane. _The fighter plane flew across the range._

4. On the stove bubbled the chocolate pudding. _The chocolate pudding bubbled on the stove._

5. Spring comes after winter. _After winter comes spring._

6. A grandfather clock stood against the wall. _Against the wall stood a grandfather clock._

7. Through the woods hiked the weary scouts. _The weary scouts hiked through the woods._

8. Tulips and daffodils grew along the fence. _Along the fence grew tulips and daffodils._

9. A pirate ship appeard out of the mist. _Out of the mist appeared a pirate ship._

10. Behind the house stood a pine forest. _A pine forest stood behind the house._

11. Across the sky twinkled the light of the satellite. _The light of the satellite twinkled across the sky._

12. Down the road trotted a riderless pony. _A riderless pony trotted down the road._

13. My best friend stood beside me. _Beside me stood my best friend._

14. Between the jagged cliffs flowed the river. _The river flowed between the jagged cliffs._

15. Throughout the book appeared colorful illustrations. _Colorful illustrations appeared throughout the book._

16. Tiny fish swam beneath the surface of the pond. _Beneath the surface of the pond swam tiny fish._

17. A family of bears lived in the cave. _In the cave lived a family of bears._

18. From the kitchen came the wonderful smell of challah. _The wonderful smell of challah came from the kitchen._

Lesson 16
Complements: Direct and Indirect Objects

A complement completes the meaning of a verb. It may be one word or a group of words. One kind of complement is the direct object. A direct object answers the question *what?* or *whom?* after an action verb.

Mario picked some **flowers** for the mantel. (Mario picked what?)
Liu trusts her **sister** completely. (Liu trusts whom?)

A direct object may have more than one part.

The farmer carried the **calf** and the **lamb** through the floodwaters.

▶ **Exercise 1** Draw one line under the simple subject and two lines under the simple predicate. Circle the direct object. At the end of the sentence, write the word *what?* or *whom?* to tell which question the direct object answers.

Astronomers study celestial (bodies.) what?

1. Early astronomers observed the (heavens) constantly. what?

2. The movements of the sky fascinated (them.) whom?

3. Often they created (myths) and (stories) explaining the stars. what?

4. To learn more, our class visited the (planetarium) yesterday. what?

5. Mr. Simpson told (us) about the solar system. whom?

6. Then we named the (planets) in order from the sun. what?

7. All the planets orbit the (sun.) what?

8. On its surface, tiny Mercury resembles our (moon.) what?

9. However, Mercury lacks an (atmosphere) and a (moon.) what?

10. Venus possesses a poisonous (atmosphere.) what?

11. The spacecraft photographed the (surface) of Venus. what?

12. Clouds covered the (surface.) what?

13. We told (Mr. Simpson) about our studies. whom?

14. First, Earth contains rocky (material.) what?

15. A moon orbits our home (planet.) what?

16. Earth's atmosphere supports many (forms) of life. what?

17. My friend studies (Mars) and (Jupiter.) what?

18. Some <u>people</u> <u>plan</u> a⬭trip⬭ to Mars. _what?_____

19. <u>Mr. Simpson</u> often <u>studies</u> the⬭moon⬭ through a telescope. _what?_____

20. <u>He</u> <u>prefers</u> the⬭moon⬭ to everything else in the solar system. _what?_____

Another kind of complement, the indirect object, answers these questions following an action verb: *to whom? for whom? to what?*

The child threw her **father** and **mother** a kiss. (The child threw a kiss to whom?)
Keanu bought **them** some popcorn. (Keanu bought popcorn for whom?)
The crowd gave our **team** a cheer. (The crowd gave a cheer to what?)

▶ **Exercise 2** **Write *D.O.* above the direct objects and *I.O.* above the indirect objects.**

       I.O.   D.O.
Mr. Stephens read us a legend about the wind.

       I.O.   D.O.
1. Ms. Bailey gave our class a lecture on weather.

       I.O.   D.O.
2. She teaches college students weather forecasting.

       I.O.   D.O.
3. Our science teacher, Mr. Stephens, sent her an invitation.

       I.O.   D.O.   D.O.
4. She brought us weather maps and other data.

       I.O.   D.O.
5. We showed her our ideas for the weather forecasts.

       I.O.   D.O.
6. She offered the class her opinion.

       I.O.   D.O.
7. Mr. Stephens showed us pictures of the first thermometers and barometers from the seventeenth century.

       I.O.   D.O.
8. Weather stations once gave others information on current conditions by telegraph.

       I.O.   D.O.
9. By the late nineteenth century, organizations were providing forecasters standards for weather records.

       I.O.   D.O.
10. In turn, these records provide meteorologists statistics.

       I.O.   D.O.
11. Recent technology gives them more help.

       I.O.   D.O.
12. Satellites send professional forecasters information from space.

       I.O.   D.O.
13. Computers offer them numerical models for predictions.

       I.O.   D.O.
14. These models save meteorologists time.

       I.O.   D.O.
15. The predictions give people warnings about bad weather.

       I.O.   D.O.
16. Ms. Bailey drew our class a graph of weather trends.

Lesson 17
Subject Complements and Object Complements

Certain words in sentences complete the meaning of linking verbs. These words are called **subject complements** because they further identify or describe the subject. The linking verbs used in such sentences include all forms of the verb *be*, as well as the verbs *become, seem, remain, feel, taste, smell, appear, look, grow, stay,* and *sound*.

The two kinds of subject complements are **predicate nominatives** and **predicate adjectives**. A **predicate nominative** is a noun or pronoun that follows a linking verb and identifies or renames the subject.

Harold is our **quarterback**. (What word identifies Harold?)
Reggie Lee remains my **friend**. (What word identifies Reggie Lee?)

A **predicate adjective** is an adjective that follows a linking verb and describes the subject.

Her paintings look **mysterious**. (What word describes the paintings?)
The swimmer was **powerful**. (What word describes the swimmer?)

▶ **Exercise 1 Identify the italicized word(s) in the following sentences as either a predicate nominative, *P.N.*, or a predicate adjective, *P.A.***

P.A.   The new car was *bright* and *shiny.*

P.N. **1.** Mr. Kravitz may become our new science *teacher.*

P.N. **2.** That object in the tree is a *pineapple.*

P.N. **3.** That train robbery remains an unsolved *mystery.*

P.N. **4.** This book on whales is a *gift* from my sister.

P.N. **5.** Jayelle and Simon are the best *performers* in the play.

P.A. **6.** These old apples smell *rotten.*

P.A. **7.** Both Tanya and Rick seemed *cheerful* after the exam.

P.N. **8.** Tika's favorite reptiles are *crocodiles, lizards,* and *turtles.*

P.A. **9.** These pears don't appear *fresh.*

P.A. **10.** The runners look *weary* but *triumphant.*

P.N. **11.** Stella became *chairwoman* of the committee.

P.A. **12.** The soaked and exhausted scouts looked *miserable.*

P.N. **13.** Red, yellow, and blue are primary *colors.*

P.A. **14.** The cut flowers looked *dry* and *lifeless.*

P.A. **15.** My uncle has been *ill.*

___P.N.___ **16.** The sculpture in the park remains his greatest *accomplishment.*

___P.N.___ **17.** First prize in the contest will be a *trip* to Grand Canyon.

___P.A.___ **18.** The runners felt *jubilant* after the race.

___P.N.___ **19.** Her orchard's main crops were *apples* and *cherries.*

___P.N.___ **20.** The Conways and the Hopes seem good *friends.*

Object complements are words that identify or describe a direct object in a sentence. They answer the question *what?* after a direct object in order to complete the meaning of the direct object. An object complement may be a noun, a pronoun, or an adjective.

The mayor apppointed Ken **treasurer.** (Noun)
The dog considers the sofa **his.** (Pronoun)
Residents think the new structure **ugly.** (Adjective)

▶ **Exercise 2 Draw one line under the direct object. Draw two lines under the object complement.**

I find school elections good experience.

1. Our science club chose Gayle the chairperson.

2. Gayle considers astronomy the most compelling science.

3. We, on the other hand, consider her starstruck.

4. I, for example, find botany fascinating.

5. I named my science project "Fabulous Flowers."

6. Other club members call me silly.

7. I will make them botanists by next year.

8. My fellow members will never elect me president.

9. However, they may appoint me lowly notetaker.

10. Several scientists in the club make geology a priority.

11. They call earthquakes and volcanoes marvelous.

12. But then, they consider liquid lava an occasion for celebration.

13. Horace declared Mount Saint Helens his favorite volcano.

14. Of course, the chemistry fans think chemistry a treat.

15. They consider all test tubes theirs.

16. Lena and Ty will make chemistry their major.

☑ Unit 2 **Review**

▶ **Exercise 1** **Draw a vertical line between the complete subject and the complete predicate.
Label each direct object** *D.O.* **and each indirect object** *I.O.* **Draw one line under each predicate
nominative. Draw two lines under each predicate adjective. Circle each object complement.**

                  I.O.   **D.O.**
Fred | gave Dave a baseball.

                    I.O.   **D.O.**
1. Jason | threw Antonio the ball.

                       D.O.
2. The club | named Moira (president.)

3. This salsa | tastes spicy.

4. Mr. Kotlinski | may become our new soccer coach.

                      D.O.
5. Wilson and Kurt | wrote letters to their friends in Japan.

6. First prize | will be a trip to Hong Kong.

7. The conclusion of Noah's paper | was a surprise.

                 I.O.   **D.O.**
8. Corky's dog | brought Sally a torn slipper.

            D.O.   **D.O.**
9. Giorgio | wrote the agenda and gave a copy to each member of the group.

10. The ship's course | seemed unusual.

11. At the conference were | representatives from forty nations.

12. Hiking and camping | are Lee's favorite activities.

                 D.O.
13. Juanita | considers math her best (subject.)

14. Hawaii's flowers | are breathtaking.

15. My friend Heidi | was the leader at the golf tournament.

             I.O.   **D.O.**
16. Alex | baked the class pumpkin bread.

                        D.O.
17. The judges | called Colin's science fair project (extraordinary.)

                 D.O.
18. My cousin Jessica | wants a new stereo.

19. Across many miles traveled | the colorful caravan.

             D.O.
20. Martha | bought some lace in Brussels.

Cumulative Review: Units 1–2

▶ **Exercise 1** Underline nouns once and verbs twice. Draw a vertical line between each complete subject and complete predicate. Label adjectives *Adj.*, articles *A.*, adverbs *Adv.*, direct objects *D.O.*, and indirect objects *I.O.*

                   A.D.O.   A.
1. Omar and Alicia|took a trip to the museum.

              I.O.   A. Adj.   D.O.
2. Kristy|sent Aunt Sue a lovely lamp.

                      A.   Adj. D.O.
3. Julia|wrote and directed the funny play.

    A.   Adv.   A. Adj.   D.O.
4. The supplier|accidentally delivered the wrong material.

    A.   Adv.   A.   I.O.   Adj.   D.O.
5. The lawyer|carefully asked the witness several questions.

              A. D.O.   A. D.O.   A.
6. Aaron|ate the apple and threw the core into the wastebasket.

   Adj.   Adv.
7. Those students|are being honored today.

      A.   Adj.   Adj.
8. On the counter were|handmade boxes of every description.

   Adj.   Adj.   Adv.   A. Adj. D.O.
9. Our swimming team|easily won the large trophy.

   Adj.   Adj.   A. Adj.   A.
10. Nora's incredible singing|was the best part of the program.

                   A.   Adj.   D.O.
11. Francis|scrubbed and waxed the kitchen floor.

                 I.O.   Adj.   D.O.
12. Someone|had been giving Demetrius mysterious gifts.

                Adj.   Adj. Adv.
13. Both Claudia and her brother|have been looking tense lately.

  A.   Adj.   Adv.   Adj. D.O.
14. The rainy weather|had severely limited our activity.

          I.O. A. Adv.   Adj.   D.O.
15. You|offered me a nearly perfect plan.

         A.   Adj.   Adj.   D.O.   A.
16. Someone|left an unfinished jigsaw puzzle on the table.

        A.   Adj.   Adv.   A. Adj.
17. Dr. Connor, a medical missionary,|carefully walked across the barren field.

         A. Adj.   A.
18. Julio|became the best shortstop on the team.

   A.   Adj.   Adv.   A.   D.O.
19. The panting racers|swiftly turned the corner.

                    I.O.   A.D.O.   A.
20. Lisa and Jacques|made Mrs. O'Brien a pie from the strawberries they picked.

Grammar

Unit 3: Phrases

Lesson 18
Prepositional Phrases

A **prepositional phrase** begins with a preposition and usually ends with a noun or a pronoun, called the **object of the preposition**. (For a list of prepositions, see Unit 1, Lesson 10, page 69.) The object may be compound or may have modifiers.

Our stockpile **of snowballs** was depleted quickly.
This pudding is made **with milk and bread.** (compound object)
I brought back film footage **of the horrible storm.** (object with modifier)

A prepositional phrase acts as an **adjective** when it modifies a noun or a pronoun. A prepositional phrase acts as an **adverb** when it modifies a verb, an adjective, or an adverb.

David tried every pair of skis **in the lodge.** (adjective phrase modifying the noun *skis*)
You can come **to the party.** (adverb phrase modifying the verb phrase *can come*)

▶ **Exercise 1** Circle each prepositional phrase in the following sentences.

We met (in the lobby) (after school.)

1. My sister took her books (off the table) (at dinnertime.)

2. (At the party,) we met students who did not go (to our school.)

3. Which (of the movies) is your favorite?

4. Tim sat motionless (for a long time.)

5. We ran (toward the water) when we reached the beach.

6. Sheila always gets nervous (before a performance.)

7. (Inside the auditorium) people talked loudly (until the end) (of the show.)

8. I ran (around the table) and hid (beneath the chair.)

9. Sue promised me her recipe (for stew.)

10. Cheers filled the stadium (throughout the football game.)

11. Would you rather live (in Alaska) or (in Africa?)

12. (By two o'clock) (on the day) (of the bake sale,) all (of the cookies) had been sold.

13. Derek looked (behind the garage) and saw his roller skates.

14. The four (of us) swam laps (in the pool) (after school.)

15. We laughed (at the joke), though it wasn't very funny.

16. Marty proved she could compete (against any member) (of the other team.)

17. Did you travel (by car) or (by train?)

18. The students were encouraged (in their efforts)

19. The parking garage (below the mall) is always full.

20. He studies hard, and his grades are always (above the average.)

▶ **Exercise 2 Circle each prepositional phrase in the sentences below and draw an arrow to the word or words it modifies.**

Sarah looked (through the telescope.)

1. The captain slipped (on the wet deck.)

2. We went (to the movie) (at the last minute,)

3. Which (of the barbells) is heavier?

4. Melissa earned the money (for her new dress.)

5. When Jo forgot her key, she knocked (on the window.)

6. The boy (in the red jacket) plays (on my soccer team.)

7. The doctor told him that joining the track team would be healthful (for him)

8. She was taught table manners (at a young age.)

9. We found sticky paw prints (on the kitchen floor.)

10. Let's meet the new coach (at four o'clock.)

11. Bill hit the ball (into the bleachers)

12. Each (of the girls) wanted some pizza.

13. The computer (in the lab) was used frequently.

14. The school band performed (during the half-time show.)

15. Did you pass your driving test (with flying colors?)

16. (At the museum) we saw paintings and sculptures.

Lesson 19
Participles and Participial Phrases

A **participle** is a verb form that acts as an adjective. It modifies a noun or pronoun.

The car screeched down the (twisting) road. (The participle *twisting* modifies the noun *road*.)

A participle can be present or past. A present participle ends in *-ing*. A past participle usually ends in *-ed*.

A participle with complements and modifiers is called a **participial phrase**. A participial phrase acts as an adjective. It can be in different positions in a sentence. If a participial phrase falls at the beginning of a sentence, it is usually followed by a comma.

Screeching loudly, the car pulled into the service station.

▶ **Exercise 1** **Circle the participle or participial phrase in each sentence.**

(Growing up in an active family,) Carla had acquired many athletic skills.

1. (Being a good kicker,) Carla tried out for the football team.

2. She wanted to be the team's (leading) kicker.

3. (Playing for her middle school team,) she felt ready to compete.

4. However, many other students, (having equal experience,) also decided to try out for the team.

5. (Startled by the number of competitors,) Carla grew nervous.

6. Did all of them have a (winning) record?

7. (Glancing at her competitors,) she discovered that three of them were female.

8. (Considered unique in middle school,) Carla was not prepared to meet other female kickers.

9. A girl (named Molly) introduced herself to Carla.

10. She had been a (celebrated) middle school kicker, too.

11. Carla, (worried about the tryouts,) made a nervous joke.

12. Molly's (determined) pacing showed that she was also nervous.

13. (Breathing deeply,) Carla began to calm down.

14. The coaches (holding the tryouts) gave each student a ball.

15. (Smiling at Molly,) Carla suggested they help each other practice.

16. Molly nodded and gave a (relieved) sigh.

17. (Running after the football,) both girls forgot to be nervous.

18. They had a contest with the other two girls (waiting in the stands.)

19. (Working together) Carla and Molly kicked more field goals than the other team.

20. A coach (watching them) insisted they try out first.

▶ **Exercise 2** **Circle the participial phrase and draw an arrow to the noun or pronoun it modifies.**

Donato sat at his desk, (listening to a classmate's oral report.)

1. (Waiting patiently) Donato organized his notes.

2. His oral report, (inspired by the World Cup competition) was about a famous soccer player.

3. (Reading his first note card) he remembered that soccer is called "football" in many countries.

4. This sport, (played around the world) is growing in popularity.

5. (Keeping that in mind) he thought his classmates would enjoy his report.

6. The student (standing in front of the class) finished her report.

7. (Clearing his throat) Donato approached the lectern.

8. A friend (sitting in the first row) smiled at him.

9. His teacher, (seated in the back) instructed him to begin.

10. (Placing his note cards on the lectern) he introduced his topic.

11. (Speaking carefully) he explained that Edson Arantes do Nascimento was known as Pelé.

12. (Playing for a minor league "football" club) Pelé tried to earn a place on a major league team.

13. The Brazilian athlete, (rejected by several teams) joined the Santos Football Club.

14. This team, (led by Pelé) won two world club championships.

15. Pelé, (continuing to play) headed the Brazilian national team that won three World Cup titles.

16. (Retired from the game in 1975) he decided to play for the New York Cosmos.

17. (Aided by his presence) the Cosmos won the North American Soccer League championship

in 1977.

18. (Retiring again) Pelé received the International Peace Award.

Lesson 20
Gerunds and Gerund Phrases;
Appositives and Appositive Phrases

A **gerund** is a verb form ending in *-ing* that is used as a noun.

Sewing has never interested me.

A **gerund phrase** is a gerund with any complements or modifiers needed to complete its meaning.

Her enthusiastic cheering drew people from yards away.
Moving the chair was not easy.

▶ **Exercise 1** **Circle the gerund or gerund phrase in each sentence.**

(Running for class president) requires a lot of work.

1. I like (eating healthful foods).

2. (Recycling) gives our family a sense of accomplishment.

3. (Quitting) is almost never the best solution.

4. (Cheryl's delicious cooking) keeps her restaurant popular.

5. (Leafing through photos) is a good way to remember old times.

6. We enjoyed (painting the barn.)

7. (Doing the yard work) made us tired.

8. (The whistling of the wind) makes the house seem lonely.

9. (Constant bickering) was making the twins a nuisance.

10. (Pacing the floors) can relieve tension for some people.

11. (Public speaking) was the class assignment everyone feared.

12. (Skating) was Karen's favorite pastime.

13. (The dog's loud barking) made it difficult to hear the television.

14. Miranda enjoyed (exploring new places.)

15. (His unique singing) made him a good candidate for the choir.

16. My hobbies, (cycling and reading,) keep me busy.

17. We wanted to win, but (playing a good game) was just as important.

18. Her greatest hope was (finding her long-lost sister)

19. (Capturing the enemy) was the mission in the latest video game.

20. (Traveling) is a good way to see the world.

An **appositive** is a noun or pronoun placed next to another noun or pronoun to further identify it.

My brother **David** is an engineer.

An **appositive phrase** contains an appositive and any words that modify it. An appositive phrase is usually not essential to the meaning of a sentence. Appositives are often set off by commas.

My brother David, **an engineer in Philadelphia**, enjoys his job.

▶ **Exercise 1 Circle the appositive or appositive phrase in each sentence.**

Dontonio, (my science partner,) helped me write the lab report.

1. Mariel, (a dancer in her own right,) watched the ballerinas dance.

2. My doctor, (Dr. Enriquez,) recently moved to our neighborhood.

3. Nancy's dog (Molly) never barks at anyone.

4. Meagan, (a hard-working student,) will run for class president.

5. The noise, (a piercing wail,) made us cover our ears.

6. The Bears, (the team in the red jerseys,) are going to the playoffs.

7. That museum has several paintings by the French Impressionist painter (Monet.)

8. Tom, (the actor on the left,) has performed in many musicals.

9. My friend (Rachel) came to see me march in the band.

10. The Wright brothers, (Orville and Wilbur,) are credited with the first flight.

11. She lives in Seattle, (the capital of Washington.)

12. Our local newspaper, (*The Sentinel,*) printed a picture of my stepfather with his award.

13. Mrs. Ito, (my sixth-grade teacher,) was a chaperone at the dance.

14. *Animal Farm* is a book by the acclaimed author (George Orwell.)

15. Was that Krista, (the captain of the drill team)?

16. Willie Mays, (the famous home run hitter,) signed one of my baseball cards.

17. During biology, (my first class of the day,) we dissected frogs.

18. *Frankenstein,* (a novel by Mary Shelley,) has been the basis for many films.

Lesson 21
Infinitives and Infinitive Phrases

An **infinitive** is a verb form usually preceded by the word *to*. In this case, *to* is not a preposition, but a part of the infinitive verb form. An infinitive can be used as a noun, an adjective, or an adverb.

I love **to gather** flowers in the spring. (infinitive as a noun)
Our plans **to visit** Civil War battlefields changed drastically. (infinitive as an adjective)
Your address is difficult **to remember**. (infinitive as an adverb)

An **infinitive phrase** includes an infinitive and any complements and modifiers needed to complete its meaning.

Many animals can learn **to recognize people**.

▶ **Exercise 1** **Above each infinitive, write *n* if it is used as a noun, *adj.* if it is used as an adjective, and *adv.* if it is used as an adverb.**

                                                                 adj.
Choosing a setting for a novel is not a decision to make hastily.

                                    adj.
1. An author must choose the right setting to make a novel memorable.
                              adv.
2. For some writers, it was easy to find the best setting.
   n   n
3. To live in London is to have the perfect setting.
                           adv.
4. A novelist can find it interesting to create plots based on the city's rich history.
                                adj.
5. As the center of government, it is the place to witness politics in action.
   adv.
6. To see a great opera, one would also travel to London.
   adv.
7. To shop, a character would head for Oxford Street.
                              adj.
8. There are many parks for a hero or heroine to walk through.
   adv.
9. To visit the oldest royal park, one would go to St. James's.
                           adv.
10. At Regent's Park it is fun to view the Zoological Gardens.
             n
11. At Trafalgar one likes to admire the statue of Lord Nelson, the hero of the battle of Trafalgar.
                 adj.
12. Perhaps the character to write about is Lord Nelson.
                adj.
13. In his day, the place to be was a London district called Mayfair.
          adj.
14. The author to read was Jane Austen.
   adv.
15. To purchase one of Miss Austen's books, one went to Hatchard's on Piccadilly.

adj.
16. Later in the nineteenth century, London became the setting to read about in books by

Charles Dickens.
adj.
17. His old house is an interesting place to visit.
n
18. Dickens liked to stroll through London gathering ideas for characters.
adv.
19. Read one of his books to determine what life was like at the time.
n
20. Think of other authors who chose to place their stories in London.

▶ **Exercise 2 Circle the infinitive or the infinitive phrase in each sentence.**

Sherlock Holmes is known for his ability (to solve baffling mysteries).

1. Sir Arthur Conan Doyle has come (to be well-known as the creator of Sherlock Holmes.)

2. Conan Doyle received a degree in medicine and decided (to work as an eye specialist.)

3. Unfortunately, he was unsuccessful in his attempt (to make a good living.)

4. He wrote his first book (to make money.)

5. Conan Doyle used a doctor he knew (to be the model for Sherlock Holmes.)

6. The time he spent with his friend helped him (to develop the characteristics of Holmes.)

7. Holmes became known for his ability (to observe).

8. Readers were able (to appreciate the fictional detective's inquisitive nature.)

9. Holmes always used his sharp wit (to solve a mystery.)

10. Conan Doyle was knighted (to recognize his defense of the British in one of his books.)

11. That is how he came (to be called "Sir.")"

12. Conan Doyle created the character Dr. Watson (to assist Holmes in his mysteries.)

13. "My dear Watson" is one of the famous phrases (to come from the Sherlock Holmes mysteries.)

14. He often chose (to write books with odd titles.)

15. *The Red-Headed League* is another book title that is hard (to forget.)

16. At one time, Conan Doyle chose (to kill off the legendary detective.)

17. Readers called for him (to bring Holmes back.)

18. Conan Doyle went on (to write fifty-nine more books featuring Sherlock Holmes.)

19. Holmes's signature pipe and hat are items that readers are likely (to remember.)

20. (To see Sherlock Holmes on television and in movies) is not unusual.

Lesson 22

Distinguishing Participial, Gerund, and Infinitive Phrases

The three types of verbal phrases, participial, gerund, and infinitive, are closely related to verbs. However, they do not function as verbs, but as nouns, adjectives, and adverbs. The easiest way to distinguish the phrases is by the way they function in a sentence and by their forms.

- An infinitive phrase can function as a noun, an adjective, or an adverb. Infinitives are usually preceded by the word *to*.
- Participial phrases function as adjectives. Present participles end in *-ing*. Most past participles end in *-ed*.
- Gerund phrases function as nouns. Gerunds end in *-ing*.

▶ **Exercise 1** **Identify the phrase in italics as *I* for infinitive, *G* for gerund, or *P* for participial.**

__G__   Harold will never forget *fumbling in the big game.*

__P__   **1.** She collects figurines *made in the thirties.*

__G__   **2.** *Buying fire extinguishers* is a good way to save lives.

__P__   **3.** *Practicing constantly,* Mike improved his tennis game.

__P__   **4.** The science lab contains many jars *labeled as dangerous.*

__G__   **5.** Jim's goal, *getting elected,* was achieved through hard work.

__I__   **6.** Dan has never been one *to complain about his problems.*

__G__   **7.** There is no excuse for *reckless driving.*

__I__   **8.** My younger sister likes *to slide down the big hill.*

__G__   **9.** *Baking brownies* is our favorite activity on a rainy day.

__P__ **10.** *Laughing at his jokes,* we nearly fell off our chairs.

__P__ **11.** *Putting in extra time,* Ben finished his work.

__I__ **12.** The lawyer argued *to set the record straight.*

__G__ **13.** *Combining the ingredients* is the easy part.

__P__ **14.** Laura was irritated by the wet towels *lying on the carpet.*

__P__ **15.** *Using a flashlight,* Julia found her ring in the dark.

__I__ **16.** Fines were imposed *to discourage littering.*

__I__ **17.** She suggested several books *to read before the test.*

_____P_____ **18.** The admiral wore a jacket *decorated with many medals.*

_____G_____ **19.** *Getting ahead in business* is my uncle's primary goal.

_____I_____ **20.** *To do a tough job well* can be rewarding.

▶ **Exercise 2** **Circle the infinitives and infinitive phrases in each sentence below. Then change each infinitive to a gerund and write the gerund form on the line at the left.**

_____Adding_____ To add sound effects to a production is called dubbing.

_____reducing_____ **1.** According to researchers, to reduce your fat intake can be healthy.

_____Installing_____ **2.** To install a smoke detector is usually a good idea.

_____Burning_____ **3.** To burn leaves is against the law in some places.

_____wearing_____ **4.** Jackie hates to wear long underwear.

_____raising_____ **5.** My mother's main concern was to raise healthy children.

_____failing_____ **6.** My stepbrother reminded me that to fail was no disgrace.

_____Coughing_____ **7.** To cough during the performance would have been rude, so I walked outside.

_____losing_____ **8.** Since we were playing our arch rivals, to lose the game would have been humiliating.

_____Biting_____ **9.** To bite the apple could have been fatal for Snow White.

_____being_____ **10.** Some people think that to be shy is a pleasant quality.

_____Sleeping_____ **11.** To sleep late is a treat for Don, who has a paper route.

_____performing_____ **12.** According to my choir director, to perform in the choir is an honor.

_____Knocking_____ **13.** To knock down the toy clowns was the biggest challenge at the school festival.

_____riding_____ **14.** My grandfather loves to ride his bicycle.

_____Forgetting_____ **15.** To forget the accident was a difficult task for Joanie.

_____playing_____ **16.** The children like to play outdoors.

_____Playing_____ **17.** To play our school song before a game is a band tradition.

_____watching_____ **18.** Katie likes to watch her younger brothers.

_____Computing_____ **19.** To compute the figures will require a calculator.

_____Mowing_____ **20.** To mow the whole lawn took four hours.

Unit 3 **Review**

▶ **Exercise 1 Label each word or phrase in italics using the abbreviations below.**

Pr. - prepositional   *I* - infinitive   *P* - participial   *G* - gerund   *A* - appositive

              A   G

My cousin *Martin* says *flying* is the only way to travel.

         A   Pr.

1. Teddy, *a professional*, was not eligible *for the prize*.

        P

2. *Serving his country bravely*, my brother returned home a hero.

        A   I

3. My friend *Kay* had several assignments *to complete*.

   G   Pr.

4. *Running* is not necessary, since we have plenty *of time*.

             A   Pr.   I

5. Philadelphia, the City *of Brotherly Love*, is a popular place *to visit*.

     I

6. *To learn calculus* is challenging for me.

    G

7. *Dialing* is not necessary now that we have a touch-tone telephone.

     Pr.   G

8. *For relaxation*, my dad turned to *walking*.

        P   Pr.

9. *Eating the leftover food*, the pilot survived *for weeks*.

        P

10. *Writing several popular books*, the author became a celebrity.

     Pr.   I

11. *For technical reasons* the ground crew needed *to delay the flight*.

     I   Pr.

12. *To identify the alternatives*, the president consulted *with his advisers*.

        A   I

13. My friend *Paul* is preparing *to study medicine*.

     P   Pr.

14. *Using my computer*, I typed my term paper *for English class*.

        A   Pr.   Pr.

15. Kari, *my best friend,* has lived *near me since first grade*.

   Pr.   Pr.   Pr.

16. *At midnight* can you meet me *in the kitchen for a snack*?

        P

17. *Claiming ignorance*, the witness was dismissed.

               A

18. Maya Angelou, *the famous poet*, wrote that particular poem.

     G   Pr.

19. *Blending two families together* can be difficult *for some people*.

    P   Pr.

20. *Receiving my tickets*, I packed *for the trip*.

Cumulative Review: Units 1–3

▶ **Exercise 1** **Draw a vertical line between the subject and predicate of each sentence. Underline each noun. Circle each verb. Label each participle *P*, each gerund *G*, and each infinitive *I*.**

I
To become a good pianist | requires great concentration.

1. Autumn | is her favorite time of the year.

I
2. She | loves to rake leaves.

G
3. Galloping her horse through fields | is another favorite activity.

P
4. Enjoying the crisp air, Miki | rides her horse in the park.

I
5. She | hopes to gather her friends together this week.

G
6. They | enjoy riding, too.

P
7. Stavros | rides the horse trained in Kentucky.

P   I
8. His horse, named Whirlwind, | was trained to race.

G
9. Whirlwind | prefers ambling.

I
10. Stavros | likes to amble, too.

11. Miki and her horse, Star, | are more adventurous.

P
12. Roaming through the fields, they | explore the changes fall brings.

I
13. Miki | wants to watch the leaves turn different colors.

G
14. Photographing the trees | preserves their beautiful appearance.

I
15. Miki | is putting together an album of pictures to show her biology class.

P
16. She | took pictures of budding leaves in the spring.

P
17. She | then took pictures of young flourishing trees.

P
18. She | will take pictures of grown trees during the winter.

P
19. Placing the photographs in sequence, she | will display the life of a leaf.

20. She | will describe beneath each photograph what is happening.

Unit 4: Clauses and Sentence Structure

Lesson 23
Main and Subordinate Clauses

There are two types of clauses: main and subordinate. A main clause contains a subject and a predicate. This type of clause is also called independent, because it can stand alone as a sentence.

The baby cried.

A subordinate, or dependent, clause contains a subject and predicate but cannot stand alone. This type of clause must be used with a main clause in order to make sense. It usually begins with a subordinating conjunction, such as *after, although, as, as if, because, if, since, so that, than, unless, until, when, where,* or *while;* a relative pronoun such as *who, whose, whom, which, that,* or *what;* or a relative adverb, such as *when, where,* or *why.*

The baby cried **when the dog barked loudly.**

▶ **Exercise 1** **Draw one line under the subordinate clause or clauses in each sentence.**

While I hem the skirt, will you finish the blouse?

1. After the storm cleared, the flight took off.

2. You will learn to speak Spanish if you practice.

3. I know a girl who sings in the chorus.

4. Although English is my favorite subject, I also like algebra.

5. We can go to the mall unless you are too busy.

6. Madeline is from a part of France where few people speak English.

7. The judge, who was angered by the outburst, slammed her gavel down.

8. When we arrived at the hotel, we discovered that our reservation had been cancelled.

9. Though many of us stood in line, only a few people bought concert tickets.

10. Maggie, whose birthday is in July, has already decided what she wants.

11. The restaurant where we used to eat dinner went out of business.

12. I peeled the potatoes while mother shredded the carrots.

13. Because the subject was complicated, Brad studied very hard.

14. Whenever we visit the zoo, Emma and I look for the giraffes first.

15. Dawn's letter had a sad tone, <u>as if something had gone wrong</u>.

16. <u>Until Diana learned to trust</u>, she had very few friends.

17. The computer <u>that Jill bought a year ago</u> is already outdated.

18. <u>Because the epidemic had grown worse</u>, the area hospitals were overcrowded.

19. <u>Whenever we go to the dentist</u>, she encourages us to brush.

20. My uncle reads at the dinner table, a habit <u>that I consider rude</u>.

▶ **Exercise 2** **Underline the main clause in each sentence. Then circle the subordinate clause.**

(When you finish your drawing,) <u>you may frame it</u>.

1. <u>The kitten ran</u> (when the children came near it.)

2. <u>Chad has quit his job</u> (so he can devote more time to his studies.)

3. (If the door is open,) <u>you can go right into the house</u>.

4. <u>Players</u> (who wish to join the team) <u>may sign up today</u>.

5. <u>Dr. Thomas returned to the site</u> (where we first saw the unusual rocks.)

6. <u>Do you remember the time</u> (when we stayed up all night?)

7. <u>My cousin</u> (who lives in Saudi Arabia) <u>came to visit last summer</u>.

8. (After I had written the letter) <u>I mailed it</u>.

9. <u>Africa had changed</u> (since the last time I was there.)

10. (When we reached the top of the mountain,) <u>we felt tired but proud</u>.

11. <u>Mitch lives in the building</u> (where the burglary happened.)

12. (Although we were worried about Jason) <u>we did not want to show our nervousness</u>.

13. (When the list of winners was announced,) <u>Kelly ran to claim her prize</u>.

14. <u>We watched</u> (as the archaeologists dug up the dinosaur remains.)

15. (Because Antonio loves water sports,) <u>we bought him water skis for Christmas</u>.

16. (Before he sat down) <u>Rick took off his jacket</u>.

17. <u>Sarah spun around</u> (as if she were an ice skater.)

18. (When she was given an example,) <u>Tessa could do just about any math problem</u>.

19. (When the clouds lifted,) <u>the sun shone brightly</u>.

20. (When the teacher is speaking) <u>we are not supposed to interrupt</u>.

Lesson 24
Simple and Compound Sentences

A **simple sentence** contains one main clause and no subordinate clauses. The simple sentence may not appear to be simple. It may have a compound subject or a compound predicate. It may also contain modifiers. As long as it has only one main clause, it is a simple sentence.

Li-Ching and Maria sang a duet.

A **compound sentence** contains two or more main clauses that are usually joined by a comma and a coordinating conjunction.

Maria sang one of her own songs, **and** Robert danced.
Maria sang, Robert danced, **and** Li-Ching played the piano.

▶ **Exercise 1** **Write *s* if the sentence is simple or *c* if it is compound.**

___S___ Marcus and Wolfgang, brothers from Germany, toured the United States and Canada last Spring.

___S___ **1.** The polio vaccine was developed by Jonas Salk and Albert Sabin.

___S___ **2.** My little brother Jake got a toy in his breakfast-cereal box.

___C___ **3.** We watched the baseball game, and we went for ice cream afterward.

___C___ **4.** A red car pulled up to the house, and a girl climbed out.

___C___ **5.** One of the remotes controlled the stereo, and another controlled the television.

___S___ **6.** The doctor determined the cause of Gina's health problem.

___C___ **7.** Collin played well, but Andrea had the highest score.

___S___ **8.** The rescue helicopter landed on top of the hospital.

___C___ **9.** Jim didn't take good notes, but Mary helped him study for the test.

___C___ **10.** The battery was dead, and the gas tank was almost empty.

___S___ **11.** The parade moved from the boulevard to the park.

___C___ **12.** Laura's new coat was blue, and her hat was burgundy.

___S___ **13.** The library was empty and quiet.

___S___ **14.** My grandfather made his fortune in the computer industry.

___S___ **15.** Monique is interested in protecting animal rights.

___S___ **16.** The change jingled loudly in my pocket.

___S___ **17.** Claire worked hard and earned a lot of money.

___S___ **18.** Zach and Amanda helped out at the car wash.

___C___ **19.** You can help with the dishes, or you can wash the car.

___C___ **20.** We helped the neighbors rake leaves, and they helped us wash windows.

▶ **Exercise 2** Write *c* next to each compound sentence.

___C___   We picked up our lunch, and we ran to the park.

_____ **1.** The Statue of Liberty was created by the French sculptor, Frederic Auguste Bartholdi.

___C___ **2.** Bartholdi studied painting and architecture in Paris, and his first sculpture was shown in 1883.

_____ **3.** The original name of the statue was "Liberty Enlightening the World."

___C___ **4.** The statue was planned to honor the centennial celebration of 1876, but the statue was not completed until later.

_____ **5.** The statue was given to the United States by France in 1886.

_____ **6.** The statue is often called "Miss Liberty."

___C___ **7.** Gustave Eiffel created the statue's internal structure, and his engineering method is used today.

_____ **8.** Eiffel later designed France's Eiffel Tower.

___C___ **9.** The statue is hollow to allow visitors inside, but it weighs approximately 450,000 pounds.

_____ **10.** Tremendous fundraising was required for Bartholdi to complete the colossal statue.

___C___ **11.** Americans were asked to provide the pedestal for the statue, and they did.

_____ **12.** An American, Richard Morris Hunt, designed the pedestal.

_____ **13.** The site chosen for the statue was Bedloe's Island in New York Harbor.

_____ **14.** The statue and its pedestal together would reach 305 feet.

___C___ **15.** It is made of copper, but the statue now appears green due to weathering.

_____ **16.** The statue was unveiled in 1886 and became the tallest human-made structure at that time.

_____ **17.** In the 1980s the statue was restored for the 1986 centennial celebration.

_____ **18.** A plaque inside the statue displays a poem by the poet Emma Lazarus.

___C___ **19.** The poem welcomes immigrants to the United States, and it continues to inspire immigrants today.

_____ **20.** The Statue of Liberty has come to signify the wealth of opportunities available in the United States.

Lesson 25
Complex and Compound-Complex Sentences

Grammar

A **complex sentence** contains one main clause and one or more subordinate clauses.

When she heard the applause, Beth felt proud.

A **compound-complex sentence** has more than one main clause and one or more subordinate clauses.

Although we had difficulty deciding, we finally chose a destination, and Dad bought the airline tickets.

▶ **Exercise 1 Circle the number in front of each complex sentence.**

(a.) We went to the eastern United States for our vacation although we'd been there before.

(1.) Frederick Douglass, who fought to end slavery, was a leader in the abolitionist movement.

2. Born Frederick Bailey in 1817, he grew up as a slave on a Maryland plantation.

3. Unlike most slaves, Douglass learned to read and write.

(4.) He escaped to the North in 1838, where he changed his name to avoid being caught.

(5.) After he spoke at a meeting of the American Anti-Slavery Society in 1841, Douglass became a spokesman for the society.

6. In his speeches, Douglass recalled life as a slave, and he called for an immediate end to slavery.

7. His autobiography, *Narrative of the Life of Frederick Douglass,* was published in 1841.

8. His book was popular in the North and in Europe.

9. Douglass became known as a leader in the crusade against slavery.

10. Douglass's notoriety jeopardized his freedom.

(11.) He spent two years in the British Isles, where he tried to win support.

12. In 1841 Douglass became the editor of the *North Star,* an antislavery newspaper.

13. He married Anna Murray in 1838, and the two had five children together.

(14.) When the Underground Railroad began, Douglass helped slaves escape to the North.

(15.) During the Civil War, Douglass wanted it known that the war was a move to abolish slavery.

(16.) He served as an advisor to President Lincoln, who saw Douglass as a representative for African Americans.

(17.) In 1862, Lincoln issued the Emancipation Proclamation, which freed slaves in places not held by Union troops.

(18) Although slavery was abolished with the Thirteenth Amendment, Douglass pursued the right of blacks to vote.

19. He became a U.S. Marshal in 1877 and was later appointed consul general to Haiti.

(20) Douglass continued to fight for reform until his death in 1895, when he collapsed following a woman suffrage meeting.

▶ **Exercise 2** Draw one line under each main clause and two lines under each subordinate clause. Then write *c* if the sentence is complex or *cc* if the sentence is compound-complex.

____c____   As we neared the hot-air balloon festival, the sky looked like a fairyland.

____c____   1. Until they were called home, the children played happily.

____cc____ 2. When we went to the opera, we saw Luciano Pavarotti, but we didn't get to see Placido Domingo.

____cc____ 3. Although I didn't brew it long, the coffee tastes bitter, and I will not drink it.

____c____   4. As the morning bell rang, the students rushed quickly into class.

____c____   5. I have always volunteered at the hospital because I enjoy helping others.

____cc____ 6. After the election is over, I will call you with results, and hopefully, our candidate will have won.

____c____   7. Dr. May was the only doctor who was available in the middle of the night.

____c____   8. Kelsey will finish her paper by noon, which is the deadline for the project.

____c____   9. My journalism teacher, whose opinion I respect, told me my article was good.

____cc____ 10. Since no one had a question for the speaker, the lecture ended early, and we went out for hamburgers.

____c____   11. When my sister went to college, my parents got her a used car.

____cc____ 12. After the doctor examined her, Darcy still felt ill, but she felt better in the morning.

____c____   13. The dog finally caught the ball as it drifted into the neighbor's yard.

____c____   14. As long as you keep your eyes open, you will see the exit ramp.

____c____   15. Although he did not understand the reasons, Josh accepted the divorce.

____c____   16. Since he has learned English, Miguel has been more outgoing.

____cc____ 17. Paul's speech will emphasize the budget because we must reduce the deficit, and his book will say the same.

____c____   18. The park where we used to play is now the site of a shopping mall.

Lesson 26
Adjective Clauses

An **adjective clause** is a subordinate clause that modifies a noun or pronoun. Remember that a subordinate clause contains a subject and verb but cannot stand alone. An adjective clause usually begins with a relative pronoun, such as *who, whom, whose, that,* and *which,* or a subordinating conjunction, such as *where* or *when.*

The book **that I lent him** is now overdue. (The adjective clause modifies the noun *book.*)

Sometimes the relative pronoun or subordinating conjunction is left out.

The book **I lent him** is now overdue.

An adjective clause can be essential or nonessential to the meaning of a sentence. An essential adjective clause is an adjective clause that cannot be omitted from a sentence without changing its meaning. A nonessential adjective clause can be omitted from a sentence, and the meaning of the sentence will remain the same.

Essential: The player **who batted last** scored the winning run.
Nonessential: Jerome, **who batted last**, is the best player on the team.

▶ **Exercise 1** Underline the adjective clause, and circle the noun or pronoun it modifies.

The (lamb) that Dena showed at the fair placed second in its division.

1. The basketball (player) whom I admired most retired last year.

2. The (company) that I worked for last summer went out of business.

3. The (Battle of Gettysburg,) which lasted three days, ended in victory for the Union soldiers.

4. The (chair) that we bought at the garage sale looks great in the living room.

5. The (telegraph,) which was the forerunner of the telephone, transmits signals over a wire.

6. The (swimmers) who won the meet were treated to dinner.

7. Do you remember the (time) when we marched in the parade?

8. The (spaghetti) that Duane made for dinner tasted great.

9. The (pier) where we docked the boat is the one on the left.

10. The (author) who wrote the book was signing autographs at the bookstore.

11. Rich was the (chef) whose secret recipes everyone wanted.

12. The (contributor) who made the large donation was never identified.

13. The (suburb) that we live in is undergoing many changes.

14. My parents were married in the (park) where they met.

15. The (coin,) which was shiny and new, was given to me by my grandfather.

16. The (surgery) that was supposed to cure her only made her feel worse.

17. Music and dancing are (hobbies) that we both love.

18. The (people) who are unable to attend will be invited again.

19. Ian found a (book) that someone had left in the gym.

20. Frank Lloyd Wright is recognized as the (man) who changed modern architecture.

21. The (stairs) that led to the attic were creaky.

22. Jessica found a (bird) that had fallen out of its nest.

23. The (skyscrapers) that rose above the city were shrouded in fog.

24. Juan is the (boy) who plays all intramural sports.

25. The (trail) they followed was marked with handkerchiefs.

26. His (speech,) which made perfect sense to me, was misinterpreted by some.

27. (Cyclists) who wear helmets have a better chance of surviving accidents.

28. The (clothes) that hung on the line were just washed.

29. The (student) who played Tiny Tim is in my geometry class.

30. I remember the (year) when I got my first bike.

31. The (experiment,) which worked perfectly, proved that the substance was soluble.

32. Luke remembered the (day) when he nearly fell through the ice.

33. The (forecast) which called for rain, was incorrect.

34. At dark we reached the (area) where we had planned to set up camp.

35. The (place) where I belong is with my family.

36. (Those) who chose the wrong trail walked in circles for hours.

37. (People) who hoped to see the comedian up close were disappointed.

38. The (bus) that picks us up in the morning is not the (one) that drops us off after school.

39. (Plays) he has directed have won many awards.

40. (Anyone) who wants to join the army must be disciplined.

41. The (books) that had been missing were found in the basement.

42. That (elephant,) which is indigenous to Africa, cannot survive in the cold.

43. (Anyone) who tried to change Kyle's mind failed miserably.

44. The picnic (lunch) that we packed this morning should feed the whole group.

45. (Students) who want to go on the field trip must bring a permission slip.

▶ **Exercise 2** Underline the adjective clause in each sentence. Write *N* next to the nonessential clauses and *E* next to the essential clauses.

___E___   Players who are always on time for practice set a good example for their teammates.

___N___ **1.** My rollerskates, which I paid fifty dollars for, are now too small for me.

___E___ **2.** The city that we visited on vacation was my father's home town.

___E___ **3.** The kicker who missed the field goal was disappointed for days.

___N___ **4.** The call, which was unexpected, came on a Saturday night.

___E___ **5.** The program that we were watching was interrupted.

___E___ **6.** The house that we lived in for nine years has been sold.

___E___ **7.** The boy whose bike had been stolen cried loudly.

___E___ **8.** Food that is not stored properly will spoil.

___N___ **9.** The camels roamed the desert, where water was scarce.

___N___ **10.** Stephanie studied every night, which helped her become a better student.

___E___ **11.** Materials that are not recyclable go in the other bin.

___N___ **12.** The piano, which had been tuned recently, sounded wonderful.

___E___ **13.** The data that we gathered was of no use to us.

___N___ **14.** The oil, which was leaking everywhere, caused quite a mess.

___N___ **15.** My friend, who goes to a different school, came to visit me.

___N___ **16.** Helen grew up during the fifties, when times were much different.

___E___ **17.** One thing that my father and I shared was a love of fishing.

___N___ **18.** The quarry, which was not safe to swim in, was being filled with dirt.

___N___ **19.** Those flowers, which have a strong scent, make me sneeze.

___N___ **20.** Dogwood trees, which are very beautiful, can be white or pink.

▶ **Exercise 3** Insert an adjective clause to modify the noun or pronoun in italics. Answers will vary.

The *lake,* ___which looked so glassy yesterday,___ had whitecaps today due to the high winds.

1. The *video game* ___that Gustavo purchased___ is difficult for beginners.

2. There is the *table* ___that holds the expensive vase___ .

3. Eli found a *puppy* _____that needed a home_____.

4. The *campground* _____where we stayed_____ was nearly full.

5. *Anyone* _____who completes the test_____ can be on the team.

6. My *cousin* _____who lives in Houston_____ comes to visit often.

7. The *driver* _____whose car was damaged_____ was not responsible for the accident.

8. This is the *firefighter* _____who saved Rita's cat_____.

9. In the *desert,* _____which is very dry_____, plant and animal life are scarce.

10. I forgot about the *appointment* _____that Mom made for me_____.

11. The *actor* _____who won the award_____ gave an acceptance speech.

12. The car wash was held in the *morning,* _____when traffic was heavy_____.

13. The bowling *league* _____that won the tournament_____ celebrated for two hours.

14. At the start of the *meeting* _____that Ms. Richards attended_____, breakfast was served.

15. Joy read a *magazine* _____that was left on the coffee table_____.

16. José spent the *money* _____that he earned last week_____ on a gift for his sister's birthday.

17. The mountain *trail* _____that the guide recommended_____ was steep and rocky.

18. Vanessa goes to the *gym* on Main Street, _____which provides daily aerobics classes_____.

19. Our first *assignment,* _____which Yolanda finished_____, was due on Tuesday.

20. The sea *air* _____that surrounded us_____ gave us a chill.

▶ **Writing Link** **Write a paragraph describing your neighborhood that includes at least three or more adjective clauses.**

_____

_____

_____

_____

_____

_____

_____

_____

Lesson 27
Adverb Clauses

An **adverb clause** is a subordinate clause that modifies a verb, an adjective, or an adverb. It is used to tell *when, where, why, how, to what extent,* or *under what conditions.* An adverb clause is usually introduced by a subordinating conjunction.

I cry **whenever I see a sad movie.** (The adverb clause modifies the verb *cry.* It tells *when.*)

An adverb clause that seems to have missing words is called **elliptical**. The words that are left out are understood in the clause.

Steve runs faster **than I** [run].

▶ **Exercise 1** **Underline the adverb clause in each sentence.**

When they arrived at the space camp, the aspiring astronauts grew nervous.

1. After I finished doing the dishes, I helped my dad mow the lawn.

2. The little girl was upset because her puppy was lost.

3. That old house looked spookier than any other house in the neighborhood.

4. Jeremy left for the football game before I could offer him a ride.

5. Jennifer will go on the retreat unless it rains.

6. Dino ran the 100-yard dash much faster than I did.

7. Because the sweaters were on sale, Stuart bought three.

8. Eve was more interested in geography than her brother was.

9. Will you wait in the car until it's time to leave for school?

10. Alex waxed the car until it looked brand new.

11. We met where his street intersects mine.

12. I heard a strange noise when I turned on the computer.

13. While it was snowing outside, Simon was daydreaming about sunny beaches.

14. The band began a food drive so that we could help the hungry.

15. Because she couldn't find an opener, Sandy didn't open the can.

16. Whenever I go to that restaurant, I run into a friend.

17. I dropped my wallet as I was crossing the street.

18. You will see a gas station <u>wherever you look in that city</u>.

19. <u>Although I had never seen my aunt before</u>, I recognized her instantly.

20. Grandma and Grandpa have lived in the same house <u>since they were married</u>.

21. The charity event will be a success <u>as long as it doesn't rain</u>.

22. <u>Whenever we ice-skate</u>, we put on our mittens.

23. He will go away <u>unless you apologize</u>.

24. <u>Wherever we went</u>, we put up flyers announcing the play.

25. <u>If we understood the rules</u>, we would be able to play the game.

26. We walked slowly away from the barking dog <u>because it frightened us</u>.

27. <u>Because he is a fine athlete</u>, Terry will compete for a scholarship.

28. Tim has been driving everywhere <u>since he got his driver's license</u>.

29. Rosa grew taller <u>than her older sister</u>.

30. <u>While we were on the plane to Hawaii</u>, I had a wonderful dream.

31. We rode the bus <u>because the car was being serviced</u>.

32. <u>After Sabine went back to France</u>, we promised to write letters every week.

33. Sean is a better cook <u>than I</u>.

34. You will do well on the essay questions <u>as long as you answer each question completely</u>.

35. Grandpa bought the telescope <u>because my brother loves to look at the stars</u>.

36. I like to exercise <u>as soon as I get up each morning</u>.

37. Those chemicals are not dangerous <u>unless they are combined</u>.

38. <u>After they left the theater</u>, John and Kim went out to dinner.

39. <u>Whenever I get a cold</u>, I feel miserable.

40. We will stick to the schedule <u>as long as there are no objections</u>.

41. My muscles ached <u>after I did the exercises</u>.

42. <u>Though he was in no immediate danger</u>, we were still concerned.

43. The audience was restless <u>until the performance began</u>.

44. We had a substitute teacher <u>because our regular teacher was ill</u>.

45. Sherry has a heavier southern accent <u>than I have</u>.

▶ **Exercise 2** Underline the adverb clause in each sentence. Circle the verb, adverb, or adjective it modifies.

While they were in the shelter of the cliff, Mali and Aaron (felt) safe from the storm.

1. Whenever I move my rook, she (takes) my bishop.

2. Because he was under oath, the witness (answered) honestly.

3. We (stayed) until the end of the program.

4. Although I am busy, I (will help) you paint the room.

5. Ryan (felt) awful until he took the medicine.

6. Bridget (walked) away as if she were angry.

7. While the first coat of paint dried, we (rested.)

8. Helena sings (better) than Lisa.

9. Raymond was feeling (worse) than I was feeling.

10. The telephone (rings) whenever I take a shower.

11. While I'm at the store, I (can get) you something.

12. The discussion made me (angrier) than it made him.

13. Because I need extra money, I (baby-sit) every weekend.

14. Though it took a long time, we (waited) patiently.

15. The ride is (safe) as long as you wear your safety belt.

16. When the time came to volunteer, Maryann (raised) her hand first.

17. Kevin (was frustrated) because he couldn't solve the problem.

18. Rebecca can climb (higher) than I can climb.

19. Because she believes in protecting the environment, Julie (recycles.)

20. Whenever she sang, audiences (cheered.)

▶ **Exercise 3** Underline each adverb clause and adjective clause. Write *adv.* if the underlined clause is an adverb clause or *adj.* if it is an adjective clause.

adj.   The first person whose name is called will be the team leader.

adv.   **1.** I call on Malcolm whenever I need help with algebra.

adv.   **2.** The horse will respond as long as you give the signals correctly.

adj.   **3.** Ernesto had many fine qualities that made him very popular.

adv.   **4.** The twins agreed to stay home as long as we agreed to bring them something.

adj.   **5.** Anyone <u>who calls the office</u> will hear the recording of Jane's message.

adv.   **6.** Jamie sneaked up on me <u>while I was eating my lunch</u>.

adv.   **7.** <u>Since there was no time to argue</u>, we quickly decided to vote on it.

adj.   **8.** The book <u>that I cherish the most</u> is the one on this shelf.

adv.   **9.** <u>Although I was not injured</u>, the accident gave me quite a scare.

adj.   **10.** The runners <u>who finished the race</u> were out of breath.

adv.   **11.** I look for these dolls <u>wherever I go</u>.

adv.   **12.** I found a dollar <u>as I was walking to Joel's house</u>.

adj.   **13.** The scarecrow <u>that stood out in the rain</u> was soaking wet.

adv.   **14.** We looked for fireflies at night <u>whenever we had time</u>.

adj.   **15.** Ruth gave her jacket to someone <u>who needed it more</u>.

adj.   **16.** The turkey, <u>which was in the oven</u>, smelled delicious.

adj.   **17.** The telephone <u>that I got for my birthday</u> was a pleasant surprise.

adv.   **18.** Derek panicked <u>after he saw his new haircut</u>.

adj.   **19.** Ben Franklin, <u>whose picture appears on the one-hundred-dollar bill</u>, was a famous

statesman and scientist.

adv.   **20.** Doug was proud <u>after he completed his term paper</u>.

▶ **Writing Link** **Write a paragraph about a family pet. Use at least three adverb clauses.**

_____

_____

_____

_____

_____

_____

_____

_____

_____

_____

_____

_____

Lesson 28
Noun Clauses

A **noun clause** is a subordinate clause that is used as a noun. A noun clause may be used as a subject, a direct object, an indirect object, an object of a preposition, an appositive, or a predicate nominative.

A noun clause usually begins with one of these words: *how, that, what, whatever, when, where, which, whichever, who, whom, whoever, whose, why.*

direct object
Cindy did not know **where the beakers were kept.**

subject
What makes them different is their ability to change colors to blend with their environment.

▶ **Exercise 1 Circle each sentence that contains a noun clause.**

(Whenever we choose to leave for the game is fine with them.)

1. The board proposed that all residents be required to recycle.

2. Whatever you choose will make a fine gift

3. Mike defended his position on the issue.

4. The community college offers a course in fencing.

5. The scientist predicted how the chemicals might react

6. Ted should have been at the swim meet an hour ago.

7. The rest of the group arrived later.

8. You may take whichever puppy you want

9. The raccoons eat whatever they can find

10. The spilled soda did not stain the carpet.

11. Many people thought that the defendant was not guilty.

12. Onlookers were disappointed when the shuttle lift-off was delayed.

13. Marla was encouraged to enter her poems in a contest.

14. Many people believe that you can do anything if you try.

15. Melissa told her teacher that her test was marked incorrectly.

16. Whatever we give will be appreciated by the charity.

17. Ethan started his own business at the age of thirteen.

18. Your opinion of the show was what I thought, also.

19. The little boy mimicked whatever Kirk did.

20. I did not hear what Brenda said.

▶ **Exercise 2** **Underline the noun clause or clauses in each sentence.**

I do not care which route we take to the cabin.

1. Sam did not know where the art exhibit was.

2. I do not know why Tonya chose to go with them instead of us.

3. I dreamed that I was the president of the United States.

4. What makes them so special is their ability to see the good in everyone.

5. The refugees were grateful for whatever they received.

6. Kay is who will be the baby-sitter.

7. Whoever was in charge of that experiment made it easy to understand.

8. That the boys had nothing in common became apparent.

9. Brent's patience and understanding were what we appreciated most.

10. Chantal was not interested in what the others wanted to do.

11. Whoever can play the piano will be the first on the list.

12. Kyle always felt that he'd like to live in Australia.

13. Ron told us that there were no seats left in the auditorium.

14. Why Jay left the party early was a mystery to everyone.

15. How anyone could dislike homemade bread amazes me!

16. How well the task is done is an important issue.

17. The principal told me that the band show was a great success.

18. That Holly had run out of gas was true.

19. What we didn't know was that the surprise was waiting for us outside.

20. That Florence was the best player was accepted by everyone.

21. Cheryl hears what she wants to hear.

22. I cannot understand how anyone can enjoy going to the dentist.

23. We gave directions to whoever asked us.

24. What Carl does not realize is that he has a great career ahead of him.

25. My friends argued about <u>how we should build the science project</u>.

26. <u>Where the exhibit will be held</u> has yet to be determined.

27. <u>Whoever made that comment</u> should be recognized.

28. <u>That we need more police on patrol</u> was the point of his speech.

29. You cannot know <u>that the test will be easy</u>.

30. <u>What the athletes wanted</u> was to do their best.

31. Your review of the novel was <u>what I believed, too</u>.

32. Our wish is <u>that the puppy will find a good home</u>.

33. No one could predict <u>how long the rally would go on</u>.

34. <u>That the candidate was qualified</u> was not an easy thing to prove.

35. Pass your paper to <u>whoever is on your left</u>.

36. Patrick was happy about <u>what happened at the tennis match</u>.

37. Joni always answered with <u>whatever she thought</u>.

38. The art students were asked <u>what the painting represents</u>.

39. <u>Why we have so little time</u> is bewildering to me.

40. Because I'm starved, <u>whatever you cook</u> will be fine with me.

41. I will call <u>whomever you wish</u>.

42. Nina could not understand <u>why the dress was so expensive</u>.

43. Many people think <u>that dogs make the best pets</u>.

44. <u>What the judges decided</u> was not acceptable to Marcus.

45. Did you know <u>that the exploration of caves is called *spelunking*</u>?

▶ **Exercise 3** **Underline the noun clause in each sentence. Then label it *d.o.* for direct object, *subj.* for subject, *p.n.* for predicate nominative, or *o.p.* for object of a preposition.**

               subj.
<u>Where they found the missing necklace</u> remains a secret.

        subj.
1. <u>That the team did not want to practice</u> was no great surprise.

                d.o.
2. I do not know <u>where she works after school</u>.

                 p.n.
3. Your opinion of the class is <u>what I think, too</u>.

     subj.
4. <u>Whoever sleeps</u> will be the victim of our practical jokes.

                     o.p.
5. We will make up a skit with <u>whatever props we are given</u>.

6. That is why I could not go to the movie.
              p.n.
   That is <u>why I could not go</u> to the movie.

7.   **d.o.**
   Will the teacher explain <u>what DNA is</u>?

8.   **o.p.**
   We paid special attention to <u>how she wove the baskets</u>.

9.   **d.o.**
   The directions did not indicate <u>where one should go</u> in case of fire.

10.   **p.n.**
   My problem is <u>that the book was due last week</u>.

11. **subj.**
   <u>Whoever has visited Chicago</u> has seen many skyscrapers.

12.   **d.o.**
   You may have heard <u>that we got a new principal</u>.

13.   **o.p.**
   Ben decided to dance with <u>whoever asked him</u>.

14.   **d.o.**
   I did not know <u>how long the debate would go on</u>.

15. **subj.**
   <u>That the bitter cold will be here soon</u> is unfortunate, but true.

16.   **d.o.**
   Ashley does <u>whatever she wants to do</u>.

17.   **d.o.**
   Hiroko asked <u>why I did not go to camp</u>.

18. **subj.**
   <u>What appeared to be true</u> was ruled out after further investigation.

19.   **o.p.**
   The mittens were left by <u>whichever person sat there last</u>.

20. **subj.**
   <u>What makes me laugh</u> is his crazy sense of humor.

▶ **Writing Link** **Write a paragraph about a book you have read recently. Use at least three noun clauses in your paragraph.**

_____

_____

_____

_____

_____

_____

_____

_____

_____

Lesson 29
Kinds of Sentences: Declarative and Imperative

A **declarative sentence** makes a statement and usually ends with a period.

Diet soda is my favorite drink.

An **imperative sentence** gives a command or makes a request. The subject "you" is understood.

(You) Report any safety violations to the supervisor.

▶ **Exercise 1 Label each sentence *dec.* for declarative sentence or *imp.* for imperative sentence.**

imp.   Always wear eye protection in the laboratory.

dec.   **1.** The backyard was flooded after the strong rains.

imp.   **2.** Come to my house after band practice.

imp.   **3.** Slowly pour the solution into the beaker.

dec.   **4.** The spaghetti was cold by the time we sat down to eat.

dec.   **5.** My glasses were bent after my little sister sat on them.

dec.   **6.** The drugstore was closed by the time I arrived there.

imp.   **7.** Go to the nearest ticket booth, and get two tickets for the concert.

dec.   **8.** My throat was sore after I had my tonsils taken out.

imp.   **9.** Send a letter to your representative if you have a complaint.

imp. **10.** Please wash my white shirt by Monday.

dec. **11.** The sand was so hot we couldn't walk on it.

dec. **12.** We've lived in the same house since I was born.

dec. **13.** An isosceles triangle has two equal sides.

imp. **14.** Have faith in my abilities.

imp. **15.** Drink your hot chocolate before it gets cold.

dec. **16.** The tent is too small for the whole family to use.

imp. **17.** When Tuesday comes, take out the trash.

dec. **18.** Jack is taller than his father.

dec. **19.** Antonio was the best gymnast at the competition.

imp. **20.** Remind me to return my library books.

dec. **21.** The family that moved in next door is very nice.

imp. **22.** Stay away from that wild horse.

imp. **23.** Call the fire department if you suspect fire.

imp. **24.** Take Mel to see the penguins.

dec. **25.** Science fiction has never interested me.

dec. **26.** Eduardo always reads the comics first.

imp. **27.** Gather your belongings and come with me.

dec. **28.** Violin music makes me sleepy.

imp. **29.** Lock the door on your way out.

dec. **30.** My science textbook had been lost all year.

dec. **31.** Linda loves to watch old westerns on television.

imp. **32.** Please wear your seat belt in my car.

imp. **33.** Stay in the hospital until you feel well.

dec. **34.** We saw _The Nutcracker_ at the theater downtown.

imp. **35.** Hold on to my hand until I can skate by myself.

dec. **36.** We played board games until midnight.

dec. **37.** Donna grew up on a farm.

imp. **38.** Watch your step on the ice.

dec. **39.** After he got a tutor, Jesse's work showed improvement.

dec. **40.** Yolanda showed me the newest dance steps.

imp. **41.** Don't touch the freshly painted walls.

imp. **42.** Smile so that I can take your picture.

imp. **43.** Read all about it in the newspaper today.

dec. **44.** The photos made me remember my childhood.

imp. **45.** Inform the guidance counselor whenever you need extra help.

Lesson 30
Kinds of Sentences: Interrogative and Exclamatory

Grammar

An **interrogative sentence** asks a question and ends with a question mark.

Are your allergies bothering you?

An **exclamatory sentence** shows strong or sudden feeling. It ends with an exclamation point.

We won the game!

▶ **Exercise 1** **Insert a question mark if the sentence is interrogative, or an exclamation point if the sentence is exclamatory.**

Don't drop that fragile vase!

1. How did you find out about the surprise party ?

2. Watch out for the falling rocks !

3. Is this the place where Lee surrendered ?

4. Were you frightened by the loud noises ?

5. When will the train be leaving ?

6. Where are the tryouts for the play held ?

7. Don't spill your drink !

8. I can't believe you said that !

9. The bell rang ten minutes ago !

10. What time does the movie start ?

11. Do you like sugar in your tea ?

12. Run as fast as you can !

13. Has Seema asked you for help with history ?

14. I caught you taking the last cookie !

15. Does the meeting start at seven ?

16. Would you pick up some eggs at the store ?

17. Do you know where Dylan is ?

18. Is that your radio ?

19. Don't be so eager !

20. Please help me find Mother's favorite earring !

21. Can you find the Big Dipper in the night sky ?

22. You scared me to death !

23. Are you allowed to stay out late ?

24. Has Marcia been asked to the dance ?

25. Is there enough time to play soccer before we go shopping ?

26. Which station do you listen to the most ?

27. Don't stand so close to the campfire !

28. Erik just took the lead !

29. Why have you been so quiet ?

30. Is this oboe yours ?

31. That's no excuse !

32. How did you hear the news ?

33. What was decided during the peace talks ?

34. Never give up !

35. I won first-chair violin !

36. Which tie looks better with this suit ?

37. Will we meet at the same time tomorrow ?

38. Was our team defeated last night ?

39. What will happen if I change my mind ?

40. I can't believe he missed that shot !

41. Where do we sign up for intramural basketball ?

42. How many cookies did Darryl eat ?

43. Do you know how to use the copier ?

44. Hurry, or we'll be late !

45. Who painted the picture hanging in the lobby ?

Lesson 31
Sentence Fragments

Grammar

A **sentence fragment** is an incomplete sentence. It may lack a subject, a verb, or both. Alternatively, it may be a subordinate clause that cannot stand alone. Correct it by adding the missing phrase or words.

Although he bought the tie for his brother. (Fragment)
Although he bought the tie for his brother, he kept it for himself. (Sentence)

▶ **Exercise 1** Write *frag.* next to each sentence fragment. Write *s* next to each complete sentence.

frag.   In the event of a disaster.

_s_   **1.** Georgia O'Keeffe became one of the best-loved American artists.

frag.   **2.** Because she had an innovative style.

frag.   **3.** Works from charcoals to watercolors to pastels.

_s_   **4.** O'Keeffe, feeling that her creations were personal, kept to herself.

frag.   **5.** By distancing herself from historians, biographers, and critics.

_s_   **6.** She developed a very individual style.

frag.   **7.** Which became apparent in 1915.

_s_   **8.** O'Keeffe studied at the Art Institute of Chicago and the Arts Students League in New York.

_s_   **9.** Her works soon came to the attention of Alfred Stieglitz, a photographer and art exhibitor.

_s_   **10.** In 1917, O'Keeffe had her first art show at the New York gallery owned by Stieglitz.

frag. **11.** Whom she later married.

frag. **12.** Paintings of flowers, some of her most famous works.

frag. **13.** Appeared in the mid-1920s.

_s_   **14.** She created many paintings that were based on the American Southwest.

frag. **15.** Where she first visited in 1929.

frag. **16.** Establishing her home in New Mexico in 1949.

_s_   **17.** *The Pelvis Series* includes some of her best work.

frag. **18.** A series of paintings of animal bones against stark backgrounds.

_____s_____ **19.** O'Keeffe's art helped to bridge the gap between American and European art of the early twentieth century.

_____frag.____ **20.** Until her death in 1986.

▶ **Exercise 2** **Tell whether you would add a subject *(s)*, verb *(v)*, or a main clause *(m)* to form a complete sentence.**

_____v_____   A blue bus carrying fifteen adults and four children.

_____m_____ **1.** As if he were in a daze.

_____v_____ **2.** Each year thousands of crops lost to flooding.

_____m_____ **3.** How to spell the words for the test.

_____s_____ **4.** Advised against eating fatty foods.

_____v_____ **5.** A heart doctor known as a cardiologist.

_____s_____ **6.** Charges no admission for students.

_____m_____ **7.** Since we forgot our skis.

_____v_____ **8.** The Smiths installing a security system in their home.

_____m_____ **9.** Which the school paper published.

_____v_____ **10.** Animals from the city zoo arriving this afternoon.

_____s_____ **11.** Warned us not to swim right after eating.

_____s_____ **12.** Are living in mobile homes until their houses are rebuilt.

_____v_____ **13.** A child singing in the chorus.

_____s_____ **14.** Gives the user plenty of information.

_____m_____ **15.** Because I cannot be at the meeting.

_____v_____ **16.** A chocolate cookie melting in the sun.

_____s_____ **17.** Every year plants trees near the school.

_____m_____ **18.** Although I bought the gift for Trisha.

_____s_____ **19.** Requires permission from a parent or guardian.

_____m_____ **20.** Hiking on lichen-covered rocky slopes.

_____s_____ **21.** Stir the hard-packed prairie soil.

_____v_____ **22.** A squirrel monkey pouncing on insects.

_____s_____ **23.** Include the prevention of water-runoff pollution.

_____m_____ **24.** One of the most livable cities in the country.

Lesson 32
Run-on Sentences

A **run-on sentence** contains two or more complete sentences written as one.

Incorrect: There was a mistake on our bill, the server took care of it. (two main clauses separated by a comma instead of a period)

Correct: There was a mistake on our bill. The server took care of it. (Break up with a period or semicolon.)

Incorrect: I ran into Margaret she is leaving for Florida tomorrow. (two main clauses with no punctuation between them)

Correct: I ran into Margaret; she is leaving for Florida tomorrow. (Break up with a period or semicolon.)

▶ **Exercise 1 Write *run-on* next to each run-on sentence.**

_____run-on_____ Prizes encourage excellence one particular prize is the Pulitzer Prize.

_____run-on_____ **1.** The Pulitzer Prize is awarded each year, it awards excellence in journalism, letters, and music.

_____ **2.** The awards were established by the powerful publisher Joseph Pulitzer.

_____run-on_____ **3.** Pulitzer owned the *St. Louis Post-Dispatch* he purchased the *New York World* in 1883.

_____ **4.** Pulitzer helped to shape the modern newspaper.

_____ **5.** He added many features to his newspapers, including sports, comics, fashions, and illustrations.

_____ **6.** Pulitzer's papers also gained a reputation for sensational reporting.

_____run-on_____ **7.** Pulitzer left money to Columbia University the awards were established in 1917.

_____ **8.** In addition to establishing the awards, his money funded a school of journalism for Columbia.

_____run-on_____ **9.** Pulitzer planned four awards for journalism and four for letters more categories were added later.

_____ **10.** The letters category includes drama, poetry, history, biography or autobiography, fiction, and general nonfiction.

_____ **11.** The Pulitzer Prizes for journalism are given for work that appears in U.S. newspapers.

_____ **12.** Each prize is $1,000, except the prize for public service, which is a gold medal.

__run-on__ **13.** Anyone may make a nomination, the nomination must include the work.

_____ **14.** Following a preliminary judging, the candidates are judged by an advisory board.

_____ **15.** The advisory board can nominate other candidates.

_____ **16.** Works with American themes seem to be preferred.

_____ **17.** The winning names are given to Columbia University trustees.

__run-on__ **18.** Pulitzer's career was ended by his failing health he had paved the way for future journalists.

_____ **19.** Joseph Pulitzer Jr., his grandson, serves on the advisory board.

__run-on__ **20.** The Pulitzer Prize is a highly regarded honor, it signifies great achievement.

▶ **Exercise 2** **Write *run-on* next to each run-on sentence.**

__run-on__ Joan went to the bank Chris waited at home.

__run-on__ **1.** Pearl Buck won a Pulitzer Prize in 1932 she was a novelist.

_____ **2.** Pearl spent much of her childhood in China because her parents were missionaries.

_____ **3.** After attending Randolph-Macon Woman's College, she returned to China and became a teacher.

__run-on__ **4.** Pearl Buck wrote many stories about Chinese life, she did not achieve success until 1931 when *The Good Earth* was published.

__run-on__ **5.** This work was recognized with a Pulitzer Prize, she continued to write novels.

_____ **6.** *The House of Earth* is a trilogy composed of *The Good Earth, Sons,* and *A House Divided.*

__run-on__ **7.** In 1935, Pearl Buck moved back to the United States she started writing biographies at this time, as well.

_____ **8.** The following year, she published biographies of her mother and father.

__run-on__ **9.** She worked on many projects, she wrote short stories, an autobiography, and more novels.

_____ **10.** Pearl Buck also wrote novels under the pen name of John Sedges.

Grammar (side margin)

Unit 4 **Review**

▶ **Exercise 1** Label the sentences below with *imp.* for imperative, *int.* for interrogative, *d* for declarative, or *e* for exclamatory.

___d___ Before leaving the house, he had a glass of orange juice.

___imp.___ **1.** Be considerate of the feelings of others.

___int.___ **2.** What class do you have first period?

___int.___ **3.** Does that old air pump still work?

___d___ **4.** We called the police when we heard the noise.

___d___ **5.** I learned that move in my karate class.

___e___ **6.** That's the silliest thing I've ever heard!

___d___ **7.** The newspaper arrived late on Sunday.

e *or* imp. **8.** Don't slam the door!

___imp.___ **9.** Use your binoculars to see the birds more clearly.

___int.___ **10.** Which of the twins volunteers at the nursing home?

___d___ **11.** Darcy's family went to New Orleans during Mardi Gras.

___int.___ **12.** What do you think are society's toughest problems?

___imp.___ **13.** Bring me a rake from the garage.

___int.___ **14.** Where is the pizza with anchovies?

e *or* imp. **15.** Watch out for that car!

___d___ **16.** Science is my favorite subject.

___int.___ **17.** Are you getting your hair cut today?

___imp.___ **18.** Give me the hammer beside you.

___e___ **19.** The magician's tricks were incredible!

___d___ **20.** Seeing our relatives over the holidays will occupy most of our time.

___imp.___ **21.** Permit the unfortunate boy to have my seat.

___int.___ **22.** What will happen to my companions?

___d___ **23.** The crowd in Madison Square Garden responded enthusiastically.

___e___ **24.** I hope you are having fun!

Grammar

Cumulative Review: Units 1–4

▶ **Exercise 1** Draw one line under each simple subject and two lines under each simple predicate. In the blank, identify the kind of sentence by writing *dec.* (declarative), *imp.* (imperative), *int.* (interrogative), or *exc.* (exclamatory).

__exc.__   How cold this winter has been!

__dec.__   **1.** The store sent the customer the wrong package.

__imp.__   **2.** Show me your hall pass.

__dec.__   **3.** The captain and the crew of the starship *Enterprise* were very experienced.   or were experienced

__int.__   **4.** How much did you pay for that dress?

__exc.__   **5.** There is smoke coming from under that door!

__dec.__   **6.** Susan went to the library to gather information for her report.

__imp.__   **7.** Please don't cut in front of the line.

__int.__   **8.** Does anyone know the location of his office?

__dec.__   **9.** Our senator campaigned to become president.

__dec.__   **10.** Their new house withstood the hurricane better than the last one.

▶ **Exercise 2** Underline the subordinate clause in each sentence. Write *adj.* (adjective), *adv.* (adverb), or *n* (noun) in the blank to tell what kind of clause it is.

__adj.__   Students who sing in the choir are dismissed early.

__adv.__   **1.** We arrived at the theater after the movie had begun.

__adv.__   **2.** My problem is how I can finish this lengthy book in one week.

__adj.__   **3.** The stylish woman who spoke at the banquet is the founder of the local department store.

__adv.__   **4.** There will be a quiz after we watch the film on the battles of the Civil War.

__n__   **5.** Sarah was worried about whether she had made the basketball team.

__adj.__   **6.** The realtor who sold us this house designed it himself.

__adv.__   **7.** We were fortunate to arrive home before the snowstorm hit.

__adv.__   **8.** Shall I wait for you at your locker while you go to the office?

__n__   **9.** No one could understand what the directions were explaining.

__adj.__   **10.** The classical music that Mrs. Griffin likes the best is by Beethoven.

Unit 5: Diagraming Sentences

Lesson 33
Diagraming Simple Sentences

Write the simple subject and the verb on a horizontal line and then draw a vertical line between them. Draw a shorter vertical line between the verb and the direct object. If there is a predicate nominative or a predicate adjective instead of a direct object, slant the shorter line toward the subject. Place an indirect object on a horizontal line under the verb, and draw a slanted line from the horizontal line to the verb. The following examples show how to diagram simple sentences.

The new student worked very hard.   Rosa and Maria gave their brother a haircut.

    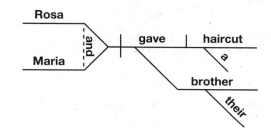

She sent me a letter.   Our results were predictable.

    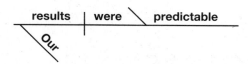

▶**Exercise 1** **Diagram the following simple sentences.**

1. Bruno finished his homework.

3. The tennis coach plays the mandolin.

2. This recipe requires sugar and oil.

4. Did Inez call anyone?

Grammar

5. My best friend and her cousin made me cookies.

6. I used my laptop computer yesterday.

7. The team played very well today.

8. Is Ruth's aunt a lawyer or a dentist?

9. The cheetah is an endangered species.

10. Write the answer clearly.

11. Can you tune your guitar?

12. Isaac and Yuri sing and play the piano.

13. Mrs. Lopez washed and waxed her truck.

14. The students completed a community project.

15. My pets include a fish, a cat, and a gerbil.

16. May I be excused?

17. Give me the licorice!

18. David grades the history quizzes.

Lesson 34
Diagraming Simple Sentences with Phrases

The following examples demonstrate how to diagram sentences with phrases.

PREPOSITIONAL PHRASE

The mother of twins drove her children to school in her new car.

GERUND PHRASE

Diagraming sentences is the subject of this lesson.

PARTICIPIAL PHRASE

The doctor found the patient studying his chart.

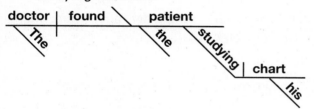

APPOSITIVE PHRASE

The dessert, chocolate cake, was a real treat.

INFINITIVE PHRASE AS ADJECTIVE OR ADVERB

Tom Sawyer is a good book to read.

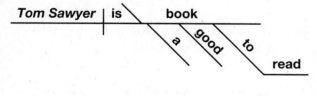

INFINITIVE PHRASE AS NOUN

My plan is to get a job.

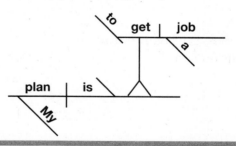

Grammar

▶ **Exercise 1 Diagram the following simple sentences with phrases.**

1. We stayed at the mall until evening.

2. Somebody sent this book to my mother by mistake.

3. The captain of the team spoke to us during practice.

4. Will you drive through the tunnel in the mountain?

5. Those girls are the Sharvy twins, Marla and Maureen.

6. Blueberries, my favorite fruit, are delicious on cereal.

7. The man in the blue sweater is Mr. Boudoulas, my English teacher.

8. Cairo, the capital of Egypt, is located on the Nile River.

9. The pitcher, taking her time, struck out our best hitter.

10. All students making the honor roll will receive special awards.

Lesson 35
Diagraming Sentences with Clauses

The following examples demonstrate how to diagram sentences with clauses.

COMPOUND SENTENCES

He removed the lid, and the small dog barked playfully.

COMPLEX SENTENCES WITH ADJECTIVE CLAUSES

The country that interests me is Kenya.

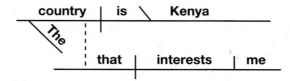

COMPLEX SENTENCES WITH ADVERB CLAUSES

Because the foreign exchange student had never been skiing, he went in my place.

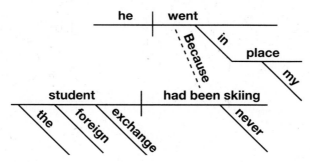

COMPLEX SENTENCES WITH NOUN CLAUSES

Elston believed that Echo was his friend.

Grammar

▶ **Exercise 1** **Diagram the following sentences with clauses.**

1. After the hurricane ceased, workers began a massive clean-up operation.

2. The class officers needed whatever help was available.

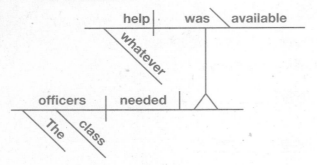

3. The press secretary spoke initially, and then the president held a news conference.

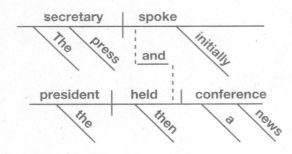

4. The nurse prepped the patient, and the doctor performed the surgery.

5. The grass needs mowing, and the rose bush needs pruning.

6. The victims wondered how this could happen to them.

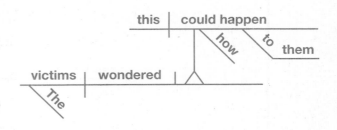

7. The author wrote short stories when she began her career.

8. After the bell rings, the principal makes announcements.

9. Claudine knows that Rupert will help.

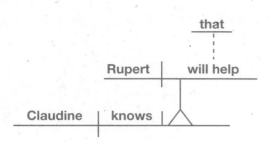

10. The ski club decided where the contest would be held.

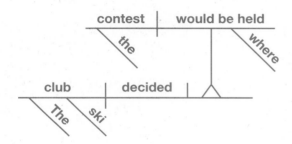

11. As far as I am concerned, you may go on the camping trip.

12. The custodian knew where the missing keys were.

13. Alligators seem slow; although they can move quickly.

14. Can you see how the treasure was lost?

15. What you choose for a career will affect your entire life.

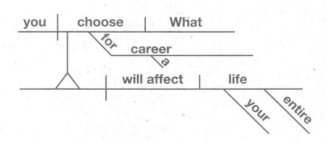

16. Jay is spending a week in New York so he will have time to attend a concert.

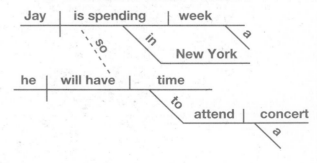

Grammar

17. You will complete the art project whenever you have the time.

18. My dad, whom you know, bought a new set of golf clubs.

19. One of the players on whom we rely was injured at the last game.

20. The treasurer warned that funds are low.

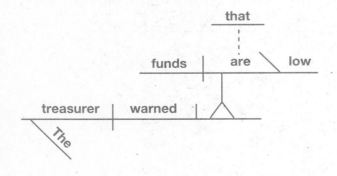

21. The tomb that held the mummy was ornately decorated.

22. The team that won the tournament was the Tigers.

23. Prizes will be awarded to whoever arrives first.

24. We wrote a poem about how we felt.

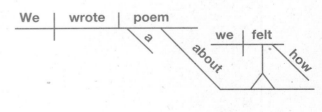

☑ Unit 5 **Review**

▶ **Exercise 1** **Diagram the following sentences.**

1. The novelist wrote movie scripts until she left Hollywood.

2. The class officers said that we could march in the parade.

3. Jessie attended the workshop to learn to paint with watercolors.

4. Maureen's goal is to play drums in Lon's band.

5. The soccer field was rocky and hard.

6. The general, a veteran of two wars, accepted the medal and addressed the crowd.

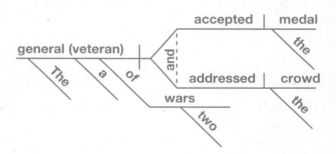

7. Gasping for air, Ella reached the top of the mountain.

8. Jim is friendly, but he must try to meet more people.

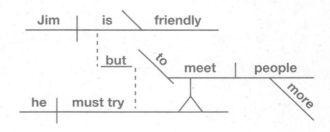

Grammar

Cumulative Review: Units 1–5

▶ **Exercise 1** Draw one line under all nouns and two lines under all verbs. Write *adj.* above any adjective, *adv.* above any adverb, and *d.o.* above any direct object. You may ignore any articles.

                adj.   d.o.
Running provides good exercise.

                      adv.
1. The prosecutor spoke convincingly to the jury.

    adj.   adj.   adv.
2. Several rose bushes are still blooming in the garden.

        adj.   adj.   adj.   d.o.   adj.
3. The department store sold its holiday decorations at half price.

      adj.   adv.   adj.
4. The hungry herd of bison grazed lazily on the open range.

               adj.   adj.   d.o.   adj.
5. Mr. Jackson gave his class bad news concerning the field trip.

    adj.   adj.
6. Which river is longer, the Nile or the Amazon?

               adj.   adj.   d.o.   adv.   adj.
7. Ms. Wong answered my sincere question in a somewhat mocking tone.

   adj.   adj.
8. A large truckload of dairy products has spilled onto the road.

           adj.   adj.   d.o.   adv.   adj.
9. I will give you my secret recipe for very moist brownies.

    adj.   adj.   adj.   d.o.
10. Many Chinese dynasties caused great changes.

                   adv.   adv.
11. The car in front of us stopped quite suddenly.

        adj.   d.o.   adv.
12. Jake called the radio station twice.

          d.o.   adj.   adj.
13. The Incas ruled one of the largest and richest empires in the world.

               adj.
14. The secret will be safe with me.

             adj.   d.o.
15. Sharon bought a tiny trinket at the bazaar.

    adv.   adj.   d.o.
16. We proudly displayed the American flag.

           adv.   adj.   d.o.   adj.
17. The ambulance has already radioed the emergency room with vital information.

          adv.   adv.   adv.
18. The interview went more smoothly today.

      adv. adv.
19. You swim very well for a novice.

        adj.   adj.   d.o.
20. Amanda teaches her parrots slang words.

▶ **Exercise 2** **Draw one line under each main clause. Draw two lines under each subordinate clause. Identify each sentence by writing *simple, compound, complex,* or *compound-complex* in the blank.**

_____compound_____ Ruben visited New Jersey, and he stayed near Atlantic City.

_____simple_____ 1. During their sailing adventure last week, the crew survived a sudden storm.

_____simple_____ 2. The Olympic team felt empowered by the cheers of their fellow countrymen.

_____compound_____ 3. The artist created miniature figurines, and his friend sold them in his shop.

_____compound-complex_____ 4. When he fell behind on the trail, Stephen wondered if he would lose sight of his group, but soon he caught up with them again.

_____complex_____ 5. Solada, while mixing up the cookies, began to wonder what she had done wrong because the dough looked strange.

_____simple_____ 6. At the hospital, the staff disposed of certain materials in a special manner to meet federal requirements.

_____simple_____ 7. The director of the play gave the actors advice.

_____compound_____ 8. Kyle is very musical, and he wants to do well at the competition.

_____complex_____ 9. While he was climbing the ladder, the firefighter slipped and nearly dropped the small animal he was carrying.

_____compound_____ 10. Families need to take vacations together, but usually their conflicting schedules make this difficult.

_____compound-complex_____ 11. After he finished writing one book, Kevin began another, and his career was on its way.

_____compound-complex_____ 12. Although the highway was now officially open, the Moehlers felt it was still not safe to travel, so they cancelled their trip.

_____complex_____ 13. The concerned and caring youth group gave food items to anyone who needed them.

_____complex_____ 14. Although I have many good memories, skating on the pond behind our home is my favorite one.

▶ **Exercise 3** **Diagram the following sentences.**

1. The daring cowboy rode the spirited mustang.

2. June enjoys Chicago-style pizza.

3. Have you read the article explaining the monarch butterfly's migration to Mexico?

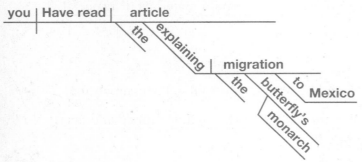

4. Renée enjoys playing the piano.

5. Recycling will help the environment.

6. You need a telescope to see the rings of Saturn.

7. To train a dog well requires much patience.

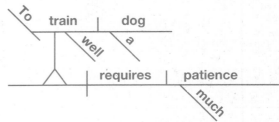

8. A police officer's job is to protect the public.

9. Sheila and Dave paid attention to what the acrobat did next.

10. They argued about who would watch the game.

Unit 6: Verb Tenses and Voice

Lesson 36
Regular Verbs: Principal Parts

Verbs have four main parts: a base form, a present participle, a simple past, and a past participle. A **regular verb** forms its past and past participle by adding *-ed* or *-d* to the base form. All verbs form the present participle by adding *-ing* to the base form. Both the present participle and past participle require a helping verb.

Base Form: The sisters **talk** to each other every day.
Present Participle: The sisters **are talking** about their summer vacations.
Past Form: The sisters **talked** earlier this morning.
Past Participle: The sisters **have talked** often about their children.

▶ **Exercise 1** Complete each sentence by writing the form of the verb indicated in parentheses.

Grandma has _____discussed_____ her childhood. (past participle/discuss)

1. Clancy is _____searching_____ for his hockey stick. (present participle/search)

2. Yesterday he _____hunted_____ high and low but with no luck. (past/hunt)

3. Clancy and his twin sister, June, have often _____wondered_____ what happened to their belongings. (past participle/wonder)

4. Last week Clancy _____placed_____ his softball and glove on the kitchen table before he went to his room to study. (past/place)

5. When he came back, Clancy _____discovered_____ his ball and glove under the stove. (past/discover)

6. Recently, June _____followed_____ a muddy trail outside, where she found the dirty boots she had left in the hallway. (past/follow)

7. Clancy and June are _____wondering_____ if they should hire a private detective to find the culprit. (present participle/wonder)

8. Clancy and June have _____decided_____ to leave one of their belongings in a certain place and then watch to see what happens. (past participle/decide)

9. They _____leave_____ a baseball glove in the kitchen. (base form/leave)

10. However, their dogs _____want_____ to go for a walk. (base form/want)

11. Fido and Spike, who _____love_____ to see them, jump up eagerly when they open the door. (base form/love)

12. On their walk, Clancy and June see that the dogs have _____burrowed_____ a spot under the fence. (past participle/burrow)

13. Curious, they hurry over to the hole the dogs have _____excavated_____. (past participle/excavate)

14. Looking into the hole, they _____howl_____ with laughter. (base form/howl)

15. There in the hole are _____resting_____ three of their missing items—a scarf, a pair of gloves, and a knee pad. (present participle/rest)

16. "We have _____solved_____ the mystery," Clancy laughs. (past participle/solve)

17. "When you see us with a ball or a glove, you know we are _____abandoning_____ you," adds June. (present participle/abandon)

18. "You _____reason_____ that if we don't have our belongings, we can't leave you," says Clancy. (base form/reason)

19. "Well," says June, "I think I _____know_____ what to do." (base form/know)

20. "From now on you can go with us and _____watch_____ from the sidelines," the twins agree. (base form/watch)

▶ **Exercise 2** **Write the three principal parts of each verb—present participle, past, and past participle.**

cough ___coughing, coughed, coughed_____

1. admit ___admitting, admitted, admitted_____

2. study ___studying, studied, studied_____

3. hike ___hiking, hiked, hiked_____

4. return ___returning, returned, returned_____

5. complete ___completing, completed, completed_____

6. refuse ___refusing, refused, refused_____

7. plot ___plotting, plotted, plotted_____

8. pitch ___pitching, pitched, pitched_____

9. dance ___dancing, danced, danced_____

10. elect ___electing, elected, elected_____

11. recycle ___recycling, recycled, recycled_____

12. conserve ___conserving, conserved, conserved_____

13. disappear ___disappearing, disappeared, disappeared_____

14. tape ___taping, taped, taped_____

15. practice ___practicing, practiced, practiced_____

Lesson 37
Irregular Verbs: Principal Parts

Irregular verbs form their past and past participle in ways different from the *-ed* and *-d* additions used for regular verbs. See the examples below for the verb *to be*.

Present Participle: I **am being** very patient with you.
Past Form: I **was** sixteen yesterday. You **were** at my party.
Past Participle: I **have been** happy today.

The principal parts of some common irregular verbs are shown below.

Base Form	Present Participle	Past Form	Past Participle
break	(am, is, or are) breaking	broke	(has, have, or had) broken
come	coming	came	come
do	doing	did	done
drive	driving	drove	driven
give	giving	gave	given
go	going	went	gone
have	having	had	had
know	knowing	knew	known
say	saying	said	said
see	seeing	saw	seen
sing	singing	sang	sung
speak	speaking	spoke	spoken
tell	telling	told	told
think	thinking	thought	thought
write	writing	wrote	written

Notice that these verbs, though irregular, still form their present participle form by adding *-ing*.

▶ **Exercise 1** Underline the word in parentheses that correctly completes each sentence. In the space provided, identify the form of the verb used as *base form, present participle, past form,* or *past participle.*

<u>base form</u>   My fish (<u>swim</u>, swimming) all day long.

<u>past form</u>   **1.** Howard (<u>spoke</u>, speaking) for one hour.

<u>past participle</u>   **2.** How many miles have you (drive, <u>driven</u>) today?

<u>past form</u>   **3.** The chorus (sung, <u>sang</u>) the school song.

<u>base form</u>   **4.** I (<u>know</u>, known) how much Carla likes horses.

<u>past form</u>   **5.** I (think, <u>thought</u>) of the answer after the test.

<u>present participle</u>   **6.** We are (<u>giving</u>, given) some money to the hunger center.

past participle	**7.**	Marsha has not (wrote, <u>written</u>) to me lately.
past participle	**8.**	The team has (<u>gone</u>, went) to the scrimmage early.
past participle	**9.**	I hope the birthday gift has (came, <u>come</u>) in time.
past participle	**10.**	She has (did, <u>done</u>) that assignment already.
base form	**11.**	My pets often (<u>break</u>, broke) things while I am away.
base form	**12.**	They (<u>say</u>, saying) we can borrow their video.
present participle	**13.**	Are you (tell, <u>telling</u>) me you have the flu?
past form	**14.**	We (seen, <u>saw</u>) the lovely sunset yesterday.
present participle	**15.**	The neighbors are (<u>having</u>, have) a party tonight.
present participle	**16.**	What are you (<u>doing</u>, done) for Thanksgiving?
past participle	**17.**	The explorer has (spoke, <u>spoken</u>) to the group before.
past participle	**18.**	She has (gave, <u>given</u>) the problem much thought.
past form	**19.**	Cara just (<u>wrote</u>, write) in her journal.
past participle	**20.**	I have (knew, <u>known</u>) Mr. Janus for years.
present participle	**21.**	That music is (driven, <u>driving</u>) me crazy!
base form	**22.**	The club members (<u>see</u>, seen) a movie once a week.
past participle	**23.**	We have (<u>thought</u>, think) of a name for the baby.
base form	**24.**	Deliveries (<u>come</u>, coming) early in our neighborhood.
present participle	**25.**	I'm (tell, <u>telling</u>) you I don't know!
past form	**26.**	The climber (gone, <u>went</u>) to the top of the cliff.
past participle	**27.**	I have (break, <u>broken</u>) two glasses today.
past participle	**28.**	They have (say, <u>said</u>) they are sorry.
past form	**29.**	I (<u>gave</u>, given) you a snack already!
past participle	**30.**	She has (driving, <u>driven</u>) that route many times.
present participle	**31.**	Who is (sang, <u>singing</u>) in the shower?
past form	**32.**	I (<u>told</u>, tell) you I would think about it.
past participle	**33.**	We have (<u>had</u>, have) enough of this noise!
past participle	**34.**	Stan has (did, <u>done</u>) his good deed for today.
past form	**35.**	I (known, <u>knew</u>) I had seen you before.
present participle	**36.**	With his new glasses, he is (seen, <u>seeing</u>) more clearly.

Lesson 38
Tense of Verbs: Present, Past, and Future

Verb tenses show time. They tell when events happen, happened, or will happen.

The present tense and the base form of a verb are the same, except for the third person singular (he, she, or it), which adds -s or -es. The verb be is also an exception to this rule.

The present tense may express an action that is repeated or ongoing. It can also express an action that is happening right now or a situation that is always true.

Malachi **plays** the trumpet well. (repeated action, always true)
I **feel** a cold draft. (right now)

The past tense expresses an action that has already occurred. In regular verbs, the past tense is formed by adding -ed or -d to the base form. In irregular verbs, the past tense takes a variety of forms. The verb be uses two past tense forms—was and were.

We **trounced** our archrivals last night. (regular)
Jackie **leapt** for the branch and missed. (irregular)

The future tense expresses an action that will take place in the future. The future tense is formed by adding will to the base form.

I **will reserve** tickets on the morning flight.
The students **will debate** the issues tomorrow.

▶ **Exercise 1 Complete each sentence by writing the form of the verb in parentheses.**

The football team _____scored_____ a touchdown. (past tense/score)

1. Cosmo _____will leave_____ for Europe Tuesday. (future tense/leave)

2. The travel agent _____planned_____ a fantastic trip for him. (past tense/plan)

3. Michelle _____wants_____ to hear all the details. (present tense/want)

4. Cosmo _____promises_____ to tell us at lunchtime. (present tense/promise)

5. All our friends _____will eat_____ under the elm tree. (future tense/eat)

6. We _____will meet_____ at noon. (future tense/meet)

7. Because he had so many things to do, Cosmo _____arrived_____ late. (past tense/arrive)

8. Michelle and our friends _____were_____ patient. (past tense/be)

9. However, I _____paced_____ around the tree. (past tense/pace)

10. Cosmo _____greeted_____ us jovially and sat down to eat his lunch. (past tense/greet)

11. "We _____will try_____ to finish eating before you begin," I said. (future tense/try)

12. "I _____will tell_____ you about my trip in a minute," Cosmo replied. (future tense/tell)

13. George _____**wanders**_____ toward the basketball court. (present tense/wander)

14. He _____**asks**_____ if anyone is interested in a game. (present tense/ask)

15. Cosmo _____**announces**_____ that he is ready to describe his trip. (present tense/announce)

16. George _____**came**_____ back just in time to hear about the journey. (past tense/come)

17. Cosmo's first stop _____**will be**_____ Rome. (future tense/be)

18. He _____**plans**_____ to visit relatives who live nearby. (present tense/plan)

19. He also _____**hopes**_____ to find the perfect plate of pasta. (present tense/hope)

20. "What about the famous places?" Michelle _____**demanded**_____. (past tense/demand)

21. Smiling, Cosmo _____**explained**_____ that he planned to see many of the well-known sights. (past tense/explain)

22. The Vittoriano _____**is**_____ a monument to Victor Emmanuel II, the first king of united Italy. (present tense/be)

23. Romans _____**constructed**_____ the Piazza del Popolo to serve as a ceremonial entrance to the city. (past tense/construct)

24. Michelle, who is interested in architecture, _____**informs**_____ us that the Spanish Steps were built from a French design. (present tense/inform)

25. I _____**began**_____ to wonder what other cities Cosmo would visit. (past tense/begin)

26. He _____**said**_____ he would also be going to Venice. (past tense/say)

27. This Italian city _____**became**_____ famous for its many canals. (past tense/become)

28. In Venice, people often _____**travel**_____ in a *gondola,* a special kind of boat. (present tense/travel)

29. Cosmo is certain he _____**will ride**_____ in one. (future tense/ride)

30. He _____**will stay**_____ in Venice for the *Biennale,* an art festival. (future tense/stay)

31. Then he _____**will journey**_____ to Paris. (future tense/journey)

32. I _____**learned**_____ about the capital of France in history class. (past tense/learn)

33. The Seine River _____**flows**_____ through the city. (present tense/flow)

34. Built for the International Exposition of 1889, the Eiffel Tower _____**looked**_____ unattractive to some people. (past tense/look)

35. However, it _____**continues**_____ to be the most recognizable symbol of Paris. (present tense/continue)

36. Cosmo _____**was**_____ quick to encourage me to take a similar trip. (past tense/be)

37. I _____**smiled**_____ ruefully and shook my head. (past tense/smile)

38. I _____**will wait**_____ until I have saved more money. (future tense/wait)

Lesson 39
Perfect Tenses: Present, Past, and Future

The present perfect tense is used to express an action that took place at some indefinite time in the past. The present perfect tense is formed with the past tense of the verb and the helping verb *has* or *have.* The present perfect tense can also be used to express an action that began in the past and continues now.

She **has read** that book.
I **have tried** several times to reach my grandmother.

The past perfect tense is used to show that one action in the past began and ended before another action in the past started. The past perfect tense is formed with the past participle of the verb and the helping verb *had.*

They **had seen** the movie before I **rented** it. (past perfect tense, past tense)

The future perfect tense is used to show that one action or condition in the future will begin and end before another event in the future starts. The future perfect tense is formed with the past participle of the verb and the construction *will have.*

By the time the school year ends, I **will have completed** ten book reports.

▶ **Exercise 1** **Draw two lines under each simple predicate in the main clause. Write the verb tense: *present perfect*, *past perfect*, or *future perfect*.**

past perfect		He had watched football all day long.
future perfect	1.	By Saturday, we will have finished our recycling project.
past perfect	2.	My dog had stolen the cat's food.
present perfect	3.	The gymnast has never lost her confidence.
past perfect	4.	The farm workers had generally gone before dawn.
future perfect	5.	By Tuesday Tisha will have landed her plane for the first time.
present perfect	6.	Raul has exhausted himself with his project.
past perfect	7.	I had turned at the wrong corner.
future perfect	8.	Before next week, Ms. Rashad will have corrected over one hundred themes.
present perfect	9.	Mother has already found her lost ring.
future perfect	10.	By mid-afternoon the tide will have gone out.
present perfect	11.	She has always wanted a book on whales.
past perfect	12.	The explorers had hoped to reach the peak by nightfall.

present perfect   **13.** My grandmother has taught me both knitting and quilting.

future perfect   **14.** They will have finished dinner before the performance.

past perfect   **15.** The flower pot had narrowly missed the bystanders.

present perfect   **16.** We have warned you about this before.

present perfect   **17.** The VCR has failed to record three times this week.

future perfect   **18.** The band will have played its program before the second half starts.

past perfect   **19.** I had snubbed her before she apologized.

past perfect   **20.** Before the speech ended, I had decided whom to vote for.

future perfect   **21.** By the time the sun rises, the icicles will have melted.

future perfect   **22.** Sue will have completed her morning exercises before her brothers get up.

present perfect   **23.** The dog has chewed her bone down to the nub.

present perfect   **24.** Trapeze artists have always fascinated me.

past perfect   **25.** The spy had switched off the light before the agents even reached the doorway.

present perfect   **26.** Kaoru has visited her brother in the hospital every day.

future perfect   **27.** By nightfall, I will have gotten very sick of the train.

present perfect   **28.** We have rehearsed this scene until it is perfect.

past perfect   **29.** The dogs had gone for hours without a walk when I came home.

past perfect   **30.** The movie had played for a half hour by the time we got there.

present perfect   **31.** Our team has won ten of its last eleven games.

future perfect   **32.** If we wait awhile, most of the crowd will have left.

future perfect   **33.** Rocco will have gotten his degree by the end of the term.

present perfect   **34.** Doug has struggled for months to learn Spanish.

present perfect   **35.** That volcano has already erupted twice this year.

past perfect   **36.** Kyra had rearranged the furniture since the last time I visited.

present perfect   **37.** I have repeatedly told you not to stand on that rickety ladder!

present perfect   **38.** You have never missed a rock concert!

future perfect   **39.** We will have fallen asleep before our parents arrive.

past perfect   **40.** The freighter had sunk before the rescue ship could reach it.

Lesson 40
Tenses of Verbs

The **present tense** expresses an action that is repeated, always true, or happening right now.

I **watch** for the early bus at Third Street. He **watches** for the early bus at Third Street.
I **am** happy. You **are** happy. He, she, or it **is** happy. They **are** happy.

The **past tense** expresses an action that has already occurred.

I **watched** for the bus and **caught** it at First Avenue. (regular and irregular verbs)
I **was** late, but the rest of the students **were** on time. (the verb *be*)

The **future tense** expresses an action that will take place in the future.

Shannon **will connect** the wires.

The **present perfect tense** expresses an action that took place sometime in the past.

I **have searched** everywhere for my telescope.

The **past perfect tense** shows that one action in the past began and ended before another action started.

I **had** already **completed** the puzzle when you came.

The **future perfect tense** shows that an action in the future will begin and end before another action starts.

I **will have swum** forty laps by the end of the hour.

▶ **Exercise 1 Draw two lines under the simple predicate in each sentence. Then write the tense of the verb in the space provided.**

__past tense__ Many citizens signed the petition.

__present perfect__ **1.** Historians have called the time from 1870 to 1890 the Gilded Age.

__present__ **2.** This name comes from a novel by Charles Dudley Warner and Mark Twain.

__past__ **3.** The novel described life in the United States at that time.

__past perfect__ **4.** Before writing the book, the authors had decided on a theme.

__past__ **5.** They wanted to expose the corruption beneath the pretty, polished surface of their world.

__present perfect__ **6.** However, the Gilded Age has produced positive results as well.

__future perfect__ **7.** We will have seen these accomplishments by the end of the year.

__past__ **8.** Victoria Woodhull was the first woman to attempt to run for president.

__past perfect__   **9.** She had asked to be on the ballot in the election of 1872.

__past perfect__   **10.** However, she had not reached the age of thirty-five by the time of the election.

__past__   **11.** In 1884, the newly formed National Equal Rights party nominated Belva Lockwood, a New York lawyer, for President.

__future__   **12.** Some prominent women will be against her candidacy.

__past__   **13.** Belva Lockwood received over four thousand votes.

__future perfect__   **14.** None of these votes will have come from women.

__past perfect__   **15.** Women had not received the right to vote yet.

__past perfect__   **16.** Women had achieved many distinctions and honors.

__present__   **17.** Many, such as Mary Bonney and Amelia Quinton, work to improve the lives of Native Americans.

__present perfect__   **18.** Colleges have opened their doors to women.

__present__   **19.** Writing is one way for women to earn money in the Gilded Age.

__future perfect__   **20.** I will have finished reading *Little Women* by Friday.

▶ **Exercise 2** **Complete each sentence by writing the form of the verb listed in parentheses.**

The submarine _____submerges_____ in the ocean. (present tense/submerge)

1. John Philip Sousa _____was_____ a famous musician of the Gilded Age. (past tense/be)

2. He _____had studied_____ music since the age of six. (past perfect tense/study)

3. He _____develops_____ an interest in band music. (present tense/develop)

4. Believe it or not, he _____will have learned_____ how to play every instrument used in military bands by the time he becomes leader of the United States Marine Corps band. (future perfect tense/learn)

5. After twelve years, he _____leaves_____ the Marine Corps band to create a band of his own. (present tense/leave)

6. He _____became_____ a composer as well as a band leader. (past tense/become)

7. Sousa _____has composed_____ many famous marches, including "Washington Post March" and "Stars and Stripes Forever." (present perfect tense/compose)

8. His marches _____have excited_____ crowds for more than a century. (present perfect tense/excite)

9. When his music was still new, Sousa's band _____traveled_____ around the world. (past tense/travel)

10. Admirers of his work _____will name_____ him the March King. (future tense/name)

Lesson 41
Verbs: Progressive and Emphatic Forms

The **progressive form** of a verb tense expresses an action that is continuing at the time referred to in the sentence. The progressive form uses the present participle of the verb with the suitable tense of the verb *be*.

Present Progressive	They **are laughing.**
Past Progressive	They **were laughing.**
Future Progressive	They **will be laughing.**
Present Perfect Progressive	They **have been laughing.**
Past Perfect Progressive	They **had been laughing.**
Future Perfect Progressive	They **will have been laughing.**

▶ **Exercise 1** Write the required form of each verb listed. Use the pronoun that heads each group as the subject of the verb.

I; past progressive/eat __I was eating._____

I

1. future progressive/sail __I will be sailing._____

2. past perfect progressive/ask __I had been asking._____

3. present progressive/arrive __I am arriving._____

4. past progressive/wait __I was waiting._____

5. present perfect progressive/move __I have been moving._____

YOU

6. future perfect progressive/swim __You will have been swimming._____

7. present progressive/testify __You are testifying._____

8. past perfect progressive/hope __You had been hoping._____

9. past progressive/play __You were playing._____

10. future progressive/go __You will be going._____

THEY

11. present perfect progressive/wonder __They have been wondering._____

12. past progressive/follow __They were following._____

13. past perfect progressive/challenge __They had been challenging._____

14. future perfect progressive/write __They will have been writing._____

15. present progressive/buy <u>They are buying.</u>

SHE

16. future progressive/rest <u>She will be resting.</u>

17. past perfect progressive/catch <u>She had been catching.</u>

18. present progressive/hide <u>She is hiding.</u>

19. future perfect progressive/knit <u>She will have been knitting.</u>

20. present perfect progressive/collect <u>She has been collecting.</u>

The **emphatic form** adds emphasis to the verb. The emphatic form uses the base form of the verb with the addition of *do, does,* or *did.*

Present Emphatic   I **do mow** the lawn every week.
Carla **does mow** hers twice each week.
Past Emphatic   Ralph **did mow** it while we were gone.

▶ **Exercise 2** **Complete each sentence by writing the emphatic verb form described in parentheses.**

Regardless of the weather, I _____<u>did visit</u>_____ the amusement park. (past emphatic/visit)

1. Despite what you say, I _____<u>did wash</u>_____ the car yesterday. (past emphatic/wash)

2. Although she hates them, Rachel _____<u>does complete</u>_____ her exercises each morning. (present emphatic/complete)

3. Even though you think you're alone, I _____<u>do understand</u>_____ your feelings. (present emphatic/understand)

4. Before I forget, Aunt Cora _____<u>did call</u>_____ after you left. (past emphatic/call)

5. Apparently the machine _____<u>does work</u>_____ on batteries. (present emphatic/work)

6. Laugh if you want to, but I _____<u>do know</u>_____ how to do a somersault. (present emphatic/know)

7. When you pass the park, _____<u>do look</u>_____ at the new monument. (present emphatic/look)

8. The electrician says he _____<u>did fix</u>_____ the outside wiring. (past emphatic/fix)

9. They hope the game _____<u>does end</u>_____ on time. (present emphatic/end)

10. I _____<u>did empty</u>_____ the garbage! (past emphatic/empty)

Lesson 42
Verbs: Compatibility of Tenses

Sometimes one event occurs before or after another event in a sentence. In these cases, it is appropriate to shift tenses.

Incorrect: By the time the police **arrived,** the thief **escaped.**

This is incorrect because the verbs are both past tense forms and suggest that the two events took place at the same time.

Correct: By the time the police **arrived,** the thief **had escaped.**

Here the tense shifts from the past (arrived) to past perfect (had escaped) to show that the thief escaped before the police arrived.

When two or more events take place at the same time in a sentence, the verb tenses must remain the same.

Incorrect: When Paul **registered** for the summer class, he **is filling** out seven forms.

This is incorrect because the tense changes from past to present, even though the events in the sentence both took place in the past.

Correct: When Paul **registered** for the summer class, he **filled** out seven forms.

▶ **Exercise 1** **Complete each sentence with the appropriate tense of the verb in parentheses.**

We went backstage to see the actor, but he _____ *had gone* _____ home. (go)

1. Taylor's family will plan their vacation before she _____ *leaves* _____ for school. (leave)

2. If she waits until ten o'clock, she _____ *will find* _____ out when they are leaving. (find)

3. I had expected her to be late, but she _____ *arrived* _____ early. (arrive)

4. Taylor says they are going to Hawaii, which _____ *was* _____ their original destination. (be)

5. By the time she left, Taylor _____ *had purchased* _____ several books about Hawaii. (purchase)

6. Last week she read about a luau, which _____ *is* _____ a Hawaiian banquet. (be)

7. If you look up the word *luau,* you _____ *will discover* _____ that it was originally the name for the leaves of the taro plant. (discover)

8. *Luau* had referred to dishes made with these leaves before the word _____ *became* _____ the name of the feast itself. (become)

9. Taylor has waited several years, so she _____ *will enjoy* _____ attending a luau. (enjoy)

10. If she remembers to bring her camera, she _____ *will take* _____ photographs. (take)

11. She had hoped for nice weather, but a storm _____ *appeared* _____ . (appear)

12. She will visit her friend Niki, whose family _____ *prepares or* will prepare *or* is preparing _____ the luau. (prepare)

13. If she watches carefully, she _____ will learn _____ how to cook the meal. (learn)

14. The host _____ had roasted _____ a pig before the guests arrived. (roast)

15. *Lau lau* is a dish that _____ consists _____ of luau leaves and pork wrapped in a ti leaf. (consist)

16. By the time she reached the luau, the others _____ had decorated _____ the table. (decorate)

17. Niki's family had expected to serve twelve dishes, but their friends _____ brought _____ three more. (bring)

18. Ti leaves cover the table at which the guests _____ will eat _____ later. (eat)

19. Before Taylor finished her poi, her host _____ had served _____ the pig. (serve)

20. The meal will not be over before the dancing _____ begins _____. (begin)

▶ **Exercise 2** Draw two lines under the two verbs or verb phrases. In the blank, rewrite the second verb or verb phrase to match the tense of the first.

Elena built a bookcase in industrial arts class, and then she paints it. _____ painted _____

1. The first Hawaiians were of Polynesian origin and come from the Marquesas Islands. _____ came _____

2. A group of immigrants left Tahiti and traveling to the Hawaiian Islands. _____ traveled _____

3. In 1778, Captain James Cook discovers the islands and will name them the Sandwich Islands. _____ names _____

4. Kamehameha I will become monarch because he seemed to be the strongest leader. _____ will seem _____

5. The islands will begin to change but continuing to develop. _____ will continue _____

6. Other nations recognized the kingdom's independence when the country adopts a constitution. _____ adopted _____

7. While Great Britain and France were fighting each other for control of the islands, Kamehameha III seeks protection from the United States. _____ was seeking _____

8. President Cleveland is against annexation, but the United States had received permission to build a naval base at Pearl Harbor. _____ receives _____

9. In 1959, Hawaii joins the Union, so flagmakers added a fiftieth star to the U.S. flag. _____ add _____

10. Many people consider Hawaii the most beautiful state, though each state will have its own unique beauty. _____ has _____

Lesson 43
Voice of Verbs: Active and Passive

Action verbs can be used in two ways—in the active voice and in the passive voice. A sentence has a verb in the **active voice** when the subject performs the action. A sentence has a verb in the **passive voice** when the action is performed on the subject.

The catcher **caught** the ball. (active voice)
The ball **was caught** by the catcher. (passive voice)

The passive voice is formed by using the past participle of the verb with a form of the helping verb *be*.

The ball **is caught** by the catcher.   (present tense)
The ball **was caught** by the catcher.   (past tense)
The ball **will be caught** by the catcher.   (future tense)

The passive voice can give variety to your writing. In general, however, the active voice is more interesting, more direct, and makes for livelier writing.

Grammar

▶ **Exercise 1** Draw two lines under the verb or verb phrase. Write *A* (active voice) or *P* (passive voice) over the verb to tell which voice it is.

P
Study hall was changed to second period.

A
1. The puppy chewed the bone.

P
2. Carla is known by everybody.

A
3. Ron fed the birds.

P
4. The kitten was found by Bev.

P
5. The baby will be fed by Dad.

A
6. Curt showed the photographs.

A
7. The dog guards the house.

A
8. The team won the trophy.

P
9. The car was washed by Sarah.

A
10. Mom will lock the door.

A
11. George took the medicine.

P
12. The data were relayed by satellite.

A
13. Curly read the minutes.

P
14. A meeting will be held by the committee.

P
15. The vote was taken by our chairperson.

A
16. The rescue planes dropped food.

A
17. The flood destroyed three towns.

P
18. The mail was delivered by Jake.

P
19. Our house will be painted by Marge.

A
20. Dad bought groceries.

▶ **Exercise 2** Write *A* over the verb if the verb is in the active voice and *P* if it is in the passive voice. Then rewrite each active voice sentence in the passive voice and each passive voice sentence in the active voice.

A
Raul planted tomatoes. _Tomatoes were planted by Raul._

P
1. Money was needed by the band. _The band needed money._

P
2. The group's budget had been depleted by inflation. _Inflation had depleted the group's budget._

A
3. The band members planned a fund-raiser. _A fund-raiser was planned by the band members._

A
4. The band members discussed several ideas. _Several ideas were discussed by the band members._

A
5. The trombone players suggested an instrument sale. _An instrument sale was suggested by the trombone players._

P
6. A car wash was proposed by the clarinet players. _The clarinet players proposed a car wash._

A
7. Several of the drummers recommended a raffle. _A raffle was recommended by several of the drummers._

P
8. That idea was liked by everyone. _Everyone liked that idea._

P
9. A new trumpet was donated by a local instrument seller, Mr. Majeske. _A local instrument seller, Mr. Majeske, donated a new trumpet._

A
10. The band members sold raffle tickets after school. _Raffle tickets were sold by the band members after school._

Unit 6 **Review**

▶ **Exercise** Draw two lines under each verb or verb phrase. Then write the tense of each verb in the blank before the sentence. Some sentences have more than one verb.

_____past_____   We rode the roller coaster.

_____future_____   **1.** Sheila will finish her homework before dinner.

____present perfect____   **2.** Our cooking class has watched three videos to learn how to prepare this dish.

____present, future____   **3.** If you crouch very quietly, you will see the raccoon.

__past perfect, past__   **4.** The alligator had disappeared by the time we reached the edge of the swamp.

__present progressive__   **5.** The teacher is talking about Thomas Edison.

_____past_____   **6.** Yesterday I toured the natural history museum.

present perfect progressive   **7.** We have been laughing at Sara's joke for five minutes.

____future perfect____   **8.** The new train will have traveled two hundred miles by noon.

____past progressive____   **9.** The playwright was hoping for a positive review.

___future progressive___   **10.** Their team will be jogging around the Lincoln Memorial.

____past emphatic____   **11.** Colleen did hear the speech by the Russian scientist.

future perfect progressive   **12.** In December, she will have been knitting that scarf for six months.

___present emphatic___   **13.** My dog, Juno, does like to jump over the fence.

past perfect progressive, past   **14.** The Tates had been expecting fifty guests, but sixty people came to the banquet.

_____present_____   **15.** Uncle Yuri sends his regards to the entire family.

____past perfect____   **16.** We had waited nearly an hour for the bus to arrive.

_____future_____   **17.** The florist will arrange a lovely centerpiece for Cousin Darla's wedding.

_____past_____   **18.** Claude sailed his boat across Lake Erie.

__present progressive__   **19.** We are watching a movie about space exploration.

present perfect progressive   **20.** Rochelle has been studying medicine for three years.

Grammar

Cumulative Review: Units 1–6

▶ **Exercise 1** Underline each simple subject once and each simple predicate twice. Label each preposition *prep.*, each direct object *d.o.*, and each indirect object *i.o.*

                        d.o. prep.
Peter took his cousin to the mall.

                          d.o.   prep.
1. Tracy suddenly left the room during the lecture.

                         d.o.
2. Ed will ski the advanced run tomorrow.

         i.o.   d.o. prep.
3. I gave Sandy the box with the blue label.

                      d.o.
4. The heavy rain replenished the crop.

                 prep.
5. The observers were excited by the meteor shower.

               prep.
6. The forward will shoot from midcourt.

                  d.o.   prep.
7. My friend Ione is writing a collection of poems.

            d.o.   prep.
8. The actor applies his makeup every night before the show.

              prep.
9. A lone tugboat struggled through the choppy water.

        i.o.   d.o.
10. Ms. Watkins asked Jenny an algebra question.

           d.o.   prep.
11. That athlete inspires many young people to stay in school.

           d.o.   prep.
12. We will telephone everyone about the party.

             prep.
13. Neil is always the first one out the door.

         d.o. prep.
14. Wilson collects insects for his science class.

               d.o.   prep.
15. The current mayor will challenge her opponent to a debate.

                 d.o.
16. The chemistry class performs two experiments each week.

         d.o. prep.
17. Her kitten hid my socks in the yard.

            i.o.   d.o. prep.
18. The guests brought their host a vase of flowers.

         d.o. prep.
19. Ben swam a mile in his best time yet.

              prep.
20. Our friends will be exhausted after the events.

$\overset{\text{d.o.}}{}$ $\overset{\text{prep.}}{}$
21. Paul rode his bicycle home through the rain.

$\overset{\text{prep.}}{}$ $\overset{\text{prep.}}{}$
22. My mother wins at chess most of the time.

▶ **Exercise 2** Label each participle *part.*, each gerund *ger.*, and each infinitive *inf.* Then write whether the sentence is *simple, compound, complex,* or *compound-complex.*

<u>   simple   </u>   Jogging is a healthy way to get in shape.

<u>   simple   </u>   **1.** Golfing is one of my favorite sports.

<u>   compound   </u>   **2.** I want to be a singer, but first I must study voice.

<u>   simple   </u>   **3.** Waiting by the fountain, Sven decided to sketch the town square.

<u>   complex   </u>   **4.** Although we had tickets, we were not allowed to enter the theater.

<u>   complex   </u>   **5.** The shivering skaters who still wish to compete should gather by the judges' table.

<u>   compound   </u>   **6.** Stretching helps Bridget to warm up, and running helps her to stay in shape.

<u> compound-complex </u>   **7.** As the train pulled out of the station, Roberto took his seat, and his fidgeting younger brother walked up and down the aisle.

<u>   complex   </u>   **8.** Unless it begins to snow, the ski resort will not be able to open.

<u>   simple   </u>   **9.** The glittering guests ascended the stairs to the awards ceremony.

<u>   complex   </u>   **10.** While Colette studies dancing, her sister studies painting.

<u>   compound   </u>   **11.** Geoff's desire to win was great, yet he skipped practice for two days.

<u> compound-complex </u>   **12.** The bell may ring, or the irritating buzzer may sound when time has expired.

<u>   simple   </u>   **13.** We are hiking to the top of the hill to do our stargazing.

<u>   complex   </u>   **14.** If the weather is mild, camping will be an option.

<u>   compound   </u>   **15.** Helga was worried, but she did not want the frightened child to know it.

<u>   complex   </u>   **16.** The flight that Ruth and Oliver wanted to take was canceled.

<u>   complex   </u>   **17.** A pulsating beat accompanied the melody as Mike played the new song he had composed.

_____compound-complex_____ **18.** You need to decide what should be done, and we need to find
inf. ... inf.
part.
willing helpers.

▶ **Exercise 3** Draw two lines under the verb or verb phrase in each sentence. Then write the
tense of the verb.

_____present perfect_____ The movie has received rave reviews.

_____past perfect_____ **1.** The polls had closed by seven o'clock that evening.

_____past_____ **2.** The water in the horses' trough froze overnight.

_____future_____ **3.** The principal will administer the test.

_____present perfect_____ **4.** Suki has seen several lunar eclipses.

_____future perfect_____ **5.** By tomorrow the council will have chosen its new president.

_____future_____ **6.** This scarf will replace the missing one.

_____present_____ **7.** My cousin attends the state university.

_____present_____ **8.** This book discusses environmental problems.

_____past perfect_____ **9.** By yesterday evening I had written thirteen letters of application for
a summer job.

_____past_____ **10.** The cartoonist at the fair drew several quick pictures of our family.

_____present perfect_____ **11.** I have given you all the facts of the case.

_____present_____ **12.** The dog barks several times during the night.

_____future perfect_____ **13.** Within an hour the rocket will have splashed down in the Pacific.

_____past_____ **14.** Katrina scoffed at the ridiculous story.

_____present perfect_____ **15.** The catcher has dropped the ball again.

_____future perfect_____ **16.** By next Sunday I will have worked four weekends in a row.

_____future_____ **17.** This device will filter our drinking water.

_____present perfect_____ **18.** They have excavated the last site.

_____past perfect_____ **19.** The sudden wind had torn the small boat from its berth.

_____past_____ **20.** Mr. Harris was happy with our oral reports.

_____present_____ **21.** Sally plans to give a party for Christy.

_____past_____ **22.** Doris and Andrew donated their profits to charity.

Unit 7: Subject-Verb Agreement

Lesson 44

Subject-Verb Agreement

The **subject and verb** in a sentence must agree. In the present tense, add *-s* or *-es* to the base form for the third-person singular.

SINGULAR	PLURAL
He **skates**.	They **skate**.
She **wins**.	They **win**.

The verbs *be, have,* and *do* change form to agree with their subjects.

SINGULAR	PLURAL
I **am** climbing.	We **are** climbing.
You **are** climbing.	You **are** climbing.
She **is** climbing.	They **are** climbing.
I **have** reached the top.	We **have** reached the top.
You **have** reached the top.	You **have** reached the top.
He **has** reached the top.	They **have** reached the top.
I **do** climb often.	We **do** climb often.
Do you climb often?	**Do** you climb often?
Does she climb often?	**Do** they climb often?

▶ **Exercise 1** **Underline the form of the verb that agrees with the subject.**

My younger brother (has, have) a large collection of toy dinosaurs.

1. Fossils (is, are) fascinating records of the past.

2. They (tells, tell) us about plants and animals of long ago.

3. Some ancient animals, such as dinosaurs, (was, were) huge.

4. A dinosaur fossil (preserves, preserve) a tooth, a bone, or even a major part of the skeleton.

5. Fossil hunters (has found, have found) dinosaur remains around the world.

6. Dinosaurs (was fixed, were fixed) in time in a number of ways.

7. Some (was frozen, were frozen) in glaciers.

8. Such a dinosaur (is, are) like the frozen food in your freezer.

9. Other dinosaurs (was caught, were caught) in tar pits and preserved there.

10. Fossil evidence (shows, show) that many dinosaurs died in a short period of time.

11. Scientists (believes, believe) that a major disaster occurred in the past.

12. Different theories (exists, <u>exist</u>) about why this happened.

13. One theory (<u>states</u>, state) that a comet collided with Earth and stirred up so much dust that the sun's light was blocked out.

14. At any rate, we (does know, <u>do know</u>) that dinosaurs no longer roam the earth.

15. Scientists (studies, <u>study</u>) dinosaur remains to find out what life was like in ancient times.

16. Stomach contents (reveals, <u>reveal</u>) what animals and plants lived at the same time.

17. Recently a fossilized dinosaur egg (<u>was found</u>, were found).

18. The unhatched baby dinosaur (have been, <u>has been</u>) preserved in the egg.

19. A fossil hunt (<u>is</u>, are) an exciting pastime.

20. Anyone who (<u>excavates</u>, excavate) a dinosaur has many stories to tell.

▶ **Exercise 2 Choose the verb in parentheses that agrees with the subject. Write your choice in the blank.**

The students _____ were _____ about to study a unit on fossils. (was, were)

1. Imagine you _____ are _____ walking in the woods one day. (is, are)

2. You _____ see _____ the dried tracks of a deer in the muddy bank along a stream. (sees, see)

3. Of course the tracks probably _____ were made _____ only days before you saw them. (was made, were made)

4. The dried tracks _____ are _____ the beginnings of a fossil. (is, are)

5. If a sudden rainstorm _____ fills _____ the tracks up with mud, the deer print will be preserved, at least for a time. (fills, fill)

6. Several materials _____ make _____ good fossils. (makes, make)

7. A bone _____ is _____ good fossil material because of its hardness. (is, are)

8. Animal shells also _____ produce _____ good fossils. (produces, produce)

9. Despite their softness, jellyfish _____ do leave _____ fossil imprints. (does leave, do leave)

10. Sometimes an insect _____ is fossilized _____ in amber. (is fossilized, are fossilized)

11. Amber _____ is _____ the hard sap of very old trees. (is, are)

12. As an insect sticks in the amber, the amber _____ hardens _____ around it. (hardens, harden)

13. Most fossils, however, _____ have formed _____ in layers of rock. (has formed, have formed)

14. Animal skeletons fall to the bottom of rivers and lakes, where they _____ are covered _____ with mud or silt. (is covered, are covered)

15. If the animal's skeleton is hard, it _____ makes _____ a better fossil. (makes, make)

Lesson 45
Subject-Verb Agreement and Intervening Prepositional Phrases

The subject of a sentence is never contained within a prepositional phrase. The verb must agree with the subject of the sentence, not the object of a preposition.

The **color** of the thunderclouds **worries** me. (The subject is *color,* a singular noun. *Of the thunderclouds* is a prepositional phrase with a plural object. However, the verb *worries* agrees with the singular subject.)
The **players** on the team **have** new uniforms. (The subject is *players,* a plural noun. *On the team* is a prepositional phrase with a singular object. However, the verb *have* agrees with the plural subject.)

▶ **Exercise 1** **Underline the verb in parentheses that correctly completes the sentence by agreeing with the subject.**

A vase of roses usually (stand, <u>stands</u>) on the piano.

1. The rain forests of the earth (occurs, <u>occur</u>) in places where there is much rainfall.

2. The rain forest ecosystem, to biologists, (<u>is</u>, are) the source of much diversity.

3. Rain forests in a tropical area (is, <u>are</u>) warm and humid.

4. The number of tree species (<u>is estimated</u>, are estimated) to be about 3,000.

5. The area around the trees (<u>is filled</u>, are filled) with mosses, vines, and other water-loving plants.

6. The rain forest, with complex food chains, (<u>recycles</u>, recycle) nutrients constantly.

7. No dead plants on the ground (is, <u>are</u>) left there for long.

8. Plant matter from different species (<u>decays</u>, decay) quickly and is reused as food.

9. Plant life, with many animal species, (keep, <u>keeps</u>) the rain forest teeming with noise and motion.

10. The mammals of a rain forest (includes, <u>include</u>) leopards, jaguars, bats, and different monkeys.

11. Hoots, chirps, and roars from every corner (echoes, <u>echo</u>) throughout the day.

12. An explorer of rain forests also (<u>thrills</u>, thrill) at the wide variety of colorful birds.

13. Scientists interested in insects (has discovered, <u>have discovered</u>) hundreds of new species.

14. The animals on the forest floor (numbers, <u>number</u>) far fewer than those that live in the trees.

15. Not every traveler to these tropical paradises (<u>focuses</u>, focus) on animals.

16. Some visitors on a search for new healing substances (looks, <u>look</u>) at medicinal plants.

17. Students of the rain forest (is alarmed, <u>are alarmed</u>) at its rate of destruction.

18. Businesses of every kind (destroys, <u>destroy</u>) many acres each day.

19. Earth with its many problems (<u>needs</u>, need) this valuable source of life.

20. Many groups with an interest in the rain forest (works, <u>work</u>) hard to preserve this treasure.

▶ **Exercise 2** **Underline the verb in parentheses that agrees with the subject.**

A rainfall of several hours (<u>soaks</u>, soak) the ground.

1. Ecosystems with little water (is called, <u>are called</u>) deserts.

2. The rainfall from many years often (<u>does</u>, do) not equal the amount that falls in one year elsewhere.

3. Still, clusters of plant life (is, <u>are</u>) common in some deserts.

4. Temperatures in a desert (varies, <u>vary</u>) by many degrees.

5. In fact, people from another region (is, <u>are</u>) surprised to learn that deserts can be cold.

6. Deserts at high elevation or latitude (<u>have</u>, has) freezing temperatures.

7. Deserts of America (reaches, <u>reach</u>) daytime temperatures of over one hundred degrees.

8. Temperatures at night (measures, <u>measure</u>) many degrees cooler.

9. Deserts, in spite of their dryness, (<u>are</u>, is) home to an amazing variety of animals and plants.

10. Species in a desert (has, <u>have</u>) different adaptations to the lack of water.

11. Sharp spines on a cactus (serves, <u>serve</u>) as leaves and help prevent water loss.

12. The root systems of cacti (<u>spread</u>, spreads) out to collect as much water as possible.

13. The roots on a mesquite tree (extends, <u>extend</u>) far into the earth, looking for sources of water.

14. A cactus with flowers (<u>makes</u>, make) an attractive houseplant.

15. Visitors to the desert (expresses, <u>express</u>) surprise at the wide spaces between plants.

16. A desert area with few plants (<u>conserves</u>, conserve) the available water better than an area with many plants.

17. Animals with little need for water (does, <u>do</u>) best in the desert.

18. Oils from dry seeds (provides, <u>provide</u>) the kangaroo rat all the liquid it needs.

19. Camels of the Sahara (stores, <u>store</u>) water in their fatty humps.

20. Animals with adaptability (thrives, <u>thrive</u>) in a land of little water.

Lesson 46
Subject-Verb Agreement and Linking Verbs

In sentences with linking verbs, the verb agrees with the subject, not with the predicate nominative.

The **flowers** in the pot **are** a **gift**. (The verb, *are,* agrees with the subject, *flowers,* not the predicate nominative, *gift.)*

The **result** of the experiment **was** more effective **medications**. (The verb, *was,* agrees with the subject, *result,* not the predicate nominative, *medications.)*

▶ **Exercise 1** **Underline the verb in parentheses that agrees with the subject.**

Jake's excuse for tardiness (is, are) his morning chores.

1. Outdoor activities (seems, seem) the best method for teaching the nature class.

2. The total cost (was, were) hundreds of dollars more than we expected.

3. Exercising and dieting (remains, remain) a healthful way to live.

4. The game scores (was, were) a major disappointment.

5. Jana's injured teeth (is, are) a source of much pain to her.

6. Pinks and oranges (makes, make) a beautiful sunset.

7. My greatest success this year (is, are) my grades.

8. The Porpoises (is, are) the best swimming team in town.

9. The band director's biggest disappointment (remains, remain) the clarinets.

10. The man's remarks (was, were) an embarrassment to his listeners.

11. Our most important resource (is, are) our children.

12. The Carters (is, are) a happy couple.

13. The two lovely monuments (remains, remain) a testament to human courage.

14. The two robberies (was, were) a mystery to the police.

15. The problem (is, are) too many cooks in the kitchen.

16. The cause of the accident (was, were) faulty brakes.

17. The noisy neighbors (was, were) a constant problem.

18. The cost of pollution (is, are) higher medical bills.

19. The reason for the delay (is, are) the strikes in the trucking industry.

20. The sounds of the birds (was, were) the only disturbance.

▶ **Exercise 2** Draw one line under the simple subject. Draw two lines under the verb in parentheses that agrees with the subject.

The <u>results</u> of the election (is, <u>are</u>) finally available.

1. Bill's best <u>feature</u> (<u>is</u>, are) his beautiful brown eyes.

2. Your <u>postcards</u> from Hawaii (was, <u>were</u>) a welcome treat.

3. The library <u>books</u> (is, <u>are</u>) a donation from a patron.

4. The <u>videos</u> about whales (is, <u>are</u>) my favorite present.

5. The gas <u>tanks</u> on those trucks (is, <u>are</u>) a safety problem.

6. Angie's and Carla's <u>haircuts</u> (looks, <u>look</u>) a sight!

7. The <u>joy</u> of Stella's life (<u>is</u>, are) her nieces and nephews.

8. Last night's <u>losses</u> (seems, <u>seem</u>) a shame.

9. A <u>change</u> in diet and lifestyle (<u>remains</u>, remain) his only hope for recovery.

10. The falling <u>leaves</u> (becomes, <u>become</u>) a blanket of red and gold.

11. The <u>result</u> of last night's poor score (<u>was</u>, were) extra hours of practice for the team.

12. The <u>delivery</u> (<u>was</u>, were) several truckloads of appliances.

13. The pioneers' light <u>source</u> (<u>was</u>, were) candles.

14. Our worst <u>problem</u> (<u>is</u>, are) the bats in the attic.

15. The pep club's <u>donation</u> (<u>was</u>, were) two dozen boxes of used clothing.

16. Endangered <u>species</u> (is, <u>are</u>) a continuing environmental problem.

17. The <u>result</u> of Bob's knee injury (<u>was</u>, were) torn ligaments.

18. The individual bright <u>colors</u> (becomes, <u>become</u>) a dull blur at dusk.

19. The main <u>issue</u> in the campaign (<u>is</u>, are) taxes.

20. The genie's <u>gift</u> (<u>was</u>, were) three wishes.

▶ **Writing Link** Write three or four sentences about a report you have prepared for one of your classes. Make your verb agree with your subject in each sentence.

_____

_____

_____

_____

_____

_____

Lesson 47
Subject-Verb Agreement in Inverted Sentences

In most sentences the subject comes before the verb. However, some inverted sentences begin with a prepositional phrase followed by the verb and then the subject. The verb in such sentences must always agree with the subject, not the object of the prepositional phrase.

               V   S   V   S
Up the tree **crawls** the **bear**.   Up the tree **crawl** the **bears**.

In sentences that begin with *here* or *there,* do not confuse either word with the subject. Look for the subject following the verb.

       V   S   V   S
There **is** a **bear** in that tree.   Here **come** the **bears** down the tree!

Questions are inverted sentences. In such constructions, a helping verb often comes before the subject.

    V   S   V   V   S   V
Does the **bear live** in a den?   **Do** the **bears fish** for salmon?

▶ **Exercise 1** Draw a line under the subject. Choose the verb in parentheses that agrees with the subject, and write it in the blank.

On the sidelines _____**stand**_____ many eager <u>players</u> ready for action. (stand, stands)

1. _____**Are**_____ <u>you</u> _____**prepared**_____ for the festivities tomorrow? (Is prepared, Are prepared)

2. Here _____**are**_____ the <u>fliers</u> about the founder's day celebration. (is, are)

3. Beside that bench _____**is**_____ a <u>stack</u> of decorations. (is, are)

4. On the walls _____**hang**_____ the <u>decorations</u> we already put up. (hangs, hang)

5. Along the sidewalks _____**extends**_____ a long <u>banner</u>. (extend, extends)

6. Here _____**comes**_____ <u>Luella</u>, the chairperson of the committee. (comes, come)

7. In her hands _____**is**_____ a <u>list</u> of tasks to be completed. (is, are)

8. _____**Do**_____ a <u>few</u> of those tasks _____**interest**_____ you? (Does interest, Do interest)

9. Under the trees _____**gather**_____ the <u>people</u> who want to help. (gather, gathers)

10. From the apartment building _____**pour**_____ the <u>sounds</u> of the band practicing. (pours, pour)

11. There _____**was**_____ an <u>article</u> about this event in today's paper. (was, were)

12. _____**Does**_____ the <u>paper</u> _____**support**_____ our plans? (Does support, Do support)

13. There on the sidewalk _____**wait**_____ the <u>photographers</u>. (waits, wait)

14. Down the street _____**moves**_____ a <u>series</u> of floats. (moves, move)

15. _____Do_____ the <u>photographers</u> _____shoot_____ a picture of the floats? (Does shoot, Do shoot)

16. Behind the floats _____soar_____ three huge <u>balloons</u>. (soars, soar)

17. There _____is_____ a <u>photograph</u> of our founder on each of them. (is, are)

18. _____Does_____ the <u>crowd</u> _____recognize_____ the photographs? (Does recognize, Do recognize)

19. From the crowd _____come_____ <u>sounds</u> of enjoyment. (comes, come)

20. There _____are_____ good <u>reasons</u> to plan another celebration next year. (is, are)

▶ **Exercise 2** Draw a line under the subject. Choose the verb in parentheses that agrees with the subject and write it in the blank(s).

Near one of those curbs _____stands_____ a bus-stop <u>shelter</u>. (stand, stands)

1. _____Does_____ a rock <u>concert</u> _____sound_____ like a good idea? (Does sound, Do sound)

2. Here _____are_____ some <u>suggestions</u> for our next fund-raiser. (is, are)

3. From her agent _____comes_____ a <u>message</u> from rock star Linda Light. (comes, come)

4. On her every word _____hangs_____ our <u>committee</u>. (hangs, hang)

5. Into the building _____hurry_____ the <u>workers</u>. (hurry, hurries)

6. Into the newspapers _____goes_____ a <u>notice</u> of her appearance. (goes, go)

7. Up on the wall _____appear_____ many enticing <u>posters</u>. (appears, appear)

8. On the radio _____airs_____ an <u>announcement</u> about the concert. (airs, air)

9. _____Does_____ the <u>printer</u> _____have_____ our tickets ready? (Does have, Do have)

10. _____Do_____ the ticket <u>sellers</u> _____know_____ the correct price? (Does know, Do know)

11. Here _____is_____ a <u>review</u> of Linda's concerts last week in Detroit. (is, are)

12. There _____are_____ several <u>songs</u> that she did as an encore. (is, are)

13. Across the gym _____yells_____ <u>Grayson</u> for help with the electronic system. (yells, yell)

14. Outside the building _____parks_____ a <u>reporter</u> from the local paper. (parks, park)

15. Inside the office _____ring_____ the <u>phones</u>. (rings, ring)

16. There _____is_____ a huge <u>demand</u> for tickets. (is, are)

17. Here _____are_____ the <u>passes</u> we need to keep for the press. (is, are)

18. _____Does_____ the school radio <u>station</u> _____plan_____ to tape the concert? (Does plan, Do plan)

19. Behind the curtain _____sits_____ the <u>microphone</u>. (sits, sit)

20. In all our hearts _____lurks_____ <u>anticipation</u>. (lurks, lurk)

Lesson 48
Subject-Verb Agreement and Special Subjects

A **collective noun** names a group (see Lesson 1, pp. 47–48). In a sentence, a collective noun is **singular** when it names the group as a whole. It is **plural** when it refers to individual members of a group.

Singular: The team **takes** the bus.
              The cast **rehearses** the play.
Plural: The team **get** regular physical exams.
              The cast **sign** autographs for the audience.

Some nouns ending in -s, such as *mumps, measles,* and *mathematics,* take singular verbs. Other nouns ending in -s, such as *scissors, pants, binoculars,* and *eyeglasses,* take plural verbs. Many nouns that end in -ics are either singular or plural, depending on the context.

Singular: Mathematics **is** my favorite subject.
Plural: My pants **are** muddy from the river.
Singular: Politics **is** that professor's area of expertise.
Plural: That candidate's politics **were** dirty during the campaign.

A noun of amount can refer to a single unit, in which case it is singular. It can also refer to several individual units, in which case it is plural.

Singular: Ten **weeks is** the period of the first term.
Plural: Ten **weeks are** needed to complete that research.

▶ **Exercise 1** Underline the subject. Fill in the blank with the verb in parentheses that agrees with the subject in the context of the sentence.

The recycling <u>club</u> _____asks_____ for the entire neighborhood's support. (asks, ask)

1. The <u>band</u> _____plays_____ school songs at halftime. (plays, play)

2. <u>Congress</u> _____plans_____ to adjourn early this session. (plans, plan)

3. <u>Measles</u> _____is_____ no longer the dread disease it once was. (is, are)

4. The six <u>months</u> _____have dragged_____ since my best friend moved. (has dragged, have dragged)

5. The <u>orchestra</u> _____dresses_____ in black for concerts. (dresses, dress)

6. My <u>family</u> _____is_____ sick with the flu. (is, are)

7. Your <u>binoculars</u> _____were_____ a big help at our star party. (was, were)

8. Seven <u>feet</u> _____is_____ a long distance to jump. (is, are)

9. Three <u>eggs</u> _____are_____ too many for this recipe. (is, are)

10. <u>Athletics</u> _____was_____ the only thing Jack wanted to pursue. (was, were)

11. The <u>cast</u> _____ **were** _____ each bringing a dish to the theater party. (was, were)

12. <u>Statistics</u> _____ **show** _____ a link between smoking and lung cancer. (shows, show)

13. Twenty <u>dollars</u> _____ **is** _____ too much for this video. (is, are)

14. My doctor says <u>aerobics</u> _____ **is** *or* **are** _____ a good way to get fit. (is, are)

15. Your <u>scissors</u> _____ **were** _____ under the desk. (was, were)

16. Twenty-four <u>hours</u> _____ **pass** *or* **passes** _____ very slowly when you're waiting for a test grade. (passes, pass)

17. The <u>committee</u> _____ **tries** _____ to finish its work. (tries, try)

18. Fifty <u>stories</u> of the building _____ **are** _____ finished. (is, are)

19. My <u>eyeglasses</u> no longer _____ **work** _____. (works, work)

20. <u>Aerobics</u> _____ **are** _____ exercises that strengthen the heart and lungs. (is, are)

▶ **Exercise 2** Underline the subject. Fill in the blank with the verb in parentheses that agrees with the subject in the context of the sentence.

Two <u>years</u> _____ **pass** _____ before Gwen returns to her hometown. (passes, pass)

1. _____ **Are** _____ your <u>pliers</u> on the workbench? (Is, Are)

2. _____ **Is** _____ <u>politics</u> his specialty? (Is, Are)

3. The <u>public</u> _____ **wants** _____ campaign reform. (wants, want)

4. The six o'clock <u>news</u> _____ **covers** _____ local events. (covers, cover)

5. These <u>trousers</u> _____ **do** _____ not match my shirt. (does, do)

6. The <u>committee</u> _____ **chooses** _____ a recycling plan today. (chooses, choose)

7. Three <u>months</u> _____ **constitutes** _____ a season. (constitute, constitutes)

8. _____ **Is** _____ fifty <u>cents</u> enough for a tip? (Is, Are)

9. <u>Athletics</u> _____ **was** _____ the subject of discussion at the school board meeting. (was, were)

10. <u>Measles</u> _____ **is** _____ usually a childhood disease. (is, are)

11. The science <u>faculty</u> _____ **is** _____ meeting at the museum. (is, are)

12. The music <u>faculty</u> _____ **were** _____ all at the concert. (was, were)

13. Ten <u>dollars</u> _____ **was** _____ the amount of the refund. (was, were)

14. Our <u>team</u> usually _____ **wins** _____ two out of three games. (wins, win)

15. But the <u>team</u> usually _____ **loses** _____ to the Eagles. (loses, lose)

16. Often the <u>team</u> _____ **give** _____ away their caps as souvenirs. (gives, give)

Lesson 49
Subject-Verb Agreement and Compound Subjects

Some sentences have more than one subject. A **compound subject** that is joined by *and* or *both...and* is usually plural. However, some compound subjects have two parts that make up one unit. These take a singular verb.

Plural:	Molly and Mabel **are racing**.
Plural:	Both Aunt Fran and Uncle George **have arrived**.
Singular:	Milk and cookies **is** a good snack.

Compound subjects joined by *or, nor, either...or,* or *neither...nor* always have a verb that agrees with the closer subject.

Singular:	Either Mark or Carlo **was** the winner.
Singular:	Neither the Morgans nor Mr. Hale **is** coming to the dinner.
Plural:	Neither the book nor the calendars **are** on sale.

When a compound subject is preceded by *many a, every,* or *each,* the subject takes a singular verb.

Many a student and teacher **has come** to Ms. Randolph for advice.
Every Tom, Dick, and Harry **has** an opinion.
Each tree and fence post **is covered** with political signs.

▶ **Exercise 1** Draw a line under the compound subject of each sentence. Choose the verb in parentheses that agrees with the subject, then write it in the blank.

Many a <u>bird</u> and <u>squirrel</u> _____visits_____ our backyard feeders. (visit, visits)

1. Every <u>orchard</u> and <u>farm</u> _____was damaged_____ by the storm. (was damaged, were damaged)

2. <u>Spaghetti</u> and <u>meatballs</u> _____is_____ a regular meal at our home. (is, are)

3. Neither <u>Grace</u> nor her <u>sisters</u> _____take_____ the early bus. (takes, take)

4. Either the <u>squirrels</u> or the <u>opossum</u> _____chews_____ through the storage boxes. (chews, chew)

5. The <u>bat</u> and the <u>ball</u> _____are_____ Ed's. (is, are)

6. Every <u>seed</u>, <u>nut</u>, and suet <u>ball</u> _____was eaten_____. (was eaten, were eaten)

7. Each <u>bird</u> and field <u>mouse</u> _____is_____ hungry. (is, are)

8. Both <u>movies</u> and <u>books</u> _____are_____ enjoyable. (is, are)

9. Neither the <u>soup</u> nor the <u>casserole</u> _____is_____ hot. (is, are)

10. Either <u>Lani</u> or <u>Marcia</u> _____skates_____ in the race today. (skates, skate)

11. Both my <u>shoes</u> and <u>socks</u> _____are_____ full of burrs. (is, are)

12. Either my <u>dad</u> or my <u>brothers</u> _____meet_____ me at the bus station. (meets, meet)

13. Neither the <u>dogs</u> nor the <u>cat</u> _____likes_____ too much sun. (likes, like)

14. Every <u>earring</u>, <u>necklace</u>, and <u>bracelet</u> _____was sold_____ at the fund-raiser. (was sold, were sold)

15. Each <u>geranium</u> and <u>lily</u> _____is_____ blooming. (is, are)

16. Many a <u>horse</u> and <u>cow</u> _____has lived_____ in this barn. (has lived, have lived)

17. Both my <u>arms</u> and <u>legs</u> _____ache_____ after a long climb. (aches, ache)

18. The <u>producer</u> and <u>director</u> _____disagree_____ over the script. (disagrees, disagree)

19. <u>Ham</u> and <u>eggs</u> _____is offered_____ for breakfast at that restaurant. (is offered, are offered)

20. Either the <u>coach</u> or the <u>players</u> _____have_____ to answer the letter. (has, have)

21. Neither the <u>jacket</u> nor the <u>shoes</u> _____fit_____. (fits, fit)

22. <u>Lox</u> and <u>bagels</u> _____is_____ Jacob's favorite snack. (is, are)

23. Many a <u>spy</u> and <u>traitor</u> _____was caught_____ by the detective. (was caught, were caught)

24. Either the <u>washer</u> or the <u>drier</u> _____is running_____. (is running, are running)

25. Both <u>Jesse</u> and <u>Malachi</u> _____are_____ honor students. (is, are)

26. Each <u>video</u> and <u>CD</u> _____is_____ half price. (is, are)

27. Every <u>surfboard</u> and <u>sailboat</u> _____is rented_____. (is rented, are rented)

28. Many a <u>captain</u> and <u>first mate</u> _____has swerved_____ to avoid that wreck. (has swerved, have swerved)

29. Neither the <u>cat</u> nor her <u>kittens</u> _____are sleeping_____. (is sleeping, are sleeping)

30. Each <u>chair</u>, <u>desk</u>, and <u>table</u> _____is covered_____ with books. (is covered, are covered)

31. Neither the <u>chairs</u> nor the <u>table</u> _____fits_____ in the truck. (fits, fit)

32. Both <u>Rhoda</u> and <u>Pallas</u> _____score_____ well on spelling tests. (scores, score)

33. <u>Oil</u> and <u>vinegar</u> _____makes_____ a good salad dressing. (makes, make)

34. Neither the <u>horses</u> nor the <u>cow</u> _____is_____ restless. (is, are)

35. Neither the <u>hurricane</u> nor the <u>tornadoes</u> _____are expected_____ to hit here. (is expected, are expected)

36. Many a <u>plaintiff</u> and <u>defendant</u> _____has passed_____ through these doors. (has passed, have passed)

37. Each <u>cap</u> and <u>gown</u> _____is reserved_____. (is reserved, are reserved)

38. Both <u>soccer</u> and <u>softball</u> _____are_____ favorites of mine. (is, are)

Lesson 50
Subject-Verb Agreement and Intervening Expressions

Certain expressions seem to create a compound subject but do not. *Accompanied by, as well as, in addition to, plus,* and *together with* are expressions that introduce phrases that tell about the subject. However, the subject remains singular and takes a singular verb.

The **President,** as well as the Cabinet, **is expected** tonight.
The **mayor,** accompanied by her staff, **eats** lunch in the cafeteria.

▶ **Exercise 1 Draw a line under the subject. Then write in the blank the form of the verb in parentheses that agrees with the subject. Use the present tense of the verb.**

Joe, as well as his brothers, _____ delivers _____ papers in the morning. (deliver)

1. Folk, in addition to rock, _____ is _____ my favorite music. (be)

2. Weight lifting, as well as wrestling, _____ takes _____ strength. (take)

3. Jupiter, plus Saturn, Uranus, and Neptune, _____ is _____ a gas planet. (be)

4. The truck, as well as a car and a bus, _____ is _____ involved in the wreck. (be)

5. The players, plus the coach and manager, _____ travel _____ by bus. (travel)

6. A hoe, in addition to a rake and a ladder, _____ is _____ missing from the garage. (be)

7. The singer, accompanied by her bodyguards, _____ arrives _____ tonight. (arrive)

8. The doctor, together with a large staff, _____ treats _____ many patients. (treat)

9. A plane, in addition to a service truck, _____ sits _____ on the runway. (sit)

10. Nancy, plus her parents and grandparents, _____ goes _____ to Florida for the holidays. (go)

11. My bicycle, as well as my skates, _____ needs _____ repair. (need)

12. The toolshed, together with the garage and the greenhouse, _____ sits _____ near the stream. (sit)

13. The bank, as well as the arcade, _____ opens _____ tomorrow. (open)

14. The VCR, plus the compact-disc player, _____ makes _____ a good holiday gift. (make)

15. The watermelon, as well as the cantaloupe, _____ is _____ ripe. (be)

16. Dan, in addition to his friends, _____ seems _____ depressed. (seem)

17. The Big Dipper, accompanied by the Little Dipper, _____ circles _____ the polestar. (circle)

18. The city, as well as the suburbs, _____ votes _____ today. (vote)

19. The bike, plus the skates and the skis, _____ belongs _____ to Oona. (belong)

20. Cereal, together with fruit and milk, _____ provides _____ a good breakfast. (provide)

▶ **Exercise 2** Draw a line under the subject. Then write the form of the verb in parentheses that agrees with the subject. Use the present tense of the verb when you write it.

Lisa's paycheck, in addition to her friend's income, _____helps_____ pay the bills. (help)

1. A helicopter, as well as a light plane, _____searches_____ for the missing hikers. (search)

2. The mail carrier, plus the grocery delivery boy, _____fears_____ the dog. (fear)

3. The bear, in addition to her cubs, _____lives_____ in that den. (live)

4. Bread, as well as cheese, _____goes_____ well with hot soup. (go)

5. Mr. Marcos, accompanied by his sons, _____builds_____ log cabins. (build)

6. The trapeze artist, in addition to her partner, _____performs_____ in each show. (perform)

7. Cory, accompanied by his nephew, _____pilots_____ his own plane. (pilot)

8. The gray suit, accompanied by a vest, _____looks_____ good on Mark. (look)

9. The candidate, as well as her opponent, _____speaks_____ tonight. (speak)

10. Sandy, plus Gerry and Pam, _____runs_____ several miles each weekend. (run)

11. Science, together with geography, _____is_____ my favorite class. (be)

12. My savings, plus a little extra, _____give_____ me enough for my mother's present. (give)

13. Grandma, plus my Aunt Clara, _____visits_____ regularly. (visit)

14. A moat, together with armed knights, _____surrounds_____ the castle. (surround)

15. Tod, accompanied by his parents, _____meets_____ many people on his travels. (meet)

16. Juan, as well as Mike, _____plays_____ shortstop for the baseball team. (play)

17. Mel, in addition to Madonna and Roy, _____has_____ the flu. (have)

18. The puppy, as well as her mother, _____chases_____ everyone around the yard. (chase)

19. Mr. Randolph, accompanied by his family, _____is_____ driving across the country. (be)

20. Hail, as well as rain, often _____accompanies_____ a tornado. (accompany)

▶ **Writing Link** Write three or four sentences about the activities you do with your family or friends. Write at least two sentences that use one or more of the phrases you learned about in this lesson. Be sure your verbs agree with your subjects.

_____

_____

_____

_____

_____

Lesson 51
Subject-Verb Agreement and Indefinite Pronouns as Subjects

Not all subjects are nouns. Many subjects consist of indefinite pronouns. A verb must agree in number with an **indefinite pronoun** used as a subject.

Singular: Everything about the party **was** perfect.
Singular: One of the windows **is** broken.
Singular: Nothing on television tonight **interests** me.
Plural: Many of our friends **study** Spanish.
Plural: A few of the trees **are** stunted.

Some pronouns can be either singular or plural, depending upon the nouns to which they refer in the sentence.

Singular: All of the punch **is** gone.
Plural: All of the players **are** exhausted.

Indefinite pronouns fall into three groups, as shown in the following chart.

INDEFINITE PRONOUNS

Always Singular	each	everyone	nobody	anything	
	either	everybody	nothing	someone	
	neither	everything	anyone	somebody	
	one	no one	anybody	something	
Always Plural	several	few	both	many	
Singular or Plural	some	all	any	most	none

▶ **Exercise 1** Draw one line under the indefinite pronoun subject. Draw two lines under the correct form of the verb.

Several of my friends (swim, swims) on the school team.

1. Many of the passengers (is, are) unhappy with coach service.

2. A few of the swimmers (was, were) ready to leave the pool.

3. Everything in the window (look, looks) expensive.

4. Something in the basement (has, have) eaten the vegetables.

5. One of the dogs (hunt, hunts) alone.

6. Some of the tomatoes (was, were) spoiled.

7. Everybody in the class (has, have) voted.

8. No one (answer, answers) the phone at the Caldwells.

9. <u>Nothing</u> (seem, <u><u>seems</u></u>) to please Linda.

10. <u>All</u> of the grass (<u><u>is</u></u>, are) brown from the drought.

11. <u>Anybody</u> who was there (know, <u><u>knows</u></u>) that Randy gave a good speech.

12. <u>One</u> of the contestants (<u><u>was</u></u>, were) late.

13. <u>Nobody</u> in our class (like, <u><u>likes</u></u>) the new movie.

14. <u>Several</u> of the squirrels (has, <u><u>have</u></u>) raided the sunflower sack.

15. <u>Most</u> of the class (<u><u>do</u></u>, does) push-ups each morning.

16. <u>None</u> of the mothers (like, <u><u>likes</u></u>) this arrangement.

17. <u>Everything</u> at the museum (<u><u>was</u></u>, were) fascinating.

18. <u>Both</u> of my aunts (is, <u><u>are</u></u>) from Poland.

19. <u>Nobody</u> in the audience (understand, <u><u>understands</u></u>) the play.

20. <u>None</u> of the players (was, <u><u>were</u></u>) tired.

21. <u>Many</u> of the old pirate ships (has been, <u><u>have been</u></u>) lost in that area.

22. <u>Neither</u> of the deer (use, <u><u>uses</u></u>) the salt lick.

23. <u>Several</u> of the class officers (was, <u><u>were</u></u>) ill.

24. <u>Nothing</u> on the menu (interest, <u><u>interests</u></u>) me.

25. <u>One</u> of the defendants (<u><u>has</u></u>, have) pleaded not guilty.

26. <u>Several</u> of the judges (has, <u><u>have</u></u>) ruled on their cases.

27. <u>Everybody</u> in the room (<u><u>was</u></u>, were) freezing.

28. <u>Several</u> of the high-school students (<u><u>earn</u></u>, earns) money after school.

29. <u>Somebody</u> in our community (<u><u>has</u></u>, have) won that huge prize.

30. <u>All</u> (is, <u><u>are</u></u>) well with the world.

31. <u>Both</u> of the twins (<u><u>sing</u></u>, sings) in the choir.

32. <u>Someone</u> (<u><u>has</u></u>, have) painted the old chairs.

33. <u>Few</u> of the people polled (<u><u>approve</u></u>, approves) of the new policies.

34. <u>All</u> of the spaghetti (<u><u>was</u></u>, were) gone.

35. <u>Everyone</u> here (<u><u>has</u></u>, have) finished lunch.

36. <u>One</u> of the babies in the nursery (<u><u>is</u></u>, are) crying.

37. <u>Few</u> of the people invited (is, <u><u>are</u></u>) coming.

38. <u>Anyone</u> at all (<u><u>is</u></u>, are) eligible to enter the race.

Name _____ Class _____ Date _____

 Unit 7 **Review**

▶ **Exercise 1** Underline the subject of each sentence. Then, choose the verb in parentheses that agrees with the subject and write it in the blank.

Katia _____ looks _____ forward to singing in the choir. (look, looks)

1. The nerves in my body _____ tingle _____ when I am excited. (tingle, tingles)

2. Here _____ lies _____ the tomb of the unknown soldier. (lie, lies)

3. Down by the schoolyard _____ plays _____ Julia, as well as Paul. (play, plays)

4. All of the campers _____ prepare _____ for the coming storm. (prepare, prepares)

5. Tarzan _____ swings _____ from a vine. (swing, swings)

6. The coaches of the football team _____ plan _____ for the big game. (plan, plans)

7. _____ Does _____ the Senate, as well as the House, approve the bill? (Do, Does)

8. Peppermint candy, as well as fruitcake and eggnog, _____ is _____ traditionally served during the holidays. (is, are)

9. Across the European countryside _____ travel _____ Killile and Mary. (travel, travels)

10. The Vietnamese pot-bellied pig, as well as the common dog or cat, _____ makes _____ a great pet! (make, makes)

11. The books _____ were _____ a heavy load. (was, were)

12. Into the street _____ gallop _____ the horses! (gallop, gallops)

13. The Olympic team _____ train _____ hard with personal coaches. (train, trains)

14. Electronics, as well as mechanics, _____ is _____ a very lucrative field. (is, are)

15. Hotcakes and sausage _____ is _____ my favorite meal. (is, are)

16. My cat _____ eats _____ his food when no one is watching. (eat, eats)

17. The distance from my house to the shopping mall _____ spans _____ many kilometers. (span, spans)

18. The audience _____ roars _____ with laughter. (roar, roars)

19. Bridget and Mary Jo _____ visit _____ their new neighbors downstairs. (visit, visits)

20. A few of the lights _____ do _____ not work. (do, does)

Cumulative Review: Units 1–7

▶ **Exercise 1** Label each noun *con.* if it is concrete, *abst.* if it is abstract, *col.* if it is collective, and *prop.* if it is proper. Underline each conjunction.

    prop.   abst.   con.
Kanya felt happiness when she saw her new house.

        abst.   con.
1. Fritz's pride was hurt when he fell, but there were no other injuries.

        abst.   abst.   con.   con.
2. Neither anger nor jealousy would help the candidate win the election.

        col.   con.   con.   con.   con.
3. The gaggle of geese rested peacefully by the shore of the lake until the dog arrived.

           col.   con.   abst.
4. If the entire family pitched in to help, they still might be able to make it to the game on time.

    prop.   con.   col.   con.
5. Abe will plan little surprises for his family as long as he has a part-time job.

      prop.   abst.
6. Walt Whitman once wrote: "Peace is always beautiful."

      abst.   col.
7. High aspirations keep many people motivated.

        prop.   con.   con.   col.
8. Whenever Sally sees a rainbow, she thinks of an imaginary pot of gold.

    con.   con.   con.
9. The heather in the fields was beautiful with its purplish-pink leaves.

        con.   prop.
10. We read the newspaper while we were waiting for Sid.

        col.   prop.   con.   prop.
11. As long as our group was visiting New York City, we went for a walk in Central Park.

        con.   abst.   col.
12. Because it was a dreary day, listlessness was felt throughout the class.

      col.   con.   con.   con.
13. The water-skiing team wore wet suits whenever the water or weather was too cold.

    con.   con.   con.
14. Many students were feeling better about school because of the peer-helper program.

    abst.   con.   con.   con.   con.
15. Anxiety ran high as the competitors for the leading roles waited for the results of the auditions.

    prop.   con.   abst.   abst.
16. Janet thought a video camera would be the best way to preserve family memories.

    prop.   con.   con.
17. Kenji ate cookies as long as there were some on the plate.

      col.   abst.   con.
18. The committee resolved their differences so that the meetings would run successfully.

    con.   con.   con.
19. The students returned to their desks before the bell rang.

      con.   abst.   con.
20. The gruff old man showed such gentleness to the stray dog.

Name _____ Class _____ Date _____

▶ **Exercise 2** **Write the correct form of the verb asked for in the blank. Underline each prepositional phrase.**

Dayung _____disposed_____ of the oil in the proper manner. (past tense of *dispose*)

1. The Morgans _____have accumulated_____ hundreds of travel brochures during their travels throughout the years. (present perfect tense of *accumulate*)

2. The wind _____arranged_____ the snow into awesome drifts. (past tense of *arrange*)

3. The highway patrol _____will caution_____ all travelers about the icy road conditions. (future tense of *caution*)

4. The tutor _____had enabled_____ Kacie to do a better job on her test. (past perfect tense of *enable*)

5. Winning this medal _____surpasses_____ my every expectation! (present tense of *surpass*)

6. Mom _____has disinfected_____ the thermometer after each use. (present perfect tense of *disinfect*)

7. Marty _____consoles_____ anyone who has also suffered a personal loss. (present tense of *console*)

8. The boy _____had cradled_____ the injured bird in his arms all the way home. (past perfect tense of *cradle*)

9. The climbing expedition hopefully _____will have reached_____ the summit before the blizzard hits. (future perfect tense of *reach*)

10. The gull _____swooped_____ down eagerly to the water for its food. (past tense of *swoop*)

11. For the special occasion, the couple _____will have surrounded_____ themselves with family and friends. (future perfect tense of *surround*)

12. The vines _____had twisted_____ themselves around the fence. (past perfect tense of *twist*)

13. Attending the conference _____will energize_____ the staff in preparation for the year ahead. (future tense of *energize*)

14. After his long illness, Marcos _____has felt_____ behind in his schoolwork. (present perfect tense of *feel*)

15. Vanesa _____alienates_____ herself from negative influences. (present tense of *alienate*)

16. You _____will have operated_____ the lathe and other machines by the end of this semester. (future perfect tense of *operate*)

17. The horses _____ will gallop _____ slowly around the arena before the competition begins.
(future tense of *gallop*)

18. On tests, we all _____ endeavor _____ to do our best. (present tense of *endeavor*)

19. I _____ had _____ never _____ tasted _____ better food in my entire life. (past perfect
tense of *taste*)

20. Myra's hands _____ will freeze _____ without her gloves. (future tense of *freeze*)

▶ **Exercise 3 Draw one line under the complete subject in each sentence. Draw two lines under
the correct form of the verb.**

Every hill and valley (is, are) a beautiful sight each fall.

1. Immunization (remain, remains) a requirement for school enrollment.

2. Each of the workers on the crew (paint, paints) at a different speed.

3. Every teacher in the school (evaluate, evaluates) each student's progress.

4. Neither the cake nor the cookies (has, have) been touched.

5. (Do, Does) the hunters wear safety clothing?

6. Across the shaky bridge (rattle, rattles) the antique cars.

7. Uncle Bob and Aunt Joan (thrill, thrills) to the music of the Glenn Miller Band.

8. Neither of the teams, the Falcons or the Knights, (is, are) this year's conference champion.

9. Each rowboat and canoe (is, are) being repainted for the next tourist season.

10. The attorneys in the case (make, makes) an appeal tomorrow.

11. Slick roads and fog (is, are) a major concern for travelers.

12. The newspapers on the stand (was, were) sold out by noon.

13. Every quiz, paper, and test (has, have) been a concern for Joel.

14. None of the members of the audience (applaud, applauds) loudly.

15. Over the horizon (appear, appears) the posse.

16. Ham and cheese (seem, seems) to be my favorite sandwich.

17. Every car, truck, and bus (go, goes) across this bridge to reach the island.

18. Snowmobiling in the northern woods (is, are) a wonderful winter sport.

19. One of the fishermen (has, have) lost his rod and reel in the lake.

20. "Early to bed and early to rise" (is, are) a good suggestion to live by.

Unit 8: Using Pronouns Correctly

Lesson 52
Personal Pronouns: Case

Pronouns that are used to refer to persons or things are called **personal pronouns**. Personal pronouns have three **cases**, or forms, called **nominative**, **objective**, and **possessive**. The case of a personal pronoun depends on how it is used in a sentence. The chart below lists the personal pronouns, their cases, and their uses.

Case	Singular Pronouns	Plural Pronouns	Function in Sentence
Nominative	I, you, she, he, it	we, you, they	subject or predicate nominative
Objective	me, you, her, him, it	us, you, them	direct object, indirect object, or object of preposition
Possessive	my, mine, your, yours, her, hers, his, its	our, ours, your, yours, their, theirs	replacement for possessive noun(s)

We gathered in the cafeteria for a meeting.   Taylor brought **her** to the game.
Dan thought the disc was **yours**.

▶ **Exercise 1 Underline the correct pronoun.**

Bring the packages to (they, <u>them</u>).

1. When the early settlers arrived in this country, (<u>they</u>, them) had little time for school.

2. Those who wanted (them, <u>their</u>) children to read would teach (they, <u>them</u>) at home.

3. There were no schools for (<u>their</u>, them) children to attend.

4. The most important subject for (their, <u>them</u>) was how to plant.

5. As the settlements grew, formal education became more important to (they, <u>them</u>).

6. Reading, writing, and arithmetic helped (they, <u>them</u>).

7. Education became a community effort, and the entire community benefited from (<u>it</u>, its).

8. Schoolhouses were generally built on land not suitable for farming, and the school yard rarely had any trees in (<u>it</u>, its).

9. Early schoolhouses were heated by smoky fires. Later (<u>they</u>, them) had stoves.

Grammar

10. Families sent a load of firewood when (<u>they</u>, their) sent (them, <u>their</u>) children to school.

11. Since paper was expensive, little of (<u>it</u>, its) was used.

12. Each family made (it, <u>its</u>) own ink from ink powder.

13. Handwriting was very important. (<u>It</u>, Its) was often considered more important than spelling.

14. Stitching samplers was a way a young girl could show (she, <u>her</u>) sewing skills and (she, <u>her</u>) knowledge of the alphabet.

15. Since the Bible was often the only book a family owned, (<u>it</u>, its) was usually the first reader.

16. A male teacher was expected to have a more disciplined way about (he, <u>him</u>).

17. A woman was expected to quit teaching after (<u>she</u>, her) married.

18. Schoolmasters often used discipline that today would seem very cruel to (we, <u>us</u>).

19. A schoolmaster would sometimes punish (him, <u>his</u>) students physically.

20. One of the rules for students was this: Respect (<u>your</u>, yours) schoolmaster. Obey (he, <u>him</u>) and accept (him, <u>his</u>) punishments.

▶ **Exercise 2 Label each italicized pronoun *nom.* (nominative), *obj.* (objective), or *pos.* (possessive) case.**

    nom.   pos.
They shook *their* clothes to get out the sand.

    pos.
1. *Our* country's history is full of exciting tales about settling the West.
   nom.   pos.   pos.
2. *We* may not realize what *our* ancestors went through to settle *our* great country.
                            pos.
3. In the 1840s, the pioneers began *their* trek across the Great Plains and the Rocky Mountains.
   nom.   pos.   pos.
4. *They* encountered many hardships on *their* treacherous journey to *their* new homes.
                                   obj.   pos.
5. These adventurers had to plan wisely to know what to take with *them* because *their*

    lives depended on these decisions.
                  pos.   pos.   pos.
6. The Conestoga wagon, with *its* broad-rimmed wheels and *its* white canvas roof, was *their*
                             obj.
    home for the journey that would take *them* many weeks.
            pos.   pos.
7. Upon reaching *their* destination, the pioneers had to choose a place to build *their* homes and

    plant crops.
                           obj.   pos.
8. This planting would provide *them* with food for *their* first winter.
   nom.   nom.   nom.
9. *It* was not an easy life for the pioneers, but *they* found *they* were all willing to help each other.
    nom.   nom.
10. If *you* had lived in the 1840s, would *you* have moved west?

Lesson 53
Pronouns with and as Appositives; After *Than* and *As*

Use the nominative case for a pronoun that is the appositive of a subject or a predicate nominative. Use the objective case for a pronoun that is the appositive of a direct object, an indirect object, or an object of a preposition.

The winners, Mitzi and **she,** collected their trophies. (nominative)
Give the tickets to the ushers, Bart and **him.** (objective)

When an appositive follows a pronoun, choose the case of the pronoun that would be correct if the appositive were omitted.

We winners collected our trophies. **We** collected our trophies. (nominative)
Give the tickets to **us ushers**. Give the tickets to **us.** (objective)

In elliptical adverb clauses using *than* and *as*, choose the case of the pronoun that you would use if the missing words were fully expressed.

I am always hungrier than **he.** (Read: I am always hungrier than he is.)
The directions puzzled Phil as much as **me.** (Read: The directions puzzled Phil as much as they puzzled me.)

▶ **Exercise 1** Underline the correct pronoun. Identify the case by writing *nom.* (nominative) or *obj.* (objective) in the blank. Some sentences have more than one pronoun to identify.

___nom., obj.___ The singers, Nora and (<u>I</u>, me), gave our friends, Sue and (they, <u>them</u>), front row seats for the concert.

___nom.___ 1. The contestants, Conrad and (<u>I</u>, me), were both nervous.

___obj.___ 2. The judges presented the winners, Sylvia and (I, <u>me</u>), with engraved plaques.

___obj.___ 3. The newspaper article described the three fastest runners on the team, Sarah, Jacques, and (I, <u>me</u>).

___nom.___ 4. The best goalies on the soccer team, Amy and (<u>she</u>, her), both wanted to play in the championship game.

___nom., obj.___ 5. The two teachers, Mr. Barnes and (<u>she</u>, her), explained the rules of the classroom to (we, <u>us</u>) students.

___nom.___ 6. The three lost campers, Rich, Manuel, and (<u>I</u>, me), returned to camp in the morning.

___obj.___ 7. The volunteers wanted to help the flood victims, Kisha and (he, <u>him</u>).

Grammar

_____nom._____ **8.** (We, Us) voters sent a message at the election.

___nom., nom.___ **9.** The two class officers, (he, him) and (I, me), have to organize the food drive before Thanksgiving.

_____nom._____ **10.** Naz and Jenny are better athletes than (they, them).

_____nom._____ **11.** No one could have been more excited than (I, me).

_____obj._____ **12.** These algebra problems confuse Rashonda as much as (I, me).

_____nom._____ **13.** Eleanor chose brighter colors for her picture than (I, me).

_____obj._____ **14.** The bus picks up An-Mei as early as (I, me).

_____nom._____ **15.** When I spilled my juice, he was more startled than (I, me).

_____nom._____ **16.** I could tell Conrad was more nervous than (I, me).

_____nom._____ **17.** No one I know is a better quarterback than (he, him).

_____obj._____ **18.** The loss of electricity was less inconvenient for me than (they, them).

_____nom._____ **19.** What do you think? (We, Us) three are the winners!

_____nom._____ **20.** When Sarah, Rhoda, and I returned from outdoor survival camp, I had more mosquito bites than (they, them).

_____nom._____ **21.** It's so frustrating. I try to work as fast as (they, them), but I always finish last.

_____nom._____ **22.** Neither of last year's leads, Ricardo or (he, him), was in the play this year.

_____obj._____ **23.** English grammar seems easy for both of the editors of the school newspaper, Joe and (she, her).

_____nom._____ **24.** The two forwards, Raoul and (he, him), shared the MVP award for the basketball team last year.

_____nom._____ **25.** I am usually satisfied with much less money than (they, them).

_____nom._____ **26.** Carlos was more disappointed than (I, me) when we were both cut from the soccer team.

_____nom._____ **27.** The two teenagers, Saul and (she, her), usually have dinner ready when their grandmother gets home from work.

_____obj._____ **28.** The new computer software was easy to master for both students, Gretchen and (he, him).

_____obj._____ **29.** We are sending blankets and winter clothes to the earthquake victims we know, Katherine and (she, her).

Lesson 54
Who and *Whom* in Questions and Subordinate Clauses

Use the nominative pronoun *who* for subjects. Use the objective pronoun *whom* for the direct or indirect object of a verb or verbal or for the object of a preposition.

Who wants to try out for the play? (nominative)
Whom did you see at the mall? (objective)
Jarod, **who** lives next door, has a trampoline. (nominative)
Gwen, **whom** he had known for years, was now an actress. (objective)

▶ **Exercise 1** **Write *who* or *whom* in the blank to make each sentence correct.**

My sister, _____who_____ likes to play basketball, is trying out for the team.

1. Franklin Delano Roosevelt, _____who_____ was elected the thirty-second president of the United States, was born in 1882.

2. He was the only child of James Roosevelt, _____who_____ descended from a well-to-do Dutch family in New York.

3. Franklin's mother, _____who_____ was named Sara Delano Roosevelt, was very devoted to him.

4. Franklin was a very athletic young man _____who_____ was an expert in boating and swimming.

5. In 1905, he married Anna Eleanor Roosevelt, _____who_____ was a distant cousin.

6. Eleanor, to _____whom_____ Sara Roosevelt objected as a wife for Franklin, was orphaned when she was ten years old.

7. At the wedding the bride was given away by another Roosevelt _____whom_____ both Eleanor and Franklin admired.

8. This Roosevelt, _____who_____ was Eleanor's uncle, was Theodore.

9. Theodore Roosevelt, _____who_____ became president when William McKinley was assassinated, was one of the most popular presidents in U.S. history.

10. In 1920, Franklin ran for vice president as the running mate for James M. Cox, _____whom_____ the voters rejected in favor of Warren Harding.

11. Less than a year later, the young, athletic Franklin, _____who_____ greatly enjoyed physical activity, was stricken with poliomyelitis.

12. His mother, _____who_____ was forever present in Franklin and Eleanor's life, wanted him to retire from politics and live as a country squire.

13. His wife, Eleanor, _____whom_____ he relied on for advice and support, urged him to remain involved in politics.

14. In 1928, Franklin Roosevelt, _____who_____ had been paralyzed by polio seven years earlier, was elected governor of New York.

15. When the stock market crashed in 1929, Herbert Hoover, _____who_____ had been elected president in 1928, was blamed for the economic disaster.

16. Many voters wondered to _____whom_____ they might turn for new leadership.

17. In 1932, the voters elected Franklin Roosevelt, _____who_____ encouraged them by saying they had nothing to fear but fear itself.

18. FDR, _____whom_____ the world will never forget, brought America into World War II to help Western Europe defend itself against Adolf Hitler.

19. FDR, with _____whom_____ the world fought for freedom in World War II, did not live to see the Allies triumph.

20. Franklin Delano Roosevelt, _____who_____ was one of the twentieth century's most skillful political leaders, is the only person elected to the U.S. presidency four times.

21. Anna Eleanor Roosevelt, _____who_____ was called Eleanor, was born in 1884.

22. Her father, Elliott, _____who_____ was Theodore Roosevelt's brother, sent her to school in England.

23. Franklin Roosevelt, to _____whom_____ Eleanor was married, embarked on a political career a few years after their wedding.

24. Eleanor and Franklin had five children, of _____whom_____ little has been written.

25. Franklin, _____who_____ was battling polio, relied on his wife to perform many tasks.

26. She, _____who_____ joined the Women's Trade Union League, also served as financial chairperson for the women's division of the state Democratic Party.

27. President Roosevelt, _____who_____ at times was considered a controversial figure, was almost outshone in some respects by Eleanor.

28. Some people made jokes about the woman to _____whom_____ the President entrusted many important jobs.

29. Franklin, _____who_____ often stayed at the White House, relied on Eleanor to tour the nation and report on current conditions.

30. Press conferences for women correspondents were instituted by Eleanor, _____who_____ broke through several gender barriers.

31. Beginning in 1936, Eleanor, _____who_____ was First Lady, wrote a daily newspaper column.

32. She wrote for people with _____whom_____ she wished to share her experiences.

33. For those to _____whom_____ she is unfamiliar, it may be difficult to understand the depth of her influence.

34. Mrs. Roosevelt, _____who_____ was concerned about the plight of children during the Depression, took an avid interest in the President's plans to help them.

Name _____ Class _____ Date _____

Lesson 55
Pronoun-Antecedent Agreement in Number and Gender

An **antecedent** is the word or group of words to which a pronoun refers or that a pronoun replaces. A pronoun must agree with its antecedent in number (singular or plural) and gender (masculine, feminine, or neuter). A pronoun's antecedent may be a noun, another pronoun, or a phrase or clause acting as a noun.

Paula brought **her** grandfather to speak to the class.

▶ **Exercise 1** **Complete the sentence by adding a personal pronoun that agrees with the antecedent. Underline the antecedent.**

Carla left _____ her _____ gloves on the kitchen table.

1. The students should have _____ their _____ books by Friday.

2. Every person must bring _____ his, her, his or her _____ own towel to gym class.

3. Many older Americans know the exact date _____ they _____ started _____ their _____ first job.

4. Only three club members paid _____ their _____ dues by the deadline.

5. If you think the colors clash, we will change _____ them _____ .

6. When my mom and her four sisters were children, _____ they _____ all shared one big bedroom.

7. Claude and Norman practice _____ their _____ sidestrokes every day.

8. Gloria works for two hours every day after _____ she _____ leaves school.

9. Sometimes people without experience are intimidated by computers. _____ They _____ needn't be.

10. Gabriel and Chad don't want to work after school, but _____ they _____ need the money.

11. Natasha and Paul found _____ they _____ share an interest in classical automobiles.

12. George and Susan both brought _____ their _____ snakes to science class when we studied reptiles.

13. Some students don't take class elections very seriously; _____ they _____ should.

14. Each participant can be very proud of _____ his, her, his or her _____ accomplishments.

15. I think my grandma is the best gardener in _____ her _____ neighborhood.

16. They finally decided Jack must have the tickets in _____ his _____ room.

17. Dad says all of _____ his _____ children spend too much of _____ their _____ time watching television.

18. Ramona and her friends left _____their_____ biology books in the library.

19. The college sends most of _____its_____ messages to students by electronic mail.

20. Abdul and Larry showed _____they_____ could hit a ball out of the ballpark.

▶ **Exercise 2** Correct each personal pronoun in italics so it agrees with its antecedent in the sentence. Cross out the incorrect pronoun, and write the correct word above it. Do not change any pronouns that already agree with the antecedent in number and gender.

their
The musicians began tuning *her* instruments.

1. Maria and Sean thought the computer was just what *they* needed to make *their* business work.
their
2. The artists displayed *her* paintings in the new gallery.
his
3. David forgot to pay *her* club dues.

4. Most students in Ms. Cynkar's class really enjoyed *their* lessons.
her
5. Kristen organized *its* desk for better efficiency.
we
6. My friends and I attended the football game; then *he* walked uptown.

7. Fred does not neglect *his* health.
He
8. Jacob likes the game of soccer. *It* plays often.
her
9. Did Kay lose the assignment sheet from *our* notebook?

10. Angela was too busy with *her* college courses.
his or her
11. The author had become accustomed to the criticism about *their* books.
their
12. The pioneers spent many hours preparing *its* homes for winter.
her
13. Martina would like to give *his* opinion on the topic.
its
14. Each animal makes *their* own unique sound.

15. Sandy succeeded in attaining *her* goal.
his
16. Did Jack lend you *their* pencil?
its
17. This tree has not yet shed *their* leaves.
his
18. Brian decided to take responsibility for *their* own chores.
he or she
19. Each student spent extra time learning the concepts *we* hadn't mastered.
his
20. At dawn, Miguel folded *their* sleeping bag and left the tent.

Lesson 56
Pronoun-Antecedent Agreement in Person

A **pronoun** must agree in person with its antecedent. When the antecedent of a pronoun is another pronoun, be sure that the two pronouns agree in person.

Bryan gave **his** old guitar to Jacob.   **We** want **our** money back!

▶ **Exercise 1 Fill in the blank with the correct personal pronoun. Underline the antecedent for each pronoun.**

Juan is planning _____his_____ vacation.

1. The students in Mrs. Nakleh's social studies class discussed how _____they_____ would spend the vacation.

2. Kristen thought her younger brothers might be frightened when _____they_____ were close to snakes.

3. Alligators are again plentiful in the Southeast, and hunting _____them_____ is now allowed.

4. Jason was spending the week with _____his_____ dad in Boston, where _____they_____ were going to watch two Celtics games.

5. Alfredo likes to be by the sea, where _____he_____ can smell the air with _____its_____ salty taste.

6. People can watch the seagulls swoop down to find _____their_____ dinner in the Boston Harbor.

7. Each businessman gave _____his_____ report at the board meeting.

8. We wanted to see _____our_____ new apartment before moving in.

9. In the spring, the robin was busy building _____its_____ nest.

10. Anita plays both volleyball and basketball, but volleyball is _____her_____ favorite sport.

11. Sam and Jose, who sing duets, agree _____they_____ need more practice before the contest.

12. Michael's father wants _____him_____ to take geometry and accelerated English next year.

13. Cats like to relax in the sun and stretch _____their_____ bodies.

14. Brett's nickname is "Stretch," which refers to _____his_____ height.

15. Nathan and Elizabeth cannot go out for pizza because _____they_____ have terrible colds.

16. That particular fish has black stripes along _____its_____ sides.

17. I saw so many things that impressed _____me_____ in Washington, D.C.

18. Colleen moved to New York to work for an <u>uncle</u> and _____his_____ wife.

19. <u>We</u>, as citizens of the United States, have to take responsibility for _____our_____ country's

success.

20. Sidney moved to the <u>city</u> of Seattle and became a member of _____its_____ city council.

▶ **Exercise 2** **Find the personal pronouns that have antecedents within each sentence or sentence group. Draw one line under the personal pronoun. Draw two lines under its antecedent. Change the personal pronoun to agree in person with its antecedent. Correct the verb if necessary.**

<u>her</u>
<u>Katrina</u> wants to finish <u>his</u> homework before dinner.

1. The first thing <u>Mario</u> realized when <u>you</u> backpacked was how heavy the pack could feel.
he

2. When <u>Connor</u> heard <u>Rose</u> sing, <u>you</u> were amazed at the high notes <u>she</u> could reach.
he was

3. <u>Barry</u> finds it hard to concentrate when there is so much going on around <u>you</u>.
him

4. <u>Jianming</u> will be the first person in <u>her</u> family to go to college, where <u>you</u> plans to study medicine.
she

5. <u>You</u> can get such sore muscles when <u>they</u> run farther than usual.
you

6. The ice was so slick that with the first step <u>I</u> fell on <u>your</u> face.
my

7. <u>I</u> just love to smell fresh bread baking when <u>you</u> get up in the morning.
I

8. Sometimes <u>I</u> am so tired when <u>you</u> get off work that <u>you</u> fall asleep without eating <u>my</u> dinner.
I *I*

9. <u>I</u> often fall asleep in the living room when <u>you</u> read late at night.
I

10. <u>I</u> looked and looked until <u>you</u> couldn't see it anymore.
I

11. My <u>mom</u> is so patient with <u>me</u>. <u>You</u> can't help but love <u>her</u>.
I

12. <u>I</u> studied so hard for this test that <u>you</u> thought <u>you</u> knew everything.
I *I*

13. When <u>they</u> turn fourteen, tell <u>them</u> <u>you</u> should consider volunteer work at the hospital.
they

14. We visited with my <u>grandparents</u>, who are so active <u>they</u> tired <u>you</u> out.
us

15. The <u>baby</u> wiggled so much <u>I</u> thought <u>I</u> were going to drop <u>him</u>.
was

16. After the <u>scouts</u> trekked up the mountain side, <u>it</u> collapsed in relief when <u>you</u> reached the
they *they*

summit.

Lesson 57
Pronoun-Antecedent Agreement with Indefinite Pronoun Antecedents

In general, use a **singular personal pronoun** when the antecedent is a singular indefinite pronoun, such as *anybody, anyone, anything, each, either, everybody, everyone, everything, much, neither, nobody, no one, nothing, one, other, somebody, someone,* or *something.* If the antecedent refers to a person and the gender is not specific, it is usually most acceptable to use *he or she, him or her,* or *his or hers.*

Each of the boys folded **his** sleeping bag.   **Anyone** can bring **his or her** favorite CD.

Use a **plural personal pronoun** when the antecedent is a plural indefinite pronoun, such as *several, both, few,* and *many.*

Both of the runners broke **their** previous records.

Some **indefinite pronouns** can be either singular or plural depending on the context of the sentence: *all, any, enough, more, most, none,* and *some.*

We will play if **enough** of the students bring **their** equipment.

▶ **Exercise 1** Write a personal pronoun that agrees with the indefinite pronoun antecedent in the sentence. Underline the antecedent.

Few of the glee club members forgot _____their_____ music.

1. Everyone has to finish __his, her, *or* his or her__ assignment before Thursday.

2. Many will find that _____their_____ uniforms from last year are now too small.

3. Does anyone disagree with me? Let __him, her, *or* him or her__ say so now.

4. Someone took the wrong jacket. If __he, she, *or* he or she__ returns it, please call me.

5. All of the computers lost _____their_____ power.

6. Many of the graduates did not even recognize _____their_____ classmates at the reunion.

7. Both of the contestants were nervous; _____they_____ kept shifting their feet.

8. After gym on Monday, only one of the boys made it to _____his_____ next class on time.

9. Everyone must pay for __his, her, *or* his or her__ ticket before boarding the bus.

10. One of these girls assembled _____her_____ own computer.

11. No one should lend __his, her, *or* his or her__ comb to anyone else.

12. Each of the girls had to show _____she_____ could make ten baskets in a row.

13. Everyone who gets a ninety or better on the final can submit ___his, her, or his or her___

     application for the accelerated course.

14. All of the band members will be in ____their____ seats ten minutes before the performance.

15. Everybody can take a break whenever ___he, she, or he or she___ needs one.

16. Neither of the girls made the team of ____her____ choice.

17. Each of the students in English class named ___his, her, or his or her___ favorite author.

18. For added security, everyone must memorize ___his, her, or his or her___ own combination.

19. Isn't it strange how all of our parents think ____they____ know just how we feel?

20. During the blackout, everyone coped in ___his, her, or his or her___ own way.

21. A few of our students don't seem to understand how ____they____ can help.

22. Remember to put everything back in ____its____ place.

23. Some of our neighbors have already shoveled ____their____ sidewalks.

24. You can keep the money you found since nobody says it belongs to ___him, her, or him or her___.

25. Several of my friends are going. ____Their____ parents say it's okay.

26. Mike said he has something important to tell me. I wonder what ____it____ is.

27. We thought we had plenty of sugar, but we ran out of ____it____ before we finished baking.

28. Most of the trees lost ____their____ leaves in Saturday's storm.

29. Do any of them know the answer? It doesn't seem ____they____ do.

30. Since most of the volunteers signed up for another rotation, ____they____ must be happy

     doing the work.

31. Neither of the students failed ___his, her, or his or her___ test.

32. Anybody would be happy to have this album in ___his, her, or his or her___ collection.

33. I will take both. Will you send ____them____ to me?

34. Some of the cheese has mold on ____it____.

35. Some of the books have very sophisticated vocabulary in ____them____.

36. Does anybody have a comb in ___his, her, or his or her___ locker?

37. Few understand how much ____they____ can contribute.

38. None of the rivers in the area overflowed ___its or their___ banks.

39. Anything you can do will be appreciated. ____It____ is more than will be done otherwise.

40. Most of the old silver had lost ____its____ shine.

Lesson 58
Clear Pronoun Reference

Make sure that the antecedent of a **pronoun** is clearly stated and that a pronoun cannot possibly refer to more than one antecedent. Do not use the pronouns *this, that, which,* and *it* without a clearly stated antecedent. If a pronoun seems to refer to more than one antecedent, either reword the sentence to make the antecedent clear or eliminate the pronoun. Avoid the indefinite use of the pronouns *you* and *they.*

▶ **Exercise 1 Rewrite each sentence to eliminate any unclear pronoun reference.** Answers may vary. Suggestions are given.

The home team played the visiting team, and they lost the game.

The home team played the visiting team, and the visiting team lost the game.

1. In the mid-1800s the best way to get a letter from New York to San Francisco was to ship it around South America, which was slow and expensive.

   In the mid-1800s the best way to get a letter from New York to San Francisco was to ship it

   around South America, but this method was slow and expensive.

2. Clipper ships took about three months to make the trip, which was too long.

   To make the trip clipper ships took about three months, which was too long.

3. Even after railroads began to be built, you couldn't take them across the country.

   Even after railroads began to be built, they did not go across the country.

4. They did not have railroad tracks between Missouri and the Pacific Coast.

   There were no railroad tracks between Missouri and the Pacific Coast.

5. This was called the "great American desert," where they didn't live.

   This was called the "great American desert," where few Americans lived.

6. Some stagecoaches crossed this land, which was very slow.

   Some stagecoaches crossed this land, but stagecoach travel was very slow.

7. You could get mail to Missouri, which was sent from New York in four days.

   Mail could be sent from New York to Missouri in four days.

8. Then the mail carriers had to cross the plains and then maneuver through the mountains, which stretched for 1,500 miles.

   Then the mail carriers had to cross the plains, which stretched for 1,500 miles, and then

   maneuver through the mountains.

Grammar

9. You could get a letter from Missouri to California in 25 days, which was almost 2,000 miles.

A letter could be sent from Missouri to California, a distance of almost 2,000 miles, in 25 days.

10. Then in 1860, they created the Pony Express.

Then in 1860, the Pony Express was created.

11. This was a series of relay stations where fresh horses and riders waited to take the mail, which were much faster than stagecoaches.

The Pony Express was a series of relay stations where fresh horses and riders waited to take the mail. It was a system that was much faster than stagecoaches.

12. They carried the mail 220 miles each day.

The Pony Express riders carried the mail 220 miles each day.

13. At first, the relay stations were 25 miles apart, which was too far for them to run at full speed.

At first, the relay stations were 25 miles apart, a distance that was too far for horses to run at full speed.

14. Intermediate depots were set up every 10 to 15 miles where you could change mounts.

Intermediate depots, where riders could change mounts, were set up every 10 to 15 miles.

15. Your mail got from Missouri to San Francisco in 10 days.

Mail got from Missouri to San Francisco in 10 days.

16. The Pony Express received no subsidy from the government, which stopped operating after a year and a half.

The Pony Express, which stopped operating after a year and a half, received no subsidy from the government.

17. The Pony Express came to be one of the most colorful episodes of the American West, which was a financial disaster.

The Pony Express, which was a financial disaster, came to be one of the most colorful episodes of the American West.

18. Then in 1861, the first telegraph lines were stretched across the country, which allowed you to send messages faster.

Then in 1861, the first telegraph lines, which allowed messages to be sent faster, were stretched across the country.

19. At almost the same time, the Pony Express stopped operating, which was very expensive.

At almost the same time, the Pony Express, which was very expensive, stopped operating.

20. In 1869, they built the first transcontinental railroad.

In 1869, the first transcontinental railroad was built.

Unit 8 Review

▶ **Exercise** **Cross out each inappropriate pronoun and write the correct word above it.**

                        her

Dominique is displaying ~~their~~ paintings in her father's office.

      We

1. ~~Us~~ students decided to change our plans.

         your   **You**

2. Choose ~~you~~ courses wisely. ~~Your~~ will only be a sophomore once.

                                             them

3. Mrs. Zimmerman and Mr. Cane are great teachers. Try to get ~~her~~ for at least one class.

   Whom

4. ~~Who~~ did you think we would choose?

                                   her   **she**   **them**

5. Sheila generally takes longer to finish ~~their~~ chores than the rest of us. Do you think ~~her~~ likes ~~it~~?

                                          I   **my**

6. I try to finish some of my homework in study hall so ~~they~~ don't have to carry home ~~their~~ books.

                                                                                      I

7. My advisor suggested I try either French or Spanish for my foreign language, but ~~you~~ won't

                  I   **I**

   know what ~~you~~ like until ~~you~~'ve tried it.

                                                  myself

8. I try to get to school early on Thursdays, but it's hard to get ~~yourself~~ going in the morning.

                                           they

9. Give George and Allen the homework from the classes ~~he~~ missed.

                   his, her, his or her

10. Everybody must see ~~their~~ advisor this week.

                                                  she

11. The co-presidents of the Service Club, Rashid and ~~her~~, are trying to organize a food drive for Thanksgiving.

                                                       their

12. The members of the football team all celebrated the victory with ~~its~~ voices raised high.

                             his, her, his or her

13. Everyone who takes art must provide ~~their~~ own pastels.

                                who

14. Ginny looks so much like her sister, ~~whom~~ is a senior, that it is hard to tell them apart.

                                              he

15. Jose's dad doesn't have to work this weekend, so ~~they~~ might be able to drive us to the game.

   Who

16. ~~Whom~~ do you think will get the soprano solo for the spring concert?

                             he

17. Our leading scorers, Ryan and ~~him~~, will get trophies at the ceremony.

                                                   I do

18. I take the bus with Sinead and Javier, but they get off before ~~me~~.

                                    she

19. Sonya sold more raffle tickets this year than ~~her~~ did last year.

                                          she

20. Neither of the girls could remember just why ~~they~~ chose this course.

                            me

21. She, together with Rhea and ~~I~~, is ready to audition now.

                                               him

22. Please give the new schedules to the co-captains, Yong and ~~he~~.

Cumulative Review: Units 1–8

▶ **Exercise 1** Label each word or phrase that is italicized to indicate its use in the sentence. Use these abbreviations: *subj.* (subject), *v.* (verb), *i.o.* (indirect object), *d.o.* (direct object), *p.n.* (predicate nominative), *app.* (appositive), or *p.a.* (predicate adjective).

           v.   d.o.

The pilot *guided* her *plane* to the runway.

  subj.   v.   d.o.
1. *Leanne,* my friend, *gave* me the *picture* on that table.

  v. i.o.
2. *Give me* your homework after school.

        app.   p.n.
3. Mr. Kwan, *the class advisor,* is a *graduate* of Harvard.

  subj.   d.o.
4. *Karen* not only ran in the marathon but also set a personal *record.*

  v. subj.
5. What *is* the *reason* for your tardiness?

  subj.   p.a.   p.a.
6. The *puppy* was *frightened* but *friendly* as the visitors arrived.

  v.   d.o.
7. I *passed* the *exam!*

  subj.   p.n.
8. My *mother* is a civil *engineer* for the government.

  v.   d.o.
9. *Close* all the animal *cages* before you leave tonight.

      v.   p.a.
10. The cake *tasted delicious.*

  subj. v.   d.o.   v.
11. *Abdul missed* the *bus* and *was* late for work.

     i.o.   d.o.
12. Joshua gave *me* a dozen *roses* for my birthday.

     subj.   v.
13. What a lousy *concert* that *was!*

  subj.   app.   p.a.
14. *Sarah, our student council president,* became *speechless.*

  v. subj.   v.
15. *Have you* ever *traveled* down the Mississippi River by steamboat?

  subj.   subj. v.   v.
16. Both the *garage* and the *car were destroyed* by the storm.

  subj.   p.n.   p.n.
17. *Franklin* was an *inventor* and a *statesman.*

    v.   d.o.
18. Please *shut* the *window* because it is raining.

  subj.   p.a.   p.a.
19. The practical *joke* was neither *clever* nor *funny.*

  v.   v. i.o.   d.o.
20. *Did* the roller coaster ride *give you* a *thrill?*

        app.   v.   d.o.
21. Mr. Sampson, the *principal, read* the morning *announcements* over the public address system.

  subj.   d.o.
22. The *director* shot some spectacular *footage* in the Alps.

  subj. v. i.o.   app.
23. Your *father gave me* this book, a *collection* of poems.

                  subj. v.
24. Stop! Your *time is* up.

▶ **Exercise 2** Draw two lines under the verb or verb phrase. In the blank, write its tense: *present, past, future, present perfect, past perfect,* or *future perfect.* Label each pronoun: *nom.* (nominative), *obj.* (objective), *pos.* (possessive).

                                                  pos.
__past__   The cat slithered across her owner's porch.

                                     pos.
__present perfect__ **1.** The Iowa farmer has planted his crops.

__future perfect__ **2.** The parade will have passed the city park by noon.

                                     pos.
__past__   **3.** The insensitive people laughed loudly at my new ideas.

                     nom.   **pos.**
__present__   **4.** I cheer tirelessly at our football games.

                    pos.   **obj.**
__future__   **5.** Your roommate will call you soon.

                        pos.   **obj.**
__past perfect__   **6.** Mom and my sister had baked the cookies for us.

                     nom.   **pos.**
__future perfect__ **7.** Maybe we will have built our new home by then.

                                          pos.
__present__   **8.** The coach always insists on faithful attendance at our practices.

__past__   **9.** The airplane landed safely after the severe storm.

                     nom.   **obj.**
__future__   **10.** When will you help with mine?

__past perfect__ **11.** The math team had solved every single problem on time.

                    pos.   **pos.**
__present perfect__ **12.** Your workers have finished their duties on time.

                    nom.
__future__   **13.** I shall always crave chocolate ice cream.

                                     obj.
__past__   **14.** The musicians' mothers made the costumes for them.

__future perfect__ **15.** The candles will have burned to nothing by tonight.

                    pos.
__past perfect__ **16.** Our president had opened the board meetings on time.

                    pos.
__present__   **17.** Sometimes our thoughts turn to the upcoming weekend.

__future__   **18.** Mia will graduate with academic honors.

__future perfect__ **19.** David will have waxed three cars by ten o'clock.

Grammar

                                     pos.   nom.

___past perfect___ **20.** The other members of our tour had taken more pictures than we.

                         pos.   pos.

___future perfect___ **21.** Your beautiful art project will have caught their attention.

                                                       obj.

___past___ **22.** At the grocery store, the flustered cashier gave her too much change.

                                  pos.

___future___ **23.** Will your parents travel to Europe?

                       nom.   pos.

___present___ **24.** We hope for good health throughout our lives.

▶ **Exercise 3** **Correct the following sentences. Cross out any incorrect words and write the changes above them. Look for subject-verb agreement, pronoun-antecedent agreement, and correct verb tense.**

                    works   **her**

Susan ~~work~~ for ~~his~~ uncle after school.

                    calls   **him, her,** *or* **him or her**

1. If the teacher ~~call~~ your name, please respond to ~~them~~.

   We

2. ~~Us~~ voters will go to the polls on Tuesday to elect our government officials.

                       make   **They are**

3. Golden retrievers ~~makes~~ wonderful family pets. ~~It is~~ easy to train, too.

  Whom

4. ~~Who~~ are you inviting to your party?

                      is   **I**

5. Concert choir ~~are~~ my favorite class. ~~You~~ am often asked to sing solos.

                                 his, her, *or* **his or her**

6. No one can register for classes without ~~their~~ advisor's signature.

       works   **She**

7. Jennifer ~~work~~ at the library. ~~Her~~ is always reading the latest best-seller.

                   has

8. The soybean crop ~~have~~ withered in the drought.

                   was

9. My most enjoyable vacation ~~were~~ hiking through the Rocky Mountains.

                         are   **Their**

10. Frank Lloyd Wright and I.M. Pei ~~is~~ famous architects. ~~His~~ work is known throughout the world.

    knows   **his**

11. Eric ~~know~~ a great deal about computer programming, but he won't share ~~its~~ knowledge.

                    visit   **they**   **their**

12. Cassie and Jess often ~~visits~~ Hawaii, where ~~she~~ can enjoy ~~his~~ favorite sport, surfing.

  Give   **them**

13. ~~Gave~~ the extra programs to Kurt and Sean. They will know what to do with ~~it~~.

                           their

14. Certain members refused to pay ~~its~~ monthly dues.

          look   **I**   **I**

15. When I ~~looks~~ at the artwork done by the seniors, ~~we~~ wonder if ~~we~~ will ever be able to do as well.

Unit 9: Using Modifiers Correctly

Lesson 59
Modifiers: Three Degrees of Comparison

Most adjectives and adverbs have three degrees: the positive, or base, form; the comparative form; and the superlative form.

The **positive** form of a modifier cannot be used to make a comparison. (This form appears as the entry word in the dictionary.)

The **comparative** form of a modifier shows two things being compared.

The **superlative** form of a modifier shows three or more things being compared.

Positive: The brown calf is **heavy.**
                The cat ran **swiftly.**
Comparative: The white calf is **heavier** than the brown calf.
                My dog ran **more swiftly** than the cat.
Superlative: The spotted calf is the **heaviest** calf in the herd.
                I ran **most swiftly** of all.

In general, form the comparative by adding -*er* and the superlative by adding -*est.* (In some cases a spelling change is required.)

green	green**er**	green**est**		loud	loud**er**	loud**est**
hot	hot**ter**	hot**test**		true	tru**er**	tru**est**
ugly	ugli**er**	ugli**est**		pretty	**pretti**er	**pretti**est

Use *more* and *most* (or *less* and *least* for the opposite) to form the degrees of comparison in the following situations:

1. adverbs that end in -*ly.*

   I see Sesto's point **more clearly** than Gabrielle's.

2. modifiers of three or more syllables.

   I think the green house is the **most attractive** house on the block.

3. whenever adding -*er* and -*est* sounds awkward.

   John was **more afraid** than Carol.

▶ **Exercise 1** **Supply the comparative and superlative forms of the following modifiers.**

POSITIVE	COMPARATIVE	SUPERLATIVE
happy	happier	happiest
1. tiny	tinier	tiniest

2. brave	braver	bravest
3. comfortable	more comfortable	most comfortable
4. long	longer	longest
5. icy	icier	iciest
6. heartily	more heartily	most heartily
7. hearty	heartier	heartiest
8. hesitant	more hesitant	most hesitant
9. big	bigger	biggest
10. just	more just	most just
11. pretty	prettier	prettiest
12. loud	louder	loudest
13. slow	slower	slowest
14. rapidly	more rapidly	most rapidly
15. shiny	shinier	shiniest
16. loving	more loving	most loving
17. low	lower	lowest
18. savory	more savory	most savory
19. wobbly	wobblier	wobbliest
20. scary	scarier	scariest

▶ **Writing Link** Write four sentences using (1) the comparative of *flat*; (2) the superlative of *keen*; (3) the comparative of *swiftly*; and (4) the superlative of *frugal*.

_____

_____

_____

_____

_____

_____

_____

_____

_____

Lesson 60
Modifiers: Irregular Comparisons

A few modifiers form their comparative and superlative degrees irregularly. Memorizing is the most helpful way to master them.

MODIFIERS WITH IRREGULAR FORMS OF COMPARISON

POSITIVE	COMPARATIVE	SUPERLATIVE
good	better	(the) best
well	better	(the) best
bad	worse	(the) worst
badly	worse	(the) worst
far (distance)	farther	(the) farthest
far (degree, time)	further	(the) furthest
little (amount)	less	(the) least
many	more	(the) most
much	more	(the) most

▶ **Exercise 1** **Complete each sentence with the correct form of the modifier in parentheses.**

The exhausted tennis champ played _____ the worst _____ match of the tournament. (bad)

1. Yosef's test score was _____ better _____ than Harold's. (good)

2. That was _____ the worst _____ day of my entire life. (bad)

3. Carrie was _____ more _____ patient than Eduardo. (much)

4. The Flying A was _____ the farthest _____ ranch from town. (far)

5. She stammered _____ badly *or* worse *or* the worst _____ during her first speech. (badly)

6. *Sand, Shells and Time* was _____ the best _____ photo in the contest. (good)

7. Anton had delved _____ further _____ into psychology than I had suspected. (far)

8. Clara garnered _____ the most _____ votes of any candidate. (many)

9. The new roof withstood the storm _____ better _____ than the shutters. (well)

10. With five children at home, Mary had _____ the least _____ free time of any member. (little)

11. Isabel was hired instead of Alan because she had _____ many *or* more _____ qualifications. (many)

12. The adoption of a baby brought Carlos and Anita _____ the most _____ joy that they had ever known. (much)

13. The woman's condition was _____ worse _____ than it was yesterday. (bad)

14. The school board's plan for redistricting received _____ less _____ enthusiasm than expected. (little)

15. Anna maneuvered her horse _____the best_____ of all the teenagers. (well)

16. Jorge batted _____the worst_____ of all. (badly)

17. Melanie walked _____farther_____ and _____farther_____ every day. (far)

18. Doctors found that the new strain of the virus was the _____worst_____ one yet. (bad)

19. Have you ever heard a _____bad *or* worse_____ speech? (bad)

20. The professor explored each topic to its _____furthest_____ detail. (far)

21. Was Mickey's rendition _____better_____ than his last one? (good)

22. Last night's storm was _____the worst_____ in twelve years. (bad)

23. The old man received _____more_____ pleasure from his radio than from his television. (much)

24. Two hundred miles was _____the farthest_____ she had ever been from home. (far)

25. I bowled _____worse_____ than last week. (badly)

26. Jim put forth his _____good *or* best_____ effort on his vegetable garden. (good)

27. "There's no sense in discussing this any _____further_____," shouted the young man. (far)

28. Which of the two children collected _____more_____ apples? (many)

29. Carla finished the marathon in _____better_____ time than Sarah or Liza. (well)

30. Many landlords allot _____the least_____ money possible for maintenance. (little)

31. Charles was upset when he found there were _____more_____ details left out of the report than were included. (many)

32. Of all the children, Rena showed the _____most_____ concern for the missing puppy. (much)

33. Both men had an ill temper, but John's was _____worse_____. (bad)

34. Vegetables grow _____best_____ of all in loose soil with lots of sun. (well)

35. The crops by the creek suffered _____less_____ from the drought than the ones on the hillside. (little)

36. Ruta was embarrassed because she had behaved _____the worst_____ of all the disappointed children. (badly)

37. The _____farther_____ Al carried the peat moss, the heavier it seemed. (far)

38. Holiday shopping seems to bring out the _____worst_____ tempers of the year. (bad)

39. A hurricane is _____worse_____ than a tropical storm. (bad)

40. The psychiatrist delved into the _____furthest_____ recesses of the man's mind. (far)

Lesson 61
Modifiers: Double and Incomplete Comparisons

Do not make a **double comparison** by using both -*er* or -*est* and *more (less)* or *most (least).*

Incorrect: A redwood grows more taller than an oak.
Correct: A redwood grows **taller** than an oak.
Incorrect: Billie is my most closest friend.
Correct: Billie is my **closest** friend.

Do not make an **incomplete** or **unclear comparison** by omitting *other* or *else* when you compare one member of a group with another.

Unclear: Mercury is closer to the sun than any planet.
Clear: Mercury is closer to the sun than any **other** planet.
Unclear: My aunt has more pets than anyone.
Clear: My aunt has more pets than anyone **else**.

Be sure your comparisons are between like things.

Unclear: The head of a gorilla is larger than a chimpanzee. (The head of a gorilla is not larger than a whole chimpanzee.)
Clear: The head of a gorilla is larger than **that of a chimpanzee.**
Clear: The head of a gorilla is larger than **a chimpanzee's.**
Unclear: Maria's hair is darker than Elke.
Clear: Maria's hair is darker than **that of Elke.**
Clear: Maria's hair is darker than **Elke's.**

▶ **Exercise 1 Circle any double or incomplete comparisons. Write *C* in the blank if the sentence is correct.**

_____   Marcia's papers are (more neater) now.

_____ **1.** One of the (most scariest) rides at an amusement park is the roller coaster.

_____ **2.** Our candidate gave the (most clearest) answer.

__C__ **3.** Leigh liked ice cream better than sherbert.

_____ **4.** Elaine finished the book sooner (than anyone).

_____ **5.** Jamaal's schedule was tighter (than Fred).

_____ **6.** Lazy students in my class are (most likeliest) to fail.

__C__ **7.** Do you like pork chops better than lamb chops?

_____ **8.** Brett can type (more faster) than I.

_____ **9.** Seth can swim faster (than anyone) on the team.

_____ **10.** New York is the (most largest) of the four cities.

_____ **11.** The patient was feeling (more better) today.

__C__ **12.** Four-cylinder engines get better mileage than eight-cylinder engines.

_____ **13.** A rabbit's ears are longer (than a cat).

_____ **14.** A teacher spends the (most largest) amount of time in preparing lessons and in grading papers.

__C__ **15.** The Joneses' house cost less than the Murphys'.

_____ **16.** Minneapolis is colder (than any city) I've lived in.

_____ **17.** My mom says that I'm the (most worst) procrastinator in the family.

__C__ **18.** Henri likes sirloin better than any other meat.

_____ **19.** Kristen is (more happier) in her job than most individuals.

__C__ **20.** English grammar is less consistent than Italian grammar.

_____ **21.** Janice has (more better) study habits than Nicole.

_____ **22.** The Irish wolfhound is the (most largest) dog I've ever seen.

_____ **23.** An eagle's claws are more powerful (than a chicken hawk).

_____ **24.** I like the Cleveland Browns better (than Los Angeles).

__C__ **25.** The new catcher is a better hitter than anyone else on the team.

_____ **26.** This oak chair is more solid (than any piece) of furniture.

_____ **27.** That is the (most tamest) horse in the stable.

_____ **28.** More (than any insect), ants and bees have an organized society.

_____ **29.** Elephants are larger (than any land animals.)

__C__ **30.** Brian was more hopeful than his friend about being selected for the team.

_____ **31.** The Nile is the (most longest) river in the world.

_____ **32.** His house was (more bigger) than ours.

__C__ **33.** Because he had many years of experience, Julio's knowledge was broader than that of any other beginner.

_____ **34.** Jenny was the (most clumsiest) gymnast on the school's team.

_____ **35.** This book is funnier (than any book) I've ever read.

_____ **36.** Don't you think Joe Montana is a better quarterback (than any football player?)

Lesson 62
Using *Good* or *Well; Bad* or *Badly*

Always use *good* as an adjective. *Well* may be used as either an adverb of manner telling how ably something is done or as an adjective meaning "in good health."

The beginning is a **good** place to start. (adjective)
You look **good** in blue. (predicate adjective)
Can you see **well** from your seat? (adverb of manner)
Aren't you feeling **well?** (predicate adjective meaning "in good health")

Always use *bad* as an adjective. Therefore, *bad* is used after a linking verb. Use *badly* as an adverb. *Badly* almost always follows an action verb.

Route 7 has **bad** curves. (adjective)
Harry's hair looks **bad**. (adjective following a linking verb)
I feel **bad** that your candidate lost the election. (adjective following a linking verb)
Carrie sings **badly**. (adverb following an action verb)

▶ **Exercise 1** **Fill each blank with the correct form of** *good, well, bad,* **or** *badly.*

It is a smart idea for a person to have a _____good_____ hobby.

1. The newly formed Riverside Writers Club was off to a ____good *or* bad____ start.

2. Margit was elected president because she edited _____well_____.

3. All seventeen members felt _____good_____ about helping each other improve their skills.

4. Consuelo found that reading others' manuscripts helped her to recognize the ____good *or* bad____ spots in her own work.

5. Receiving criticism made Sean feel _____bad_____ until he realized that such comments really helped him improve.

6. While _____bad_____ grammar plagues everyone at times, style development is also a universal concern.

7. So far, every meeting had gone ____well *or* badly____.

8. In January, the meeting was cancelled due to a _____bad_____ winter storm.

9. Dan missed the March meeting because he was not feeling _____well_____.

10. Knute Petersen (editor of the *Daily News*) presented a _____good_____ overview of local free-lance opportunities.

11. One of the most popular meetings was a talk by a magazine editor discussing _____good_____ and _____bad_____ submissions.

12. A writer's submission would be rejected if it did not fit in _____*well*_____ with the publisher's needs.

13. In April, Robert enthusiastically announced the _____*good*_____ news that he had received an assignment from *Boys' Life.*

14. He attributed the acceptance to a _____*good*_____ query letter.

15. Excitement spread through the group because each member _____*badly*_____ coveted this new plateau.

16. As the months passed, each member found ways for _____*good*_____ fellowship as well as peer help.

17. Hector's humorous stories prompted Sarah to comment, "He writes ____*well or badly*____, but I'm not sure he *is* ____*well or bad*____!"

18. The Riverside Writers Club is one of many peer support groups that provide _____*badly*_____ needed encouragement for their members.

19. Neophyte writers generally respond _____*well*_____ to peer review and encouragement.

20. If you and your friends write, forming a similar group is a _____*good*_____ investment in time and effort.

▶ **Exercise 2** Circle each incorrect use of *good, well, bad,* or *badly.* Write the correct word on the blank. Write *C* if the sentence is correct.

_____*well*_____ Not everyone does (good) at the same thing.

_____*badly*_____ **1.** Some people write (bad) and have no interest in writing at all.

_____*well*_____ **2.** A writing club would not serve their needs very (good).

_____*badly*_____ **3.** Kermit wanted (bad) to start a local theater group in his small town.

_____*C*_____ **4.** He felt this would be a way to gain some good experience in his area of interest.

_____*bad*_____ **5.** Any hope for a successful start looked (badly) at first, but Kermit was determined.

_____*good*_____ **6.** Soon everything looked (well) as more people became interested and contributed their time and effort to the cause.

_____*well*_____ **7.** The group was able to find a play that suited their needs (good).

_____*C*_____ **8.** Now was a good time to solicit money from local businesses to subsidize the first performance.

_____*badly*_____ **9.** Space to rehearse and perform was needed (bad).

_____*badly*_____ **10.** This was an exciting time, and it felt as if things would never go (bad) for the theater group again.

Lesson 63
Double Negatives

Grammar

In general, do not use a **double negative** (two negative words in the same clause). Use only one negative word to express a negative idea. Most negative words have positive forms. You can usually use positive forms to correct double negatives.

NEGATIVE	POSITIVE	NEGATIVE	POSITIVE
neither	either	none	any
never	ever	no one	any one
no	any, a	nothing	anything
nobody	anybody	nowhere	anywhere

Incorrect:	We haven't been to no concerts this year.
Correct:	We haven't been to any concerts this year.
Correct:	We've been to no concerts this year.
Incorrect:	Kathy never did nothing to justify expulsion.
Correct:	Kathy never did anything to justify expulsion.
Correct:	Kathy did nothing to justify expulsion.

▶ **Exercise 1** **Circle each phrase containing a double negative. Rewrite the phrase correctly in the blank. Write _C_ if the sentence is correct.**

would be no _or_ wouldn't be any	There (wouldn't be no) opportunity for the entire team to go to camp.
C	1. Football camp is really nothing like summer camp.
aren't any _or_ are no	2. There (aren't no) activities that are unrelated to the sport of football.
have no _or_ don't have any	3. You (don't have no) reason to be there unless you truly want to play.
doesn't leave any _or_ leaves no	4. Football camp (doesn't leave no) opportunity to sleep late.
C	5. Nobody ever went to football camp to rest!
C	6. After breakfast, which no one ever misses, conditioning activities begin.
Nothing will ever	7. (Nothing will never) protect a player from injury more than conditioning.
There are no _or_ There aren't any	8. (There aren't no) exercises that the players find easy.
don't practice anything	9. We (don't practice nothing) but drills to prepare us for the actual game.

_____ C _____ **10.** Players can never learn enough about the importance of

commitment.

▶ **Exercise 2 Circle the two negative words in each double negative. Rewrite the sentence correctly in the blank. Write *C* if the sentence is correct.** Answers may vary. Some suggestions are given.

Staying at home all summer (never) is (no) fun. ___Staying at home all summer never is any fun.___

1. The first time I went to summer camp, I (didn't) expect to have (no) fun. ___The first time I went to___ ___summer camp, I didn't expect to have any fun.___

2. When my parents dropped me off, there (wasn't)(no) one around that I knew. ___When my parents___ ___dropped me off, there was no one around that I knew.___

3. Because I was the last to arrive, I (didn't) get (no) choice of bunks. ___Because I was the last to arrive,___ ___I didn't get any choice of bunks.___

4. I (wasn't) getting (nowhere) with making my bunk until my counselor helped me. ___I was getting___ ___nowhere with making my bunk until my counselor helped me.___

5. It took a long time to fix the sheets, and I was afraid I (wouldn't) get (no) supper. ___It took a long___ ___time to fix the sheets, and I was afraid I wouldn't get any supper.___

6. In the mess hall, I sat beside Carlos, who (hadn't) made (no) friends either. ___In the mess hall, I sat___ ___beside Carlos, who had made no friends either.___

7. I (won't)(never) forget Carlos because he became my best friend at camp. ___I will never forget Carlos___ ___because he became my best friend at camp.___

8. One day when there (wasn't)(no one) around, we tied the counselor's shaving gear to the rafters. ___One day when there wasn't anyone around, we tied the counselor's shaving gear to the rafters.___

9. Carlos and I promised (not) to play (no) tricks on each other. ___Carlos and I promised not to play any___ ___tricks on each other.___

10. I (never) got bitten by (no) mosquitoes because I wore plenty of insect repellent. ___I never got bitten___ ___by any mosquitoes because I wore plenty of insect repellent.___

11. When we hiked in the woods, we (weren't) allowed to build (no) fires. ___When we hiked in the woods,___ ___we weren't allowed to build any fires.___

12. We looked for wild animals, but we (didn't) see (nothing) but birds and squirrels. ___We looked for___ ___wild animals, but we didn't see anything but birds and squirrels.___

Lesson 64
Misplaced and Dangling Modifiers

Place modifiers as close as possible to the words they modify in order to make the meaning of the sentence clear.

Misplaced modifiers modify the wrong word, or they seem to modify more than one word in a sentence. To correct a misplaced modifier, move the modifier as close as possible to the word it modifies.

Misplaced:	**Floating in the wind,** Hannah stared wistfully at the kite.
Clear:	Hannah stared wistfully at the kite **floating in the wind.**
Misplaced:	A **new man's** suit was in the closet.
Clear:	A **man's new** suit was in the closet.

Dangling modifiers seem logically to modify no word at all. To correct a dangling modifier, supply a word the dangling phrase can sensibly modify.

Dangling:	**Working all night long,** sleep was welcome.
Clear:	**Working all night long,** Francis welcomed sleep.
Dangling:	**After a valiant effort** the blaze still raged uncontrollably.
Clear:	**After a valiant effort** the firefighters still faced a blaze that raged uncontrollably.

If the word *only* is not placed immediately before the word or group of words it modifies, the meaning can be unclear.

Unclear:	Dan only has art on Monday.
Clear:	Dan has only art on Monday.
Clear:	Dan has art only on Monday.
Clear:	Only Dan has art on Monday.

▶ **Exercise 1** Circle each misplaced modifying phrase and draw an arrow to the word it should modify. If the sentence is correct, place a *C* in the blank.

_____ Ice cream was served to everyone in a dish.

_____ **1.** Proposing new menus, healthier school lunches would be offered by the new dietitian.

_____ **2.** Standing in the cool shower the summer heat didn't feel so intense to Danilo.

_____ **3.** Throw Mama from the train a kiss.

_____ **4.** Listening to the scanner, the accident sounded extremely serious to Kent.

____C____ **5.** Daydreaming quietly, Kai was reflecting on her wonderful excursion to Bermuda.

_____ **6.** Climbing down from their seats, the stands seemed to sway slightly as people left.

_____ **7.** Every week while doing the yard work, the mower seems to break down for Carl.

_____ **8.** Nicole and Isra helped prepare for the prom, working as hard as possible.

____C____ **9.** Trying not to scratch herself, Lorena was miserable because of the poison ivy.

_____ **10.** Two deer were spotted by the hunters licking the block of salt in the pasture.

_____ **11.** Thomas developed pictures for the newspaper of the football games.

_____ **12.** Climbing into bed, the tornado siren began to blow, scaring the children.

_____ **13.** At noon, Karen encountered heavy traffic driving to the bank.

_____ **14.** Erin must have found at least ten sources researching her term paper.

____C____ **15.** A delicious lunch with all the trimmings was served to the staff.

_____ **16.** The president waved to the thousands of people riding in his black limousine.

_____ **17.** The bears began eating their meal of ants rising from their afternoon naps.

____C____ **18.** With great energy, the horses entered the race track.

_____ **19.** Stumbling over another player's foot, the crowd gasped as the receiver ran on for a

touchdown.

____C____ **20.** Circling overhead, the hawk was searching for its next meal.

▶ **Exercise 2 Circle any misplaced or dangling modifier. If the sentence is correct, place a _C_ in the blank.**

_____ While rafting, the supplies had no chance of staying dry.

_____ **1.** Sleeping soundly, the alarm clock startled me with its harsh ringing.

_____ **2.** Walking along the beach, a shell cut Harry's foot.

____C____ **3.** Catching sight of our friends, we waved frantically.

_____ **4.** While mowing the yard, the mail carrier's horn announced his presence.

_____ **5.** Driving along the freeway, the deer ran into the woods.

____C____ **6.** Needing a ride to the airport, Mrs. Wiggins called a taxi.

_____C_____ 7. Because I was shy, I had some difficulty making new friends.

_____ 8. (After standing in line for half an hour), the clerk announced that the store was closed.

_____ 9. A story was told to the children (with a happy ending.)

_____ 10. (Working at my desk), the sudden noise was startling.

_____C_____ 11. Gloating over his victory, Bill bored the other wrestlers with his bragging.

_____ 12. (Running home), my heel came off my shoe.

_____C_____ 13. Draining the radiator, I replaced the antifreeze.

_____ 14. (Lost in the woods,) survival was uppermost in our minds.

_____ 15. (Lying on the couch), my snack fell to the floor.

_____ 16. (Reading intently), her entrance broke my concentration.

_____C_____ 17. Savoring each moment, Eileen and Tracy watched the sunset.

_____ 18. A holiday was given to the employees (with pay.)

_____ 19. (Walking in the woods), a squirrel darted across Tanya's path, startling her.

_____ 20. (After smiling at his girlfriend), Achim's solo went very well.

_____C_____ 21. As a successful attorney, Andrea was widely sought.

_____ 22. (Tired and hungry,) a meal and a bed sounded good to me.

▶ **Exercise 3** Insert a caret (^) to show where the word *only* should be placed to match the meaning in parentheses.

I ^ watch cartoons on Saturday mornings. (I do nothing else on Saturday mornings.)

1. The ^ green truck was speeding down the gravel road. (There was no other green truck.)

2. ^ The green truck was speeding down the gravel road. (No more than one truck was speeding.)

3. The green truck was speeding down the ^ gravel road. (There was no other gravel road.)

4. Potatoes are the main product of ^ Idaho. (No other state has potatoes as a main product.)

5. Potatoes are the ^ main product of Idaho. (There is no other major product from Idaho.)

6. Kerry played ^ soccer while attending Northridge High. (Kerry participated in no other sport.)

7. Kerry ^ played soccer while attending Northridge High. (Kerry did nothing else but play soccer while in high school.)

8. ^ Jeanne liked to drive her convertible. (No one enjoyed driving the convertible except Jeanne.)

9. Jeanne liked to drive ˄ her convertible. (Jeanne didn't like driving if the car was not her convertible.)

10. ˄ Esther got three books from the library. (No one got the same number of books as Esther.)

11. Esther got ˄ three books from the library. (Esther got no more than three books.)

12. Rover was Adam's ˄ pride and joy. (Rover was the one thing in which Adam took delight.)

13. Rover was ˄ Adam's pride and joy. (The other members of the family didn't care as much for Rover as Adam did.)

14. ˄ Airplanes are Linda's favorite mode of transportation for long trips. (Linda will make long trips on nothing but an airplane.)

15. Airplanes are Linda's favorite mode of transportation ˄ for long trips. (When the trip is short, Linda prefers some other form of travel.)

16. ˄ I bought Dad a screwdriver set for Christmas. (No one else got Dad a screwdriver set.)

17. I bought ˄ Dad a screwdriver set for Christmas. (I bought screwdrivers for no one but Dad.)

18. I bought Dad ˄ a screwdriver set for Christmas. (I bought one thing for Dad.)

▶ **Writing Link** **Write a paragraph about a family outing. Correctly use 2 or 3 modifying phrases and circle them. Use the word *only* at least once.**

_____

_____

_____

_____

_____

_____

_____

_____

_____

_____

_____

_____

_____

Unit 9 **Review**

▶ **Exercise 1** **Supply the comparative and superlative forms of the following modifiers.**

POSITIVE	COMPARATIVE	SUPERLATIVE
1. interested	more interested	most interested
2. true	truer	truest
3. luxurious	more luxurious	most luxurious
4. quick	quicker	quickest
5. nice	nicer	nicest
6. speedily	more speedily	most speedily
7. hardy	hardier	hardiest
8. charismatic	more charismatic	most charismatic
9. happy	happier	happiest
10. righteous	more righteous	most righteous
11. noble	nobler	noblest
12. clumsy	clumsier	clumsiest
13. little (amount)	less	least
14. rapidly	more rapidly	most rapidly
15. grimy	grimier	grimiest
16. caring	more caring	most caring
17. able	abler	ablest
18. savory	more savory	most savory
19. calm	calmer	calmest
20. worrisome	more worrisome	most worrisome

Grammar

Cumulative Review: Units 1–9

▶ **Exercise 1** Draw two lines under the simple predicate in each sentence. Label any direct object *d.o.* and any indirect object *i.o.*

                  i.o.   d.o.
Ms. Chung gave her students some good advice.

                        d.o.
1. Dylan returned his library books last night.

                             d.o.
2. Our advisor suggested the community project to the class.

                  i.o.   d.o.
3. Father will buy me a car for my sixteenth birthday.

                     d.o.
4. Did Keshia shovel the snow from the driveway?

                   i.o.   d.o.
5. She gave the weary mail carrier a glass of water.

                    i.o.   d.o.
6. Mr. Hayashi handed the flight attendant his ticket.

                    d.o.
7. Our house needs a new coat of paint.

                 i.o.   d.o.
8. Mai left the amiable waiter a large tip.

                 i.o.   d.o.
9. The chef promised me his recipe for moo goo gai pan.

                  i.o.   d.o.
10. Mr. Lichtenberg gave the football players a pep talk.

                  d.o.
11. Toto's makes the best pizza in town.

                 i.o.   d.o.
12. On your vacation will you send us a postcard?

                   d.o.
13. The scientist remembered the correct equation.

                     d.o.
14. This year Westland High relinquished the state title.

                 d.o.
15. The symphonic choir sang five songs at the concert.

               i.o.   d.o.
16. Tiffany wrote her grandmother a long letter.

          i.o.   d.o.
17. Please save me a piece of the cake.

                 i.o.   d.o.
18. The babysitter read the children a bedtime story.

                 i.o.   d.o.
19. The editor can give the writer suggestions on following the textbook guidelines.

                 d.o.
20. The loud, screeching noise startled Tony.

▶ **Exercise 2** Underline the simple subject. Identify the verbal or verbal phrase in each sentence by drawing a circle around it. In the blank, write whether the verbal or verbal phrase is a gerund, a participle, or an infinitive.

_____infinitive_____ The merry carolers tried (to sing together)

_____gerund_____ 1. (Reading biographies) is one of Kevin's favorite pastimes.

_____participle_____ 2. The heavy snowfall buried the (abandoned) truck.

_____participle_____ 3. A man (carrying a dozen red roses) walked into Miss Carter's classroom.

_____gerund_____ 4. Many stuntmen were used in (making this movie)

_____infinitive_____ 5. Li Cheng forgot (to register for the computer class)

_____participle/participle_____ 6. They hiked along the trail, over (decaying) logs and (snarled) underbrush.

_____gerund_____ 7. Kim made extra money by (tutoring students in math.)

_____gerund_____ 8. (Skiing) is a great winter sport.

_____infinitive_____ 9. It takes courage (to admit our mistakes)

_____infinitive_____ 10. Aisha tried (to wait patiently for the phone call)

_____gerund_____ 11. The best place for (running) is the Olentangy bike trail.

_____gerund_____ 12. (Making costumes for the school play) is a big job.

_____gerund_____ 13. We achieved a victory by (scoring a basket in the last minute.)

_____infinitive_____ 14. The tuxedo was too expensive (to buy)

_____participle_____ 15. Peg woke to the aroma of (frying) bacon.

_____gerund_____ 16. (Speaking before a large group) isn't easy for many people.

_____gerund_____ 17. My mother insisted on (returning the damaged goods)

_____participle_____ 18. The homeless man discovered the (deserted) building.

_____infinitive_____ 19. The dream of the Wright brothers was (to build the first successful airplane).

_____participle_____ 20. The (raging) wind knocked down power lines and tree limbs.

▶ **Exercise 3** Underline the correct word given in parentheses. Draw an arrow to the word it modifies.

Our school orchestra always performs (good, <u>well</u>).

1. The poison ivy itched (bad, <u>badly</u>) for at least a week.

2. What is the (taller, <u>tallest</u>) building in the country?

3. As the winter storm raged on, the city streets became (more icier, <u>icier</u>).

4. The freshly baked bread smells (<u>good</u>, well).

5. Randy has (many, <u>more</u>) baseball cards than anyone else.

6. Much to the doctor's dismay, the small child grew (<u>worse</u>, ill) each day.

7. The test that Mr. Rivera gave was the (most simplest, <u>simplest</u>) of all.

8. Mrs. Greiner cried because she felt (<u>bad</u>, badly) about the loss of her pet.

9. Jason has (the least, <u>less</u>) sales experience than Ben.

10. Wyoming is (more farther, <u>farther</u>) from here than Indiana is.

11. Sukey reads very (good, <u>well</u>) for her age.

12. We couldn't find (<u>any</u>, no) birdseed at the hardware store.

13. Calculus is a (<u>more difficult</u>, difficulter) mathematics than algebra.

14. Of the three boys, Michael is the (cuter, <u>cutest</u>).

15. Jeff wanted (<u>badly</u>, bad) to add that stamp to his collection.

16. Veronica's (badly, <u>bad</u>) attitude was the source of much of her discontent.

17. Our student teacher wore the (most ugliest, <u>ugliest</u>) dress yesterday!

18. Her father bought the (more expensive, <u>most expensive</u>) car on the lot.

19. Who scored (the most, <u>more</u>) goals during the game, Colin or Jess?

20. Of the two sisters, Carla is (the least, <u>less</u>) popular.

*U*sage

Unit 10: Usage Glossary

Lesson 65
Usage: *a* to *altogether*

Words that are similar are sometimes misused.

a, an Use *a* in front of words that begin with a consonant or "yew" sound. Use *an* in front of words that begin with any other vowel sound.

a house, **a** university; **an** animal, **an** honor.

a lot, alot *A lot* should always be two words or avoided completely.

There are **a lot** of new computer products on the market.

a while, awhile *A while* is made up of an article and a noun. *Awhile* is an adverb.

Let's think for **a while,** then we'll continue **awhile** with the lesson.

accept, except *Accept* is a verb meaning "to receive" or "to agree to." *Except* can be a verb, though it is often used as a preposition meaning "but."

I **accept** your explanation that footballs fly straight, **except** in high winds.

affect, effect *Affect* is a verb meaning "to influence." *Effect* can be a noun meaning "result" or a verb meaning "to accomplish."

Artificial lighting can **affect** the nutritional cycle of plants. (verb)
Artificial lighting can have an undesirable **effect** on plants. (noun)
Exposure to both daylight and darkness **effects** good health in plants. (verb)

ain't *Ain't* is unacceptable in speaking and writing unless used as a direct quote.

▶ **Exercise 1** Underline the correct term in each sentence.

Their kitchen has (alot, <u>a lot</u>) of modern conveniences.

1. Do not use the emergency exits, (accept, <u>except</u>) in case of fire.

2. Blue-screen matting is a common special (<u>effect</u>, affect) in television and movies.

3. Mr. Chen will be coming back to his office in (<u>a while</u>, awhile), if you'd like to wait.

4. The track coach will not (<u>accept</u>, except) applications submitted after the first of the year.

5. Matthew was studying the cause and (affect, <u>effect</u>) of historical events.

6. We waited at the restaurant (a while, <u>awhile</u>) before going out into the cold.

7. Jules was working on (an, <u>a</u>) history paper when I called.

Usage

8. Does committing too many fouls (effect, <u>affect</u>) the score?

9. It (<u>is not</u>, ain't) incorrect to omit the leading zero on some decimal numbers.

10. It should take less than (<u>an</u>, a) hour to complete this test.

---

all ready, already *All ready* means "completely ready." *Already* means "by this time."

Matthew was **all ready** to perform his gymnastics routine.
Janice was **already** capable of reading college-level textbooks.

all right, alright This should always be two words.

Any flavor of ice cream is **all right** with me!

all the farther, all the faster These are unacceptable in writing. Use *as far as* and *as fast as* instead.

Walk **as far as** you want and **as fast as** you can to build stamina.

all together, altogether *All together* means "in a group." *Altogether* means "completely."

We were **all together** for the last time at our class picnic.
Our class picnic was an **altogether** wonderful experience for everyone.

▶ **Exercise 2 Correct the word in italics. If the word is correct, write C.**

all right		Changing the drama club meeting to Thursday was *alright* with the members.
altogether	**1.**	I was *all together* astonished at the outcome of the story.
C	**2.**	The fire had *already* raged out of control when the emergency vehicles arrived.
all ready	**3.**	The architect was *already* to present his design to the construction company.
all right	**4.**	Is it *alright* to wear a striped necktie with a plaid shirt?
C	**5.**	The ice hockey player skated *as fast as* he could to get by the left wing.
already	**6.**	Cole had *all ready* toasted the bagels by the time his parents woke up.
C	**7.**	Hasan asked if it was *all right* to use a calculator during the exam.
all together	**8.**	The band members asked, "May we go *altogether* on the same bus?"
as far as	**9.**	To the lake and back was *all the farther* we had to go.
all right	**10.**	Will traveling by car be *alright* with Curtis?

Usage

Lesson 66
Usage: *amount* to *could of*

amount, number Use *amount* when referring to nouns that cannot be counted. Use *number* when referring to nouns that can be counted.

The Appalachian Mountains have a vast **amount** of fog.
We have a small **number** of dictionaries in the branch library.

bad, badly *Bad* is an adjective. *Badly* is an adverb.

This cold weather has been **bad** for the farmers.   The crops were **badly** damaged.

being as, being that These expressions should not be used in writing. Replace them with *because* or *since*.

beside, besides *Beside* means "at the side of." *Besides* means "in addition to."

My dog likes to curl up **beside** me.   There are other things in life **besides** television.

between, among Use *between* to compare one person or thing with another. Use *among* to show a relationship in which more than two persons or things are considered as a group.

The sculptor had to choose **between** marble and granite.
The trees in Oregon are **among** the tallest in the Pacific Northwest.

▶ **Exercise 1** **Underline the correct word in each sentence.**

There is a large (<u>amount</u>, number) of fat on this steak.

1. Earth's atmosphere lies (<u>between</u>, among) the surface of the planet and the edge of outer space.

2. The air we breathe contains only a small (<u>amount</u>, number) of oxygen.

3. The atmosphere consists of different elements and layers, some portions of which have been (bad, <u>badly</u>) polluted.

4. (<u>Besides</u>, Beside) human-made pollutants, gases, steam, and ash from volcanoes contribute to air pollution.

5. A large (amount, <u>number</u>) of clouds reside in the lowest part of the atmosphere, the troposphere.

6. (Beside, <u>Besides</u>), scientists can predict weather by studying the troposphere.

7. Clouds play an important role in the earth's weather (<u>because</u>, being that) they contain water.

8. The water that clouds bring as rain or snow is (bad, <u>badly</u>) needed to sustain life.

9. Stratocumulus clouds are one of the largest types of clouds, and they contain a small (amount, <u>number</u>) of light and dark areas.

Usage

10. There are other by-products of clouds (beside, <u>besides</u>) rain; electrified regions within the cloud discharge, creating lightning.

---

borrow, lend, loan *Borrow* is a verb meaning "to take something for a limited time." *Lend* means "to give for temporary use." *Loan* is a noun.

May I **borrow** your pen?   Please **lend** me your pen.   We got a **loan** from the bank.

bring, take *Bring* means "to carry from a distant place to a closer one." *Take* means "to carry from a nearby place to a more distant one."

Bring your books to me.   **Take** a jacket to the game tonight.

can, may Use *can* to indicate the ability to do something. Use *may* to indicate permission to do something.

I **can** finish reading before dinner.   **May** I finish reading after dinner?

can't hardly, can't scarcely These expressions are double negatives. Avoid using them.

I **can hardly** wait for vacation.   The driver **can scarcely** see through the snow.

could of, might of, must of, should of, would of The preposition *of* is incorrect here; use the helping verb *have* instead.

The loud noise **might have** startled the dog.

▶ **Exercise 2 Correct the word in italics. If the word is correct, write** *C.*

<u>borrow</u>   Chris would like to *loan* that book from Tina.

<u>can hardly</u>   **1.** People *can't hardly* walk when sidewalks are covered with ice.

<u>can</u>   **2.** Hot air *may* mix with cold air to cause powerful currents.

<u>bring</u>   **3.** Blizzards *take* with them a lot of snow, wind, and low temperatures.

<u>can scarcely</u>   **4.** You *can't scarcely* imagine the total destruction a tornado can cause.

<u>C</u>   **5.** Winter weather *brings* winter storms such as ice storms and blizzards.

<u>must have</u>   **6.** The tornado that hit Illinois in 1925 *must of* been the worst in history.

<u>could have</u>   **7.** There was no way this killer storm *could of* been prevented.

<u>can</u>   **8.** One *may* never be safe from a tornado in a mobile home.

<u>C</u>   **9.** Another type of violent storm is a hurricane, which *can* be tracked with satellites, airplanes, and radar.

<u>lend</u>   **10.** Before such a storm is due to hit, people *loan* each other tools and materials to board up their houses.

Lesson 67
Usage: *different from* to *regardless*

different from, different than The expression *different from* is preferred.

Although there are similarities, a clarinet is **different from** a soprano saxophone.

doesn't, don't *Doesn't* is used with *he, she, it* and all singular nouns. *Don't* is used with *I, you, we, they,* and all plural nouns.

She **doesn't** like cold weather.   We **don't** have a hockey team.

emigrate, immigrate *Emigrate* means "to go from one country to another to live." *Immigrate* means "to come to a country to live."

The entire family plans to **emigrate** from Russia next year.
Most people who **immigrate** to the United States live in coastal states.

farther, further Use *farther* to refer to physical distance. Use *further* to refer to degree or time.

We traveled **farther** today than we did yesterday.
We will discuss this topic **further** at our next meeting.

fewer, less Use *fewer* to refer to nouns that can be counted. Use *less* to refer to nouns that cannot be counted.

There are **fewer** students enrolled in the city's elementary schools this year.
It takes **less** time to travel one mile in a car than on a bicycle.

▶ **Exercise 1 Underline the correct word in each sentence.**

(Fewer, Less) than twenty people attended the student council meeting.

1. Cleveland is (farther, further) from Columbus than is Cincinnati.

2. José (doesn't, don't) want to go to the rock concert.

3. Two families recently (immigrated, emigrated) to the United States.

4. In the 1980s, (less, fewer) Vietnamese settled in the United States than in the previous decade.

5. Ahmed (doesn't, don't) think Arizona will be any hotter than Saudi Arabia.

6. Denise and Colin (doesn't, don't) share the same opinion about the movie.

7. Los Angeles is very (different from, different than) New York.

8. The tired child could not walk any (farther, further).

9. A black hole is (different from, different than) other stars because it can't be seen.

10. I have (fewer, less) than five puppies left from the litter.

good, **well** *Good* is an adjective. *Well* is an adverb.

It was a **good** book.
The team played **well**.

had of *Of* should not be used between *had* and a past participle.

I thought I **had read** this book before.

hanged, **hung** Use *hanged* when referring to death by hanging. Use *hung* in all other instances.

In the Old West, they **hanged** people for stealing a horse.
The librarian **hung** the sign on the door.

in, **into** Use *in* to mean "inside." Use *into* to indicate movement from outside to a point within.

Meet me **in** the cafeteria.
I'm going **into** the cafeteria.

irregardless, **regardless** *Irregardless* is a double negative and should not be used. *Regardless* is the only correct usage.

The mouse tried to run across the room, **regardless** of the cat.

▶ **Exercise 2 Correct the word in italics. If the word is correct, write C.**

_____well_____   Helena plays the guitar very *good*.

_____regardless_____   **1.** Our school will continue its community service projects *irregardless* of funding.

_____into_____   **2.** When my father had an aching back, he climbed *in* the bathtub very carefully.

_____C_____   **3.** Many animal species face extinction *in* the wild.

_____C_____   **4.** Tanya likes to dress *well* when she goes on a date.

_____C_____   **5.** The school drama club *hung* posters around town to advertise the school play.

_____well_____   **6.** Subway systems must be ventilated *good*.

_____had_____   **7.** The history teacher believed he *had of* explained the assignment thoroughly.

_____regardless_____   **8.** My guidance counselor said that *irregardless* of my grades, I should take geometry next year.

_____hanged_____   **9.** The mob *hung* the outlaw from a large oak tree.

_____into_____   **10.** We put our cans, bottles, and newspapers *in* the recycling bin.

Lesson 68
Usage: *this kind* to *reason is because*

---

this kind, these kinds Use *this* and *that* with singular words. Use *these* and *those* with plural words.

This kind of metal won't rust.   **These kinds** of paints are lead-free.

lay, lie *Lay* means "to put" or "to place." *Lie* means "to recline" or "to be positioned."

Lay your cards on the table.   My dog likes to **lie** in the sunshine.

learn, teach *Learn* means "to receive knowledge." *Teach* means "to give knowledge."

You can't **teach** an old dog new tricks unless it's willing to **learn**.

leave, let *Leave* means "to go away." *Let* means "to permit."

You may **leave** when you finish the test.
Don't **let** the grease settle in the pan.

like, as *Like* is a preposition and introduces a prepositional phrase. *As* is often a subordinating conjunction and introduces a subordinate clause.

This roller coaster feels **like** a jet!   We won the game **as** the final buzzer sounded.

loose, lose *Loose* means "free" or "not fitting tightly." *Lose* means "to have no longer" or "to fail to win."

These new shoes are too **loose**.   Don't **lose** your ticket.

▶ **Exercise 1 Underline the correct word in each sentence.**

(<u>This kind</u>, these kinds) of muffin is Crystal's favorite.

1. Our class (<u>learns</u>, teaches) that the animal kingdom has a well-defined social order.

2. Many animal parents (<u>teach</u>, learn) hunting and survival skills to their young.

3. Coyote cubs can make noises that sound (<u>like</u>, as) human babies crying.

4. Predatory birds won't (leave, <u>let</u>) their young move out of the nest until the babies have been prepared for life.

5. Like humans, animals quickly (<u>learn</u>, teach) to recognize their limitations.

6. Animals build their lives around (<u>these kinds</u>, this kind) of limitations because they cannot alter their environments.

7. A tiger may (<u>lay</u>, lie) its catch in a protected spot.

8. A tiger senses it should (lay, <u>lie</u>) in the shade of a tree on a hot day.

9. To thrive within their environments, animals have tools and instincts they cannot (loose, <u>lose</u>).

10. Owls have sharp eyes and strong talons to locate and capture small animals (as, <u>like</u>) field mice.

---

passed, past *Passed* is the past form and the past participle of the verb *to pass*. *Past* may be an adjective, a preposition, an adverb, or a noun.

We **passed** this building an hour ago!   Have you eaten any pizza this **past** week?
We drove **past** this building an hour ago!

precede and proceed *Precede* means "to go or come before." *Proceed* means "to continue" or "to move along."

Which selection will **precede** Beethoven's *Pastoral Symphony* in tonight's program?
You may **proceed** with your presentation.

raise, rise *Raise* means "to cause to move upward." *Rise* means "to go up."

Raise the flag at 7:30 A.M. sharp.
Does the sun **rise** over the eastern or western horizon?

reason is because This expression is redundant and should not be used.

The **reason** he left early is **that** he came down with a fever.
He left early **because** he came down with a fever.

▶ **Exercise 2 Correct the word in italics. If the word is correct, write *C*.**

_____raise_____	Please do not *rise* the blind.
_____passed_____	**1.** Yesterday, Tabitha *past* a wildlife reserve while riding her bicycle.
_____raise_____	**2.** She wants to *rise* awareness of the importance of these reserves.
reason is that	**3.** The *reason is because* wildlife contributes much beauty, scientific value, survival value, and economic value.
_____proceed_____	**4.** Scientists must *precede* with their studies of wildlife.
_____C_____	**5.** The *reason is that* they gain valuable medical knowledge through such research.
_____rise_____	**6.** Certain animals need protection so they can *raise* every morning.
_____C_____	**7.** The American bald eagle is the national bird of the United States and an important part of our country's *past*.
_____precede_____	**8.** Observation and study must *proceed* any action taken to remedy the wildlife situation.
_____C_____	**9.** This *raises* the question, "Which animals, where, how, and to what extent should hunters be permitted to hunt?"
_____passed_____	**10.** In 1973 the government *past* the Endangered Species Act.

Usage

Lesson 69
Usage: *respectfully* to *where at*

---

respectfully, respectively *Respectfully* means "with respect." *Respectively* means "in the order named."

Tim **respectfully** handed the ball back to the referee.
Blue and magenta are primary and secondary colors, **respectively**.

says, said *Says* is the third-person singular of the verb *say*. *Said* is the past tense of *say*.

He always **says** he'll call.   He **said** he would call back tomorrow.

sit, set *Sit* means "to place oneself in a sitting position." *Set* means "to place" or "to put."

You may **sit** at this table.   Please **set** the table with napkins.

than, then *Than* is a conjunction. *Then* is an adverb.

Cats are more agile **than** dogs.   Layna was a young girl **then**.

this here, that there *Here* and *there* shouldn't be used after *this* and *that*. *This* and *that* should be used alone.

We like **this** song.   I don't like **that** color.

where at *At* is a preposition and should not be used after *where*.

Where is city hall?

▶ **Exercise 1 Underline the correct word in each sentence.**

After shopping, I need to (<u>sit</u>, set) for a while.

1. Thirty years ago, cars were about 25% heavier (<u>than</u>, then) they are today.

2. I don't know (<u>where</u>, where at) the new stadium is going to be built.

3. My aunt moved into (<u>that</u>, that there) building ten years ago.

4. Maya (<u>respectfully</u>, respectively) submitted her paper to her English teacher.

5. Yesterday Tim (says, <u>said</u>) to me that he wants to learn how to snow ski.

6. Don't (sit, <u>set</u>) too many boxes on the table.

7. (Where at, <u>Where</u>) is the lunchroom?

8. To get to the lunchroom, go through (that there, <u>that</u>) door and turn to your right.

9. Dan and Alta, (<u>respectively</u>, respectfully), baked brownies and apple pie for the cast party.

10. If you need more light, (<u>sit</u>, set) next to the window.

▶ **Exercise 2 Correct the word in italics. If the word is correct, write *C*.**

respectively	The band and the orchestra will play the first and second selections listed in the program, *respectfully*.
Set	**1.** *Sit* that heavy package on the chair by the window.
where	**2.** Do you know *where* my school jacket is *at*?
C	**3.** George Foreman lost to Muhammad Ali in 1974; *then* twenty years later he beat Michael Moorer to regain the heavyweight championship.
this	**4.** Please take *this here* floppy disk to the computer lab.
Where	**5.** *Where* is the reference section of the library *at*?
sit	**6.** Let's *set* near home plate so we can watch the pitcher.
C	**7.** Our art class and our science class took tours of the art museum and underground caves, *respectively*.
That	**8.** *That there* horse is the most beautiful stallion I've ever seen.
than	**9.** A blue whale is much bigger *then* an elephant.
where	**10.** José wanted to visit the Alamo *where* Davy Crockett fought *at*.

▶ **Writing Link Write four sentences about your favorite season using four rules from this lesson.**

_____

_____

_____

_____

_____

_____

_____

_____

_____

_____

_____

_____

_____

Name _____ Class _____ Date _____

Unit 10 Review

▶ **Exercise 1** Underline the correct word in each sentence.

The car had every special feature (accept, <u>except</u>) a sunroof.

1. The city library (loans, <u>lends</u>) books that our school library doesn't have.

2. A baboon is (<u>different from</u>, different than) a gorilla.

3. Rayna dragged her heavy suitcase (<u>awhile</u>, a while) before she stopped to rest.

4. The class enjoyed the fair because the event offered (alot, <u>a lot</u>) of rides, games, and exhibits.

5. I must try to (lie, <u>lay</u>) my keys in the same place every day.

6. Benedict Arnold's treachery did not (effect, <u>affect</u>) the outcome of the Revolutionary War.

7. The nonfiction of Isaac Asimov is very popular (between, <u>among</u>) young people.

8. Henry Ford (farther, <u>further</u>) improved assembly line methods to cut the cost of producing cars.

9. The elephants at the circus performed remarkably (good, <u>well</u>).

10. The Thanksgiving Day parade (past, <u>passed</u>) my uncle's apartment in New York City.

11. Nina had a (lose, <u>loose</u>) tooth from her fall, so she went to the dentist after school.

12. Swimming is better exercise (<u>than</u>, then) jogging because it doesn't hurt the knees.

13. Mark's mother asked, "Did you (<u>bring</u>, take) your permission slip home so I can sign it?"

14. The snowstorm in Chicago (must of, <u>must have</u>) caused the delays at the airport.

15. "Mr. Stewart, (can, <u>may</u>) I leave the room to go to speech therapy now?"

16. (Irregardless, <u>Regardless</u>) of the cool water, Kaveetha went swimming in the ocean.

17. Tia threw the ball (<u>into</u>, in) the basket to win the game for her team.

18. We (preceded, <u>proceeded</u>) with the lesson even though the workbooks had not yet arrived.

19. The florist (sat, <u>set</u>) the plant on the windowsill to absorb more sun.

20. Will your parents (leave, <u>let</u>) you go to the movie with me Friday night?

21. Mrs. Chang (hanged, <u>hung</u>) a colorful mobile over her baby's crib.

22. The choir sold bakery goods to (<u>raise</u>, rise) money for the field trip.

23. The cooperation (<u>between</u>, among) the teachers and the staff has contributed to the success of the school.

24. Recycling has (all ready, <u>already</u>) helped the cleanliness of the environment.

Cumulative Review: Units 1–10

▶ **Exercise 1** Underline the pronoun in parentheses that correctly completes each sentence. Then write the type of sentence in the blank: *simple, compound, complex,* or *compound-complex.*

_____complex_____   Though Gustav prepared for the worst, (she, he) hoped for the best.

_____simple_____   **1.** Kenny is waiting for (his, their) father to give him directions.

_____complex_____   **2.** Although Sonya hopes to win the scholarship, (she, he) is saving money for college.

_____compound_____   **3.** The Woo family invited us to dinner, and (we, they) returned the compliment by taking them to a movie.

_____simple_____   **4.** George and Rafi will perform (his, their) act at the talent show.

_____compound_____   **5.** Zina liked the acrobats, but (her, his) little sister preferred the clowns.

_____simple_____   **6.** A star displayed (their, its) brilliance in the night sky.

_____complex_____   **7.** Isra's uncle, (who, whom) often entertains, makes a special punch with cranberry juice and sparkling water.

_____simple_____   **8.** Chet (himself, itself) painted the new mural.

_____complex_____   **9.** Mikasi and Poloma brought their golf clubs, even though (she, they) do not expect to have time to play more than nine holes.

_____compound-complex_____   **10.** After Grandmother went back to school, (she, they) became a reporter, and we started watching her on the news.

_____complex_____   **11.** Hugh was not excited about watching the videotape of an erupting volcano because (he, it) has seen one in person.

_____simple_____   **12.** Keith's older brother taught (them, him) how to guide a horse.

_____simple_____   **13.** Basir's family is preparing food for (them, their) Kwanza celebration.

_____complex_____   **14.** Before Marcia mails the letter, ask (her, him) to see me.

_____complex_____   **15.** The person to (who, whom) Jenny wishes to speak is on vacation.

_____simple_____   **16.** The setting sun cast (its, their) last rays over the horizon.

_____compound_____   **17.** Ms. Ortiz planted that beautiful garden (himself, herself), yet she rarely visits it.

_____complex_____   **18.** The toddler loved his well-worn coat, though (he, it) was missing two buttons.

_____complex_____ **19.** Since Mr. Conti is selling (him, <u>his</u>) computer, he might be selling some of his software, too.

_____complex_____ **20.** Marcus, (<u>who</u>, whom) collects comic books, will send some books to the local children's hospital.

▶ **Exercise 2** **Complete each sentence by choosing the correct modifier in parentheses.**

Julian is a _____better_____ tennis player than Brad. (better, best)

1. Wilson performed _____well_____ at the piano recital. (good, well)

2. The sun shone _____more brightly_____ yesterday than today. (more brightly, most brightly)

3. That was the _____worst_____ television program Nick had ever seen. (worse, worst)

4. The Spanish club had _____fewer_____ refreshments at the March meeting than at the February meeting. (fewer, fewest)

5. The special effects in this movie are the _____greatest_____ I have seen. (greater, greatest)

6. Katherine felt _____bad_____ because she missed her mother's birthday. (bad, badly)

7. Tony makes the _____best_____ minestrone soup I have ever tasted. (better, best)

8. The _____most exciting_____ part of the entire journey occurred when Regina found the buried treasure. (more exciting, most exciting)

9. The hiking trail was _____more challenging_____ than the tourists expected. (more challenging, most challenging)

10. Blake selected the role with the _____fewest_____ lines to learn. (few, fewest)

11. Roberto's lemon cake was _____good_____, but his apple pie was extraordinary. (good, well)

12. Ms. Rollins felt _____worse_____ today than she did yesterday. (worse, worst)

13. This morning's balloon flight was _____more interesting_____ than yesterday's. (more interesting, most interesting)

14. Luigi insisted that galloping his horse through the forest was the _____most exhilarating_____ experience imaginable. (more exhilarating, most exhilarating)

15. Some critics believe the musical score was composed _____badly_____, but Dante credits the composer with inventiveness. (bad, badly)

16. Because of the misunderstanding, Julia found herself _____less_____ informed about the current situation. (less, least)

17. Tanya and Clarice appeared _____more willing_____ to volunteer their time than the other members of the club. (more willing, most willing)

18. The *Silver Arrow* is considered the _____fastest_____ train in this area. (faster, fastest)

19. My father is the _____wisest_____ person I know. (wiser, wisest)

20. Bonnie has been accepted into the advanced karate class even though she is _____*younger*_____ than the other students. (younger, youngest)

▶ **Exercise 3** **Underline the word in parentheses that correctly completes each sentence.**

The weather might (<u>affect</u>, effect) the team's chances of winning.

1. Patrick asked his sister if she was feeling (alright, <u>all right</u>).

2. Everyone wanted to go ice skating (accept, <u>except</u>) Kirsten.

3. Mr. Harper (could of, <u>could have</u>) given the twins a ride to the amusement park.

4. Ronda left her term paper (<u>between</u>, among) her notebook and her history book.

5. (Irregardless, <u>Regardless</u>) of the newspaper's account of the parade, ten bands marched in all.

6. My friend (<u>emigrated</u>, immigrated) from Italy when he was five years old.

7. The color guard will (<u>precede</u>, proceed) the first regiment.

8. (<u>Lay</u>, Lie) the basket on the shelf next to the other one.

9. First Frederica will show us the dance steps. (Than, <u>Then</u>) we will try them ourselves.

10. The players (respectfully, respectively) placed their hands over their hearts during the national anthem.

11. Ryan and Luisa have (<u>already</u>, all ready) finished their science fair project.

12. Each guest will (<u>bring</u>, take) one dish to the potluck dinner.

13. Dr. Carly will sit (<u>beside</u>, besides) Aunt Rose, and Justin will sit next to Anna.

14. The catcher (don't, <u>doesn't</u>) like to chase foul balls.

15. Roosevelt High School is (<u>farther</u>, further) from our school than Polk High School.

16. Rick (<u>passed</u>, past) all the necessary tests to become a lifeguard.

17. This week our cooking class will (<u>learn</u>, teach) how to make a soufflé.

18. Please do not (loose, <u>lose</u>) the concert tickets before we reach the theater.

19. The medal-winning gymnast glided through her routine (<u>like</u>, as) a gazelle.

20. The show choir will (<u>raise</u>, rise) their voices when the music indicates a crescendo.

21. (This here, <u>This</u>) program radiates wit and charm.

22. Grandmother used her finest china to (<u>set</u>, sit) the table for Thanksgiving dinner.

23. The new job had a definite (affect, <u>effect</u>) on Priscilla's family.

24. Delia's mother (hanged, <u>hung</u>) new draperies in the living room.

*M*echanics

Unit 11: Capitalization

Lesson 70
Capitalization of Sentences

Capitalize the first word of every sentence, including the first word of a direct quotation that is a complete sentence.

The new barn was built to stable fifteen horses.
Kerry smiled and said, "**Y**ou are the best coach in the whole school."

Capitalize the first word of a sentence in parentheses that stands by itself. Do not capitalize a sentence within parentheses if it is contained within another sentence.

Participation in soccer is growing rapidly. (**S**ome think the growth is too slow.)
Enrico asked for an instrument (**h**is first choice was a tenor saxophone) for his birthday.

Do not capitalize the first word of a quotation that cannot stand as a complete sentence.

The review praised the students as "**c**aring young citizens."

Do not capitalize an indirect quotation. An **indirect quotation** gives the meaning of an original statement without repeating it word for word. It is often introduced by the word *that.*

The brochure said that **b**rown bears are plentiful in the park.

▶ **Exercise 1** **Draw three lines under each letter that should be capitalized. If a sentence is correct, write *C* in the blank to the left of the sentence.**

_____ I looked everywhere for the book. (my dad wanted to borrow it.)

_____ **1.** the striking colors of autumn leaves are admired by nearly everyone.

_____ **2.** They come in varying shades of red, orange, and yellow. (when the sun shines on yellow leaves, they look bright gold!)

_____ **3.** those who must dispose of the fallen leaves (especially sanitation workers) seldom share the enthusiasm of mere observers.

__C___ **4.** Nature's autumn array serves as a reminder that a large, recurring problem has once more arrived.

_____ **5.** Burning leaves creates a pollution problem. (all the smoke and particles fill the air.)

_____ **6.** Burning leaves is also a fire hazard. (it must be done in a well-controlled environment and watched at all times.)

_____C_____ 7. Some municipalities (for these reasons) have banned the burning of leaves.

_____ 8. local governments have devised several methods of handling this annual problem.

_____ 9. mulching (chopping leaves into fine pieces) greatly reduces the volume of trash.

_____ 10. some cities require mulching before pick-up by the sanitation department.

_____C_____ 11. One way to accomplish mulching is to use a lawn mower with a special mulching blade.

_____ 12. A local newspaper states, "mulchers save our city thousands of dollars each year."

_____ 13. trash collection costs are lowered because of the tons of leaves that do not require

disposal.

_____ 14. mobile mulchers (lawn mowers) provide direct benefits, besides saving time and labor.

_____C_____ 15. Through the process of decomposition (leaf mulch decomposes quickly), the soil

becomes well fertilized.

_____C_____ 16. A magazine article states that mulching "provides long-lasting benefits to the soil."

_____ 17. An encyclopedia (referring to mulching) explains, "it helps the soil retain water by

reducing evaporation." (the encyclopedia also states that mulching helps reduce the

number of weeds.)

_____ 18. the leaves are also excellent (along with coffee grounds and grass clippings) to use for

compost.

_____ 19. compost makes soil more fertile to improve plant production.

_____C_____ 20. It is best to allow compost to decay (about three to six months) before using it.

_____C_____ 21. Karen (an avid gardener) says that she does not break up the leaves before composting.

_____ 22. Instead, she spreads the leaves over her garden for the winter. (she later tills them into

the soil in the spring.)

_____ 23. She also states, "leaves make a good mulch for roses."

_____C_____ 24. Leaf mulch also provides food for earthworms (which contribute to the growth of plants).

_____ 25. a nature magazine states that earthworms improve the soil by keeping it loose and aerated.

_____ 26. by reducing the strain on landfills and recycling the debris, everyone benefits.

_____ 27. returning the leaves to the soil changes a liability to an asset.

_____ 28. most people still use a rake (usually metal or bamboo) to rake their leaves.

_____ 29. leaf blowers, however, have become popular replacements for lawn rakes.

_____C_____ 30. Leaf blowers can be either gas or electric (see your local hardware store).

Mechanics

Name _____ Class _____ Date _____

Lesson 71
Capitalization of Proper Nouns

Capitalize names of individuals. Capitalize titles used before a name or in place of it. Capitalize titles that specify family relationships when they are used with a person's name or in place of it.

Vincent van **G**ogh	Catherine the **G**reat	**P**ope **P**ius XII
Governor **R**ichards	How do you do, **G**overnor?	Have you seen the **g**overnor?
This is **A**unt Jane.	Where is **D**ad?	This is my **a**unt.

Also capitalize these names, terms, and titles: ethnic and national groups, languages, religious terms; organizations, institutions, political parties and their members (but not the word *party*), firms; monuments, buildings, bridges, and other structures; trade names; documents, awards, laws; geographical and calendar terms, historical events and periods; planets and other heavenly bodies; compass points (but not directional words); ships, trains, aircraft; specific school courses; titles of literary and artistic works.

Native Americans	Nobel Prize	Saturn
Swahili	Asia	the Northwest
Greek Orthodox	Rhode Island	west of town
Passover	Dallas	*Titanic*
the University of Iowa	Nile River	World Cultures II
Republican party	Elm Street	world history
Ford Motor Company	Monday	the *Iliad*
Empire State Building	February	"The Lottery"
Golden Gate Bridge	Memorial Day	*Boston Globe*
the Meadowlands	Civil War	"Stardust"
Kleenex tissues	Iron Age	*The Bull from the Sea*
the Bill of Rights		

▶ **Exercise 1 Draw three lines under each lowercase letter that should be capitalized. Strike through (B̸) each capitalized letter that should be lowercase.**

Kara's oil Portraits resemble the paintings of grandma Moses.

1. The new girl's Name was Althea Smithson.

2. His Grandfather's diary told of meeting president Roosevelt.

3. Are you one of doctor Johnson's patients?

4. Alaina works after school as a Volunteer at mercy hospital.

5. Have you met my Mother?

6. The ending was corny, complete with a rendition of "Home On The Range."

7. While in France, we must visit the eiffel tower.

8. Have you ever been to Yellowstone national park?

9. His accent was a musical mixture of english and italian.

10. Japan and the united States are separated by the pacific ocean.

11. When did president Lincoln issue the emancipation proclamation?

12. According to *the world book encyclopedia,* Henry Hudson explored hudson strait and Hudson bay while looking for the northwest passage.

13. Jerry's telescope is powerful enough to see the Moons of Jupiter.

14. Leonard Bernstein was a renowned conductor of the new york philharmonic.

15. Do you have señora Perez for Freshman Spanish?

16. Is the mississippi river one of the borders of Illinois?

17. Political unrest in the middle east caused great concern for the tourists.

18. Have you read the memoirs of the Native American chief Red Fox?

19. The Empire state building was once the tallest building in the world.

20. Our space program suffered a serious setback with the *challenger* mishap.

21. Joy earns outstanding grades in latin, english, and algebra.

22. Consuelo hopes to get a Basketball scholarship at the university of North Carolina.

23. The first african american to play in the american league was Larry doby.

24. I just had a visit from father Mulcahy.

25. Chariot races were regular features at circus maximus in Ancient Rome.

26. The Islamic book of holy writings is called the quran.

27. The adams high school french club meets every other thursday.

28. A favorite christmas story is *the gift of the magi.*

29. One of our gold depositories is located at fort Knox, Kentucky.

30. Many employees of the Chrysler corporation belong to the united automobile workers, one of the largest labor unions in the united states.

31. Maria and Harvey ate dinner at the olde town inn.

32. A joint session of congress includes members of both the house of representatives and The senate.

33. My cousin took astronomy 101 when she went to College in the Midwest.

34. I read an article about Sports Cars in last month's *car and driver* magazine.

35. During world war II, my Grandmother worked with the red cross in the philippine islands.

Lesson 72
Capitalization of Proper Adjectives

Capitalize **proper adjectives** (adjectives formed from proper nouns). Most proper adjectives fit into the following categories:

1. Adjectives formed from names of people

Victorian architecture	**J**effersonian politics
Gregorian chant	**C**linton administration
Elizabethan poetry	**N**apoleonic era

2. Adjectives formed from specific days or holidays, place names, and names of national, ethnic, and religious groups

Hungarian goulash	**C**hristmas decorations
Australian folklore	**H**ispanic students
Thursday evening	**J**ewish synagogue

▶ **Exercise 1** Draw three lines under each lowercase letter that should be capitalized. Strike through (ℬ) each capitalized letter that should be lowercase.

The carter Administration dealt with oil shortages, rising tax rates, and the iranian Hostage situation.

1. The book of japanese fairytales was beautifully illustrated.

2. Jamal and Kenny always enjoyed hearing Holiday tales.

3. Many people find it quite surprising to see gregorian chants are becoming popular these days.

4. Carlita is particularly fond of chinese food.

5. A tasty pizza topping is canadian bacon.

6. The stranger looked as though he had stepped out of a dickensian novel.

7. The company performed a wagnerian opera.

8. Many interesting tales are found in swedish folklore.

9. Communism was based on marxist doctrines.

10. Do may flowers really come from april showers?

11. Some holidays have Religious origins; others have secular roots.

12. The entire community looked forward to the annual italian festivities.

13. The tibetan Terrain can be treacherous.

14. There are german polkas as well as polish polkas.

15. The library at Main and Elm is a good example of georgian architecture.

Mechanics

16. Masaccio is credited as the founder of renaissance painting.

17. Randall Cunningham is a great american Football star.

18. The buffet menu included swedish meatballs.

19. Alice wanted to vacation on the mediterranean coast.

20. The Heritage Festival featured a thrilling demonstration of african tribal chants.

21. There are so many arthurian tales, it is difficult to separate history from myth.

22. The basketball team reviews game films every monday evening.

23. Every room of the old mansion contained a franklin stove.

24. Originating on an island in the English Channel, jersey cattle provide the richest milk of all breeds.

25. My irish setter has a mahogany coat.

26. The entire family enjoyed watching disney movies.

27. What was the highlight of your caribbean cruise?

28. Forty-one democratic governors attended the conference.

29. The United States imports large amounts of colombian coffee.

30. Israeli Troops protect all residents of the country.

31. James Borland is an english Professor.

32. Tanya played a hungarian polka on her accordion.

33. We visited a Gettysburg Battlefield on our trip.

34. Molly owned recordings of all nine Beethoven Symphonies.

35. After yom kippur services at Temple Beth Shalom, we continued to fast until sundown.

36. The Dogwood tree in the backyard has beautiful white blossoms.

37. We carved our halloween pumpkin on a warm october day.

38. Luba went to her grandmother's house for thanksgiving dinner and ate turkey.

39. I would love to own a steinway Grand Piano.

40. Beverly Sills, the great american Operatic Soprano, sang with the Metropolitan Opera.

Mechanics

✓ Unit 11 **Review**

▶ **Exercise** **Correct the capitalization in each sentence. Draw three lines under each lowercase letter that should be capitalized and a single slash (ℬ) through any capital letters that should be lowercase.**

Mr. osborne, my ℛeport on the jazz age is finished.

1. leif erikson was a norse explorer who came to north america.

2. Thick ice buries most of antarctica, the ℂontinent that surrounds the south pole.

3. *Gone With The Wind* is a classic american novel.

4. The ℙostman delivered an invitation to Achim's ℊraduation party.

5. small in stature, mother Teresa is a giant in caring.

6. The Gotham City philatelic society meets on Wednesday ℰvenings. (philately is the hobby of stamp collecting.)

7. Rolanda had great difficulty (ℌhe loves languages) deciding whether to study german or spanish.

8. Karin was honored with the employee-of-the-month award.

9. Lord Byron once wrote, "the vile are only vain; the great are proud."

10. Which roman ruler was first called caesar?

11. the hiking party gave a wide berth to the ℳild ℬoar.

12. Little John and robin hood lived in Sherwood forest.

13. The Monroe doctrine remains controversial to this day.

14. "I Want to Hold Your Hand" was a great beatles hit.

15. The first nuclear-powered submarine (the Uss *nautilus*) sailed under the ice at the North pole.

16. *ursa major* is the scientific name for the big dipper.

17. Anton studied shakespearean drama at the ℳniversity.

18. At the mortgage-burning ceremony, president Masterson received the ℱitle ℙeed from the vice president of the bank.

19. The Toyota is a ℂar that originated in japan.

20. There was no World Series in the ℳutumn of 1994 because of the ℬaseball strike.

Mechanics

Cumulative Review: Units 1–11

▶ **Exercise 1** Underline each adjective or adverb clause. Draw an arrow from the clause to the word it modifies. In the blank, write *adj.* (adjective) or *adv.* (adverb) to tell what kind of clause it is.

__adj.__   We took the highway that runs south from here.

__adj.__   **1.** There may come a time when you will need my phone number.

__adv.__   **2.** I shall visit Aspen, Colorado, if I can afford it.

__adv.__   **3.** While we were gone, Mr. Salazar cared for our pets.

__adv.__   **4.** The meeting began earlier than we had expected.

__adj.__   **5.** The city from which I came is a large metropolis.

__adj.__   **6.** The exchange student that you met was from Spain.

__adv.__   **7.** Do not give your opinion unless you are asked.

__adj.__   **8.** Sam's proudest possession was a baseball that was signed by Roberto Alomar.

__adv.__   **9.** Our soccer team played a great defensive game although they finally lost.

__adv.__   **10.** When you called, I was raking the leaves.

__adj.__   **11.** Uncle Leo, to whom I told my crazy dream, just laughed and laughed.

__adj.__   **12.** Monet is the artist whose paintings are on display.

__adj.__   **13.** The Iowa farmer, whose place I bought, moved to southern California.

__adv.__   **14.** Apply an ice pack if your knee begins to swell.

__adv.__   **15.** Whenever it storms, our roof leaks.

__adj.__   **16.** The necklace that I like is too expensive.

__adv.__   **17.** After I do my homework, I can go to the movies.

__adj.__   **18.** The house where my grandmother grew up was torn down.

__adj.__   **19.** The rancher whom we asked for directions was very helpful.

__adv.__   **20.** Hakeem, running as fast as he was able, finished the race first.

Mechanics

▶ **Exercise 2 Underline the correct word or words in parentheses.**

Sean planned the student council meeting (good, <u>well</u>).

1. The play we saw last weekend was very (<u>good</u>, well).

2. The deer ran (<u>more swiftly</u>, most swiftly) through the open field than the fox.

3. The teacher gave the students (a, <u>an</u>) example to follow as they were working out the equation.

4. Simba was the (most noisiest, <u>noisiest</u>) puppy in the litter.

5. After little preparation, he performed (bad, <u>badly</u>) on the test.

6. The principal's reprimand had little (<u>effect</u>, affect) on the unruly student.

7. A dark and shrouded figure emerged (sudden, <u>suddenly</u>) from the house.

8. Of all the fresh vegetables, I like beets (less, <u>the least</u>).

9. Matt, our star basketball player, was taller (<u>than</u>, then) Mr. Cooper.

10. The abandoned building across the street is the (<u>oldest</u>, most oldest) in the city.

11. My elderly aunt has (a, <u>an</u>) honest face.

12. (Beside, <u>Besides</u>) soup and salad, they had a croissant.

13. The peaceful protest (<u>proceeded</u>, preceded) through the capital city.

14. Bananas appear to ripen more quickly than (any, <u>any other</u>) fruit.

15. My friend never eats (no, <u>any</u>) candy.

16. The crowd listened (<u>respectfully</u>, respectively) as the minister eulogized the hero.

17. I will (<u>accept</u>, except) full responsibility for my brother's actions.

18. Columbus is (further, <u>farther</u>) south than Cleveland.

19. These hiking boots are (<u>cleaner</u>, more cleaner) than yours.

20. Mrs. Ichiko (<u>immigrated</u>, emigrated) to the United States in 1968.

21. Yesterday, it snowed so hard we (couldn't hardly, <u>could hardly</u>) see the highway.

22. (Irregardless, <u>Regardless</u>) of what my opponents say, I am (a, <u>an</u>) avid supporter of the school levy.

▶ **Exercise 3 Draw three lines under each lowercase letter that should be capitalized. For each italicized word write in the blank *com.* (common noun) or *prop.* (proper noun).**

<u>com.</u>   Two famous *landmarks* in Washington, D.C., are the lincoln memorial and the capitol.

<u>prop.</u> **1.** While in the west, our family climbed *pikes peak* in rocky mountain national park.

<u>com.</u> **2.** In american history *class* we are studying world war II.

Mechanics

com. **3.** because of the baseball *strike,* the world series wasn't held in 1994.

prop. **4.** great changes took place during the *industrial revolution.*

prop. **5.** The boat navigated the ohio river from *Cincinnati* to Louisville.

com. **6.** I read an *article* about martin luther king jr. in last sunday's newspaper.

com. **7.** The fourth of july is an american *holiday.*

prop. **8.** When in *chicago,* we went to the top of the sears tower.

com. **9.** on our *flight* from san francisco to sacramento, we flew over yosemite national park.

prop. **10.** the metropolitan museum of art is located in *new york city.*

com. **11.** For thanksgiving dinner we took grandma and grandpa to a *restaurant.*

prop. **12.** On *may* 20, 1927, charles lindbergh touched down near paris, france.

com. **13.** tutankhamen reigned as *king* of egypt from about 1347 B.C. to 1339 B.C.

com. **14.** My most difficult *courses* in school are geography and spanish.

prop. **15.** *india,* a country found in southern asia, was once a british colony.

prop. **16.** linus pauling, an american chemist, received two *nobel prizes.*

com. **17.** My sister's favorite *book* is by laura ingalls wilder.

prop. **18.** The navajo are the largest Native American group in the *united states.*

com. **19.** the indianapolis 500 automobile *race* is held every memorial day weekend.

com. **20.** The massive *steamboat* rolled lazily along the mississippi river.

prop. **21.** *pope john paul II* met with the President at the white house.

prop. **22.** The *brooklyn bridge* spans the east river from Brooklyn to manhattan island.

Mechanics

Unit 12: Punctuation, Abbreviations, and Numbers

Lesson 73
End Punctuation: Period, Exclamation Point, and Question Mark

---

Use a **period** at the end of a declarative sentence and at the end of a polite command.

Declarative Sentence: The computer room is at the end of the hall.
Polite Command: Please close the door when you leave the room.

Use an **exclamation point** to show strong feeling and indicate a forceful command.

Oh, my gosh!   What a great jacket!   Watch out!   Jump!

Use a **question mark** to indicate a direct question.

Who knows the answer to the riddle?   Is this the right bus stop?

Do not place a question mark after an indirect question (one that has been reworded so that it is part of a declarative sentence).

Jason wondered whether he would be accepted into the program.
She asked if she could hand in her paper early.

▶ **Exercise 1 Place a check in the blank next to each sentence that has correct end punctuation.**

__✔__   Where are we going after the game?

__✔__ **1.** Most people have heard of the Nobel Prize.

_____ **2.** Six prizes are given each year to outstanding people in various fields!

__✔__ **3.** The six fields are physics, medicine or physiology, literature, chemistry, peace, and economics.

_____ **4.** Do you know which one is the most recently created.

_____ **5.** The economics prize was awarded for the first time in 1969!

_____ **6.** The other prizes have been given for more than 90 years?

_____ **7.** The prizes were created by a Swedish industrialist and inventor named Alfred Nobel!

__✔__ **8.** Nobel, who lived from 1833 to 1896, became fascinated by explosives when he was working in his father's factory in Russia.

_____ **9.** The young Alfred invented a process in which an explosive called *nitroglycerine* could be exploded in a controlled situation?

_✔_ **10.** Even though he was a gifted inventor, Nobel never attended a university.

_✔_ **11.** In fact, he attended school for only one year!

_____ **12.** Nitroglycerine proved to be a dangerous material to work with, and several explosions in Nobel's factories caused many deaths?

_✔_ **13.** Among the people who died in a factory in Sweden was Alfred's younger brother, Emil.

_____ **14.** Eventually he discovered a way to mix nitroglycerine with a kind of sandy clay!

_____ **15.** The clay made the nitroglycerine more stable and less likely to explode unexpectedly?

_✔_ **16.** The new blasting product was put to many peaceful uses, such as mining, road construction, and tunnel building.

_____ **17.** Nobel's invention, which he called *dynamite,* also became a weapon of war!

_____ **18.** The inventor wondered if he could do something to promote peace and good will among people to make up for the deadly uses of his invention?

_✔_ **19.** A very rich man at the time of his death, Alfred Nobel decided his money should be used to create prizes for those who had helped the world's people.

_✔_ **20.** In this amazing way, the inventor of a deadly explosive honors people who have saved lives!

▶ **Exercise 2** **Complete each sentence by adding a period, an exclamation point, or a question mark as needed.**

I can't believe I'm going to Europe **!**

1. Sweden, the homeland of Alfred Nobel, is an interesting and beautiful country **.**

2. Do you have any idea how far north this country is **?**

3. Many North Americans are surprised to learn that Sweden is as far north as Hudson Bay **!** *or* **.**

4. In spite of its northerly location, Sweden has a temperate climate **.**

5. Winters are long and cold, but the summers can be quite warm **.**

6. In northernmost Sweden during the winter, the sun never rises above the horizon **!** *or* **.**

7. How would twenty-four hours of darkness affect you **?**

8. Many Swedes who live above the Arctic Circle combat the gloom by lighting candles **.**

9. This desire to spread light in the darkness of winter is the basis for the holiday honoring Saint Lucia, which charms each year's Nobel Prize winners **.**

10. Because of the tilt of the earth, a summer day in northern Sweden lasts for twenty-four glorious hours **!** *or* **.**

11. Swedes celebrate the warm weather and bright days on the country's most beloved holiday **.**

12. June 24, *Midsommardag*—Midsummer Day—is a glorious festival of merrymaking **.**

Lesson 74
Colons

Use a **colon** to introduce a list, especially after a statement that uses words such as *these*, *the following*, or *as follows*.

Denise has lived in these three cities: Albuquerque, Sacramento, and Boulder.

The following students should report to the guidance counselor's office: Dwight Robinson, Angela Martinez, Michael Byrne, and Li Chen.

Do not use a colon to introduce a list if the list immediately follows a verb or a preposition.

Among the prizes offered were a camera, a calculator, and a radio.

The people at the next table ordered their pizza with green peppers, onions, black olives, and anchovies.

Use a colon to introduce a long or formal quotation. A formal quotation is often preceded by words such as *this*, *these*, *the following*, or *as follows*.

The governor repeated the following words of Motavato, chief of the Southern Cheyennes: "Although wrongs have been done to me, I live in hopes. I have not got two hearts."

Use a colon between the hour and minute of the precise time, between the chapter and verse in biblical references, and after the salutation of a business letter.

1:25 P.M.	Job 6:1–8	Sir or Madam:
8:57 A.M.	Leviticus 4:22–27	Dear Ms. Rayburn:

▶ **Exercise 1** **Insert a colon where necessary. If the sentence is correct, write *C* in the blank.**

_____ You will need the following tools:a hammer, a screwdriver, and a wrench.

_____ **1.** The school bus came every morning at about 745.

__C__ **2.** The animals I liked best at the zoo were the elephants, the giraffes, the electric eels, and the baboons.

_____ **3.** Many people remember President John F. Kennedy's famous statement from his inaugural address:"Ask not what your country can do for you; ask what you can do for your country."

__C__ **4.** Don't forget the following items: a bathrobe, soap, slippers, a towel, and a washcloth.

__C__ **5.** I'll pick you up at 7:30 sharp.

__C__ **6.** The most popular sports in the United States are football, basketball, and baseball.

_____ **7.** Try to deliver the package between 1145 and 1215.

_____ **8.** I'll never forget his final words:"Don't look back—something might be gaining on you."

___C___ **9.** To whom it may concern:

_____ **10.** The following are the main steps in booting up the computer:1. turn the unit on; 2. log on; 3. select the software program you want.

___C___ **11.** Their study group had written a song using Hamlet's famous speech: "To be or not to be; that is the question."

___C___ **12.** A tin-roof sundae is made from vanilla ice cream, chocolate syrup, peanuts, and whipped cream.

___C___ **13.** This morning's reading is from the book of Luke 7:15–22.

_____ **14.** Make sure you follow this advice:Neither a borrower nor a lender be.

___C___ **15.** Ms. Richardson asked if we knew who the author of the novel was.

_____ **16.** The essay for the contest had to be on the following subject:former House Speaker Thomas "Tip" O'Neill's saying that all politics is local.

___C___ **17.** The last three people in line were Jason, Mary-Margaret, and Dawn.

_____ **18.** Our presentation consisted of the following:a report, a bulletin board, an audiotape, and a fashion show.

___C___ **19.** The following books were chosen by the group: *Middlemarch, The Old Man and the Sea, Song of Solomon, Wuthering Heights,* and *The Scarlet Letter.*

_____ **20.** When it's 11:00 in the morning in New York, it's 4:00 in the afternoon in London.

___C___ **21.** The fencing club's poster had a picture of a fencer, followed by the caption: "Fencing—try it once and you'll get the point!"

_____ **22.** My dad's favorite song has the line:"Life's a hotel at best; you're here as a guest."

___C___ **23.** To make popcorn, follow these instructions: 1. add the oil to the pan; 2. pour in the popcorn; 3. shake the pan over the heat as the popcorn pops.

_____ **24.** These are the magazines she read regularly:*Time, Newsweek, Sports Illustrated,* and *People.*

___C___ **25.** The children's favorite vegetables were corn, broccoli, peas, and carrots.

___C___ **26.** The police officer took the 6:15 train to Haverford.

_____ **27.** Angela's parents grew these crops:soybeans, corn, wheat, and oats.

_____ **28.** The following streets will be closed for curb repair:Main Street, Broad Street, High Street, M.L. King Drive, Southwest Boulevard, and Northern Lights Avenue.

Lesson 75
Semicolons

Use a semicolon to separate main clauses that are not joined by a coordinating conjunction (*and, but, or, nor, yet,* and *for*).

She can't play the saxophone, but I know she'd like to learn.
She can't play the saxophone; I know she'd like to learn.

Use a semicolon to separate main clauses joined by a conjunctive adverb (such as *however, therefore, nevertheless, moreover, furthermore,* and *subsequently*) or by an expression such as *for example* or *that is.* In general, a conjunctive adverb or expression such as *for example* is followed by a comma.

Some people in our group refused to take the assignment seriously; therefore, we received a *D* on our project.

Use a semicolon to separate the items in a series when the items contain commas.

Italians have created an almost unlimited number of pasta shapes and sizes, among them *orecchiete,* which means "little ears"; *capellini,* or "angel hair"; and *orzo,* which look like small grains of rice.

Use a semicolon to separate two main clauses joined by a coordinating conjunction when the clauses already contain several commas.

The book was very long, almost six hundred pages, and contained more than seventy-five characters, which made keeping track of them difficult; but I loved it anyway and would recommend it to anyone.

▶ **Exercise 1** **Place a check on the blank next to each sentence that is correct.**

_✔_   Kristy, who finished first, won the trophy; however, Marla won the award for most improved.

_____ **1.** Nobel Prizes are awarded each year in six areas; which are physics, chemistry, physiology or medicine, literature, peace, and economics.

_✔_ **2.** The prizes were created by Swedish inventor Alfred Nobel; they are administered by various organizations in Sweden and Norway.

_____ **3.** Five of the six prizes are given by Swedish organizations for example, the physics, chemistry, and economics prizes are awarded by the Royal Academy of Sciences.

_✔_ **4.** The sixth prize, for peace, is awarded by a committee appointed by the Norwegian parliament; how it came to receive this duty is an interesting story.

_____ **5.** During Alfred Nobel's life, Norway belonged to Sweden; and the inventor stated in his will that Norway should award the peace prize.

Mechanics

_____ **6.** Today, even though Norway and Sweden are separate and independent countries, which came about early in this century, the Norwegians have kept the right to award the peace prize, it is a source of pride to all Norwegians.

__✔__ **7.** Winners of a Nobel Prize receive a cash award from Alfred Nobel's estate; the award is currently worth about $950,000.

_____ **8.** Up to three people may share the prize, for example, the prizes in science and peace are often awarded to several people.

_____ **9.** Winners of the different prizes are usually announced in October or November; late in the year.

__✔__ **10.** Winners receive their prizes in a ceremony on December 10, the anniversary of Alfred Nobel's death; these include a gold medal, a diploma, and a check.

_____ **11.** During Nobel week in Sweden, many festivities take place; that is, banquets, dances, parties, and receptions.

__✔__ **12.** Nobel week takes place at the same time as the Swedish holiday honoring Saint Lucia; consequently, prizewinners are serenaded by groups of young girls who also take part in a pageant on December 13.

__✔__ **13.** One young girl, wearing the traditional costume of a white robe and a crown of candles, represents the saint; others dress as her attendants.

_____ **14.** Prizewinners also give lectures during Nobel week; their only obligation.

__✔__ **15.** Many famous scientists, writers, and world political figures have won Nobel Prizes; however, many others have not.

_____ **16.** The decisions of the various committees are often criticized, no one can make a perfect decision every time.

_____ **17.** Some of the greatest writers of this century were passed over by the Swedish Academy, the committee that awards the prize in literature; for example, Virginia Woolf, Marcel Proust, and James Joyce.

__✔__ **18.** Some peace prizes have also gone to controversial figures; these include Henry Kissinger, U.S. secretary of state, and Yasir Arafat, leader of the Palestine Liberation Organization.

_____ **19.** In setting up the prizes; Alfred Nobel wrote only that the prizes should go to those who have "conferred the greatest benefit" on the world's people.

__✔__ **20.** The roster of Nobel Prize winners contains some of the greatest figures in the scientific, literary, and diplomatic life of the last hundred years; no other award is held in higher regard.

Mechanics

Lesson 76
Commas and Compound Sentences

Use **commas** between the main clauses in a compound sentence. Place a comma before a coordinating conjunction (*and, but, or, nor, yet,* or *for*) that joins two main clauses.

The members of the choir went to the concert, and the artists' group went to the museum.

Many tourists visit Miami in the summer, but most people go during the colder months.

You may omit the comma between very short main clauses that are connected by a coordinating conjunction unless the comma is needed to avoid confusion.

Dad raked the leaves and I washed the car. (clear)
I went to English class and gym comes next. (confusing)
I went to English class, and gym comes next. (clear)

▶ **Exercise 1 Add commas where necessary. Cross out commas used incorrectly using the delete symbol (⌒). Some sentences may be correct.**

On Saturday we visited Capitol Hill,and tomorrow we want to visit the monuments.

1. Many important discoveries in the field of science are the result of work done by women,and the achievements of Dorothy Crowfoot Hodgkin are no exception.

2. Dorothy Crowfoot was born in Egypt and moved to England when she was a child.

3. Her parents were English educators living in Cairo,and Dorothy spent the first four years of her life in the Egyptian city.

4. Her father was interested in archaeology,and her mother shared his interest by collecting unusual plants and studying ancient methods of weaving cloth.

5. While at school in England, Dorothy first learned about the science of chemistry,and her interest was to lead her to a scientific career.

6. She became fascinated by the study of crystals⌒and even set up a small laboratory in her family's home when she was 14.

7. Certain natural substances are actually made up of tiny crystals,but many people do not know that even aspirin is crystalline.

8. Substances made of crystals can look quite different,yet all crystals share important characteristics.

9. All crystals are solid, and have regular shapes.

10. Patterns in crystals repeat themselves over and over, and crystals with flawless repetition are said to be perfect.

11. Dorothy finished high school, and she decided to attend Oxford University.

12. Dorothy studied at Oxford for four years, but then she received an offer to be an assistant to a famous chemist at the University of Cambridge.

13. She became familiar with a research technique called X-ray diffraction, and this method became one of the foundations of her career as a scientist.

14. Later she returned to Oxford to teach and do research.

15. She received a laboratory space in which to work and continued her studies of crystals, but another element soon appeared in her life.

16. She met a young man named Thomas Hodgkin, and the couple was married a short time later.

17. World War II began shortly after her marriage, but Dorothy's work was not interrupted.

18. The war led to Dorothy's first major scientific success, and her discovery was to have far-reaching consequences.

19. A British scientist named Alexander Fleming had several years earlier discovered a special mold that could destroy harmful bacteria.

20. The mold was called penicillin, and it grew naturally.

21. Doctors knew that penicillin could cure diseases caused by bacteria, yet it was available in such small quantities that it could not be used in widespread applications.

22. It was a medical dream to learn to "grow" penicillin artificially in a laboratory, for then it could be manufactured in large quantities.

23. Dorothy started to work on this problem, but it proved to be very difficult to crystallize the penicillin molecules.

24. Dorothy and her assistants analyzed the structure of penicillin using the X-ray diffraction technique, and the discoveries they made changed the history of medicine.

25. Penicillin and similar drugs can now be manufactured in large quantities, but this breakthrough could not have been achieved without the work of Dorothy Crowfoot Hodgkin's team of scientists.

Mechanics

Lesson 77
Commas in a Series and Between Coordinate Adjectives

Use **commas** to separate three or more words, phrases, or clauses in a series.

Josh caught the pass, dodged a tackler, and sprinted for the goal line.

No commas are necessary when all of the items are connected by conjunctions.

She was the kindest and wisest and gentlest person I have ever known.

Nouns that are used in pairs (*bread and butter, sweet and innocent, bacon and eggs*) are usually considered single units and should not be separated by commas. If such pairs appear with other nouns or groups of nouns in a series, they must be separated from the other items in the series.

The storm is expected to cause *thunder and lightning,* heavy rains, and gusting winds.

Place a comma between coordinate adjectives that precede a noun. **Coordinate adjectives** modify a noun equally. To determine whether adjectives are coordinate, try to reverse their order or put the word *and* between them. If the sentence still sounds natural, the adjectives are coordinate.

The sergeant ordered a slow (and) cautious (and) orderly approach.
The sergeant ordered a slow, cautious, orderly approach.

▶ **Exercise 1 Add commas where necessary. Delete (⅄) unnecessary commas. Some sentences may be correct.**

The weather today will be warm, sunny, and windy.

1. Her pen rolled off her desk, onto the floor, and under the cabinet.

2. Sheep, cattle, poultry, and swine are all raised in Ohio.

3. My mouth is watering just thinking about those big, juicy tomatoes!

4. Darnay wanted to borrow my best ⅄ red pen for the interview.

5. Would you like mashed potatoes ⅄ or baked potatoes ⅄ or scalloped potatoes?

6. The audience loved the movie, cheered at the end, and left happy and satisfied.

7. The Montinis have just put in a new ⅄ wooden deck.

8. He often said that people could either lead, follow, or get out of the way.

9. The little ⅄ brown house on Adams Street is for sale again.

10. Logging, cattle farming, and mining all pose a threat to the Amazon basin's rain forest.

11. Rita looked out on the playground, saw the child fall, and ran out to help him.

12. Thomas enjoys both hiking ⅄ and fishing.

Mechanics

13. The man had a black⸼and blue bruise on his leg,a cut on his forehead,and a scratch on his hand.

14. Don't eat the food, don't drink the water, and don't breathe the air—then you'll be fine!

15. My dad put the new lamp in our⸼dining room.

16. The spring beauty is a little⸼pink⸼and white flower that blooms in early March.

17. Alaska is the biggest state,Rhode Island is the smallest,and California has the most people.

18. The character was pictured as a rough-and-ready,ornery, and argumentative frontiersman.

19. Her favorite vegetables are carrots, green beans, and zucchini.

20. Raymont was having a hard time choosing between the Toyota⸼and the Mercury⸼and the Pontiac.

21. They took a trip to Vermont to see the beautiful⸼fall colors.

22. The woods echoed with the sounds of birds, insects, and different⸼kinds of small mammals.

23. We went on the roller coaster, the Ferris wheel, and the bumper cars.

24. The strange bird we saw was yellow⸼and blue.

25. He had never been on an airplane,a bus, or a train!

26. Wait in this line,get your ticket,and take it to the cashier.

27. My birthday was a cold and drizzly and miserable day.

28. He yelled that he was sick⸼and tired of the way they treated their cat.

29. The bus stopped in Dayton,Springfield,Columbus,and Zanesville.

30. I presented my report, asked if there were any questions, and then turned the meeting over to the president.

31. It was so hot that we took off our shoes and socks,hats,and jackets.

32. The people of the community are its most valuable,important resource.

33. The political candidate solicited money, bought TV time,and ran newspaper ads⸼for his campaign.

34. The members of the Spanish Club always served ham and bean,chicken and noodle,and vegetable beef soups on election night.

35. The red, velvety coals from the campfire were glowing in the dark.

36. The long,winding,steep trail was the cause of a hot,dusty,and exhausting hike.

37. Teri wanted the small spotted puppy, but her sister liked the big golden retriever.

38. That new restaurant makes the juiciest⸼and tastiest⸼and biggest hamburgers in town.

Mechanics

Lesson 78
Commas and Nonessential Elements

Use **commas** to set off nonessential participles and infinitives and their phrases (see Lesson 19, pp. 91-92, and Lesson 21, pp. 95-96). Do not set off essential phrases.

Waving, the man came toward us. (nonessential)
The man **waving to my mother** is my uncle. (essential)
Her goal, **to become a doctor,** has finally been achieved. (nonessential)
To win is her goal. (essential)

Use **commas** to set off nonessential adjective clauses (see Lesson 26, pp. 107–110). Do not set off essential clauses.

Bangkok, **which is the capital of Thailand,** is an intriguing city. (nonessential)
People **who live in glass houses** shouldn't throw stones. (essential)

Use **commas** to set off nonessential appositives (see Lesson 20, p. 94). Do not set off essential appositives.

My brother, **Bill,** loves cars. (nonessential—The writer has only one brother.)
My brother **Bill** loves cars. (essential—The writer has more than one brother.)

Use **commas** to set off interjections (such as *oh* and *well*) and parenthetical expressions (such as *on the other hand* and *without a doubt*).

Oh, I can hardly believe it!
Last year, **on the other hand,** you could have taken journalism.

▶ **Exercise 1 Insert commas where necessary. Delete (⌒) unnecessary commas. Some sentences may be correct.**

John went to the restaurant⌒to eat lunch.

1. Just thinking about the test⌒made her nervous.

2. Abraham Lincoln,an Illinois congressman,was born in Kentucky.

3. An old bicycle,battered and rusted,lay in the creek.

4. The actress went to school in Nashville,the capital of Tennessee.

5. Robert,breathing heavily,ran an extra lap around the track.

6. OK,you win.

7. Franklin's father, to be honest, is not interested in baseball.

8. Walking to school⌒is good exercise.

9. Russell,walking to school,wondered how the tryouts would go.

10. To save enough money to buy a pair of in-line skates⌒was his goal.

Mechanics

11. The performance, which we rehearsed for two months, was a smashing success!

12. The car, that the drunk driver hit, was totally demolished.

13. The little dog with the jeweled collar was behaving badly.

14. Oh, I suppose you're right about that.

15. Disappointed by his performance, Harry left the room.

16. Someone who is really interested in animals, should get the job at the zoo.

17. To grow cactuses at home is not easy.

18. To prevent computer damage, many people use surge protectors.

19. I have the strangest feeling, that something peculiar is about to happen.

20. Our tour guide, the young man in the safari hat, is a native of Kenya.

21. All students will, of course, be responsible for their own lunches.

22. Animals that are active at night are said to be nocturnal.

23. It was obvious that the man, getting off the plane, was her father.

24. Colorado Springs, where I was born, is in central Colorado.

25. That coat is, without a doubt, the warmest one I have ever owned.

26. Yes, I now understand the assignment.

27. A coyote, howling sadly, added a lonely feeling to the fall evening.

28. Melissa, who loves all sports, also finds writing poetry enjoyable.

29. To be a loyal friend, is an admirable quality.

30. You would enjoy Mesa Verde National Park, a place I have visited.

31. Our committee will have the list of nominees tomorrow, by the way.

32. Is the young lion, standing on that ledge, one of the zoo's new animals?

33. The Statue of Liberty is a symbol that represents opportunity.

34. The woman, sitting on the bench, is my aunt.

▶ **Writing Link** **Write a paragraph about your favorite entertainer. Use one adjective clause, one interjection, and one parenthetical expression.**

_____

_____

_____

_____

Mechanics

Lesson 79
Commas and Introductory Phrases

Use a **comma** after a short introductory prepositional phrase (see Lesson 18, pp. 89–90) only if the sentence would be misread without it. (However, a comma setting off a short introductory prepositional phrase is not incorrect.)

For the children inside, the playhouse seemed like a magical world. (comma needed to prevent misreading)

During the winter the building is drafty. (comma not needed)

Use a **comma** after a long prepositional phrase or after the final phrase in a succession of phrases.

During the exciting game's final three minutes, the fans began to cheer wildly.

In the middle of the night on the stroke of twelve, the man's eyes opened wide and he stared into the darkness.

Do not use a **comma** if the phrase is immediately followed by a verb.

In the middle of the train station stood the famous writer.

Use commas to set off introductory participles and participial phrases. (See Lesson 19, pp. 91–92.)

Growling, the dog advanced toward the wolf.
Appealing to the jury, the lawyer made her final remarks.

▶ **Exercise 1** **Place a check in the blank next to each correctly punctuated sentence.**

✔_____ Moving cautiously, the little boy climbed the tree.

_____ **1.** In baseball gloves are used by the fielders.

✔_____ **2.** During the commercial after this one, I'll try to telephone Andrew.

✔_____ **3.** By the railing was the captain's special telescope.

_____ **4.** Seeing the crash we ran out to see if we could help.

_____ **5.** Inside the calzone, were sausage, cheese, and onions.

✔_____ **6.** Standing behind the man in the blue suit, DeJuan looked impatient.

✔_____ **7.** In the small space above the closet was a frightened and mewing Mimi.

_____ **8.** Behind the dairy cows grazed in a pasture.

✔_____ **9.** Smiling, the man behind the desk motioned us to come forward.

_____ **10.** At the wheel of the sleek red sports car, was none other than my dad!

_____ **11.** At the insistence of her parents she decided to attend.

Mechanics

_____ **12.** Laughing she handed me the photograph.

__✔__ **13.** From the mouth of the cannon flew the Great Stromboli!

_____ **14.** After the game boys thanked the referee.

__✔__ **15.** Gazing intently at the scar on the stranger's face, the sheriff stood up slowly.

_____ **16.** At the beginning of the race through the downtown area, sat the timekeepers.

__✔__ **17.** To those in need of help from the Red Cross, the plane was the best sight they had ever seen.

_____ **18.** On the edge of the pond scum covered the reeds.

_____ **19.** Catching a glimpse of the rescue team's light the trapped miners let out whoops of happiness.

_____ **20.** Beneath the cold water of Lake Superior, lay the wreck of the *Edmund Fitzgerald.*

▶ **Exercise 2 Insert commas where necessary. Delete (⌄) unnecessary commas.**

After two hours of tennis, the players cooled off by swimming.

 1. Curling up in her favorite chair with a new book, Regina felt happy and calm.

 2. Under the Egyptian sand⌄lay ancient temples, statues, and buildings.

 3. For us, children are never a nuisance.

 4. At the mouth of the river on the edge of the jungle⌄lay the village.

 5. Spotting a familiar face in the crowd, the nervous performer seemed to relax a little.

 6. In the middle of the night, she was awakened by a strange tapping sound at the window.

 7. After the ridiculously expensive dinner, guests were astonished to be asked to leave immediately.

 8. Spying a fish, the seagull dived straight down into the ocean.

 9. Crying, the lost child could not be comforted.

10. Looking under the porch, I spotted a raccoon.

11. By the photograph of the pig, farmers signed their names.

12. After twelve hours of nonstop hiking, we finally came to the campsite.

13. Muttering, the man returned to the bench.

14. Settling itself on a high branch, the osprey carefully scanned the surface of the inlet.

15. To her, parents were both friends and teachers.

16. Underneath the piano⌄lay the missing string of pearls.

Mechanics

Lesson 80
Commas and Adverb Clauses and Antithetical Phrases

Use **commas** to set off all introductory adverb clauses. Use commas to set off internal adverb clauses that interrupt the flow of the sentence.

Before you sign that agreement, make sure you read it carefully.
Most people, if they eat too much, will get indigestion.

In general, do not set off an adverb clause at the end of a sentence unless the clause is parenthetical or the sentence would be misread without the comma.

Don't come to the show unless you really want to see it. (comma not needed)

Use commas to set off an antithetical phrase. An **antithetical phrase** uses a word such as *but*, *not*, or *unlike* to qualify what precedes it.

She, not Michael, should have been elected class president.
Sheep, unlike cows, do not cause heavy damage to a pasture or a field.

▶ **Exercise 1 Add commas where necessary. Delete (⅄) unnecessary commas. Some sentences may be correct.**

The juror, not the detective, leaked the news,⅄to the press.

1. If you have never heard the name of Agnes Gonxha Bojaxhiu, you're not alone.

2. Although Agnes may be the most famous person in the world, few know her original name.

3. Agnes was born where people of several nationalities lived.

4. Although both Orthodox churches and Muslim mosques were plentiful in Agnes's town, her family was Catholic.

5. After her father died, young Agnes became increasingly involved in the church.

6. She attended meetings about missionary programs whenever she could.

7. While she was attending one meeting, Agnes learned of the Sisters of Loreto.

8. These nuns performed missionary work in foreign countries, but especially in India.

9. After she expressed her interest in the Loreto nuns' activities, a priest told her to wait until she was older.

10. When she became eighteen, Agnes decided she wanted to join the missionary nuns.

11. The main headquarters of the Loreto nuns was in Dublin, Ireland, not India.

12. Agnes's family reacted differently when she told them she had decided to become a nun.

13. Her brother Lazar, after he heard the news, was shocked.

14. Since Agnes was so full of fun, he felt a nun's life would be unsuitable for her.

15. Her mother was proud, but sad.

16. She knew she might never see Agnes again if Agnes went to India.

17. To her family, it would be, almost as if their Agnes had died.

18. In 1928 Agnes went to Dublin to join the Sisters of Loreto.

19. After two years the Loreto sisters sent Agnes to India, where she started her new life.

20. When she took her vows to become a nun, Agnes Gonxha Bojaxhiu became Sister Teresa.

▶ **Exercise 2** **Draw one line under each adverb clause. Then add necessary commas.**

When she became principal, Ms. Jansen began to change the rules.

1. So that she could better serve God, Sister Teresa promised to remain in poverty, to take no pay for her work, and to own only a few things.

2. Although nuns cannot marry in the ordinary sense, many consider themselves to be brides of Jesus.

3. Sister Teresa would wear the special robe and head covering, called a habit, of the nuns wherever she went.

4. After she visited Darjeeling near the Himalayan Mountains, Sister Teresa was sent to Calcutta.

5. In 1937 Sister Teresa took her final vows so that she could consecrate her life to her faith.

6. Although her first job was teaching at a Catholic girls' school in a middle-class section of Calcutta, Sister Teresa became aware of the poverty and misery of many residents of the city.

7. Then one day in 1946, when the regular food delivery failed to arrive at her convent, Sister Teresa went into the city to buy supplies.

8. Although she knew Calcutta had some of the worst living conditions in the world, Sister Teresa was shocked at the things she saw.

9. Although convent life was peaceful, the streets of Calcutta were frightening and strange, with starving beggars and unsanitary conditions.

10. Sister Teresa, after she had this powerful experience, felt that God wanted her to work with the poor of Calcutta.

Lesson 81
Commas with Titles, Addresses, and Numbers

Use **commas** to set off titles when they follow a person's name.

Sylvia Chang, Ph.D.
Walter Jackson, mayor of Toledo
Christina Lundgren, M.D., will give the opening speech.

Use a comma after each part of an address, a geographical term, or a date.

Mason, Ohio, is the location of King's Island.
Graham's new address is 622 Van Buren Street, Richmond, Indiana 47374.
On Thursday, May 24, 1994, she received notification about the loan.

In a letter use commas as follows:

622 Van Buren Street
Richmond, IN 47374
November 11, 1996

Do not use commas if only the month and the day or only the month and the year are given. Do not use a comma between a state and a zip code.

July 12   January 1993   Columbus, Ohio 43210

Use commas to set off the parts of a reference that direct the reader to the exact source.

The quotation about overcoming oneself is from the *Lao Tzu,* Book One, Chapter 33.
Ariel, the airy spirit, makes his first appearance in Act I, Scene ii, of *The Tempest* by Shakespeare.

▶ **Exercise 1 Add commas where necessary. Delete (⅄) unnecessary commas. Some sentences may be correct.**

Her Korean pen pal's birthday was⅄August 9, 1980.

1. Please welcome our speaker tonight, Angelina Thomas, senator from New Mexico.

2. The Nobel Prize in physics is presented each year in Stockholm, Sweden.

3. However, the Nobel Peace Prize is awarded in⅄Oslo, Norway.

4. All the Nobel Prizes are awarded in a gala ceremony on December⅄10 of each year.

5. Did you know there is a Kansas City, Missouri, and a Kansas City, Kansas?

6. The return address on the envelope was Christine Lundgren, M.D., 622 Van Buren Street, Richmond, Indiana 47374.

7. When he gave his birth date as December 3, 1951, I knew he couldn't be telling the truth.

8. Richard and Sarah's address until September is 1892 Sunshine Drive, Arlington Heights, Illinois 60005.

9. It looks as if the game on March 4 will decide the conference title.

10. The archaeology lecture will be given by Leopold M. Steinhauer, Ph.D., a noted Egyptian explorer.

11. A notice in the newspaper said that the classes would begin on Monday, September 12, 1996.

12. The group's concert tour includes performances in Saginaw, Michigan, and Wausau, Wisconsin.

13. I think you'll find the answer to that question in Act III, Scene ii, of *The Merchant of Venice.*

14. My sister joined the navy in October 1992.

15. The dentist handed him a card that read "Dr. Ariella Blubaugh, D.D.S."

16. You can redeem the coupons by sending them to P.O. Box 398, Blacksburg, Virginia 24063.

17. The masquerade takes place in Act I, Scene iii, of the second part of Goethe's *Faust.*

18. Stephen's pen pal lives in Quito, Ecuador.

19. Please have your applications in by March 21.

20. I have a recommendation from Anthony Wheeler, director of the Wheeler Institute.

21. Danielle's brother in the army is stationed in Frankfurt, Germany.

22. The letter introduced the new priest as Father Jeffrey Rhoades, S.J.

23. The sweepstakes entries have to be postmarked by midnight on April 30.

24. Send the entries to Contest, 1112 Northridge Avenue, Minneapolis, Minnesota 55401.

25. Until September 1, 1985, the *Titanic,* a grand but tragic ship, sat in total darkness two miles beneath the Atlantic Ocean.

26. A demonstration of CPR will be given in the auditorium by Elaine Hollister, R.N., head of nursing at Memorial Hospital.

27. The new tape and CD store is at 505 Butler Avenue.

28. Her little brother started school on September 1, 1990.

29. Marcelina Lopez is a city councilwoman.

30. The address on the form read 901 Old Mill Road, Salida, Colorado 81201.

31. The last day of band camp is Friday, August 3.

32. I ordered my hiking boots from a Portland, Maine, company.

Lesson 82
Commas in Direct Address, Tag Questions, and Letter Writing

Use **commas** to set off words or names used in direct address.

Robin, have you ever been to the zoo?
Yes, sir, we can have lunch together this week.
Don't forget to turn in your books, class.

Use commas to set off a tag question. A **tag question** (such as *Do you?* or *Can I?*) emphasizes an implied answer to the statement preceding it.

You don't like raisins, do you?
You've read *The Outsiders,* haven't you?

Place a comma after the salutation of an informal letter and after the closing of all letters.

Dear Ruben,
Sincerely,

▶ **Exercise 1** **Add commas where necessary. Cross out commas used incorrectly by using the delete symbol (⌒). Write *C* in the blank if the sentence is correct as written.**

_____   Carlos, hand me my books.

_____   **1.** No, my friend, I don't think we shall ever meet again.

_____   **2.** We've never been to Nebraska, have we?

_____   **3.** Dear Brian,

_____   **4.** You'll try to get some sleep before the test, won't you?

_____   **5.** Excuse me, ma'am, the sign says not to feed the animals.

_____   **6.** Don't forget to call me on Saturday, Lena.

_____   **7.** He knows about the deadline next week, doesn't he?

__C__   **8.** Very truly yours, Ms. Julia Pataky

__C__   **9.** That's the bus to Little Rock, isn't it?

_____   **10.** Dad, you're the greatest!

_____   **11.** Yes, Your Honor, I am prepared for trial today.

_____   **12.** This shirt⌒doesn't make my hair look orange, does it?

_____   **13.** I guess I am disappointed, Mom, but I'll get over it.

_____   **14.** Listen, folks, and I'll let you in on a little secret.

Mechanics

_____ 15. They don't really believe that, do they?

_____ 16. Dear Grandpa,

_____ 17. That's not a very smart thing to do, is it?

_____ 18. Whoa, Brandy! Down, girl!

_____ 19. Those are Kerry's gloves, aren't they?

__C__ 20. No, Officer, I did not see the flashing lights.

_____ 21. Jenny and Jillian didn't already leave for the pool, did they?

_____ 22. All right, you guys, the party's over!

_____ 23. Yes, Your Majesty, the ambassador from Persia has arrived.

_____ 24. I don't think Deanne left a forwarding address, did she?

_____ 25. Yes, Madame Chairman, I am happy to second the motion.

__C__ 26. Miguel won first place in the judo contest, didn't he?

_____ 27. You're not paying attention, people.

_____ 28. Ricky, you shouldn't walk down the stairs with a sucker in your mouth.

_____ 29. He won't tell anyone, will he?

_____ 30. Dear Mom and Dad,

_____ 31. Attention, students.

__C__ 32. She shouldn't be messing around with that fuse box, should she?

_____ 33. All right, Bobcats, let's go out and play our best game!

_____ 34. Electricity can be dangerous if you don't know what you're doing, can't it?

_____ 35. Here, Mittens, come get your dinner.

_____ 36. Your friend, Anthony

_____ 37. The news story about us will be next, won't it?

__C__ 38. Good evening, sir. My name is Tom and I'll be your waiter tonight.

_____ 39. I couldn't have seen Tyrone at the play, could I?

_____ 40. Dear Todd and Trevor,

_____ 41. Orange juice is a lot better for you than soda pop, isn't it?

_____ 42. Go, team! Beat Washington High!

Lesson 83
Commas in Review

▶ **Exercise 1** **Add commas where necessary. Delete commas used incorrectly using the delete symbol (⌿).**

To my surprise, Aunt Mary ⌿ bought tickets to the concert for Tony, Miguel, and me.

1. Jenny and I were planning to go to the parade, but when it started to rain, we decided to stay at her apartment and listen to music.

2. Although the other team had a big lead at halftime, we were barely able to eke out a victory.

3. Uncle Mervyn likes to work in his flower garden, and Aunt Jane spends most of her time spinning wool on her spinning wheel.

4. By the time we got to town, we found that the shoe store, the sporting goods store, and the clothing store were all closed.

5. Before they could play volleyball, players had to sign up for the team.

6. Among the sites we visited on our trip to New York was the Statue of Liberty, which was so crowded we couldn't go to the top.

7. We also saw the Museum of Modern Art, my favorite spot of all.

8. Her grandparents celebrated their 50th wedding anniversary on May 3, 1994.

9. The author, ⌿ whose books I like best, ⌿ is Walter Dean Myers.

10. Dad took a picture of Max and Mimi asleep on his favorite ⌿ red ⌿ easy chair.

11. Mr. Graves ran out of the house in a hurry, slipped on a patch of ice, and wound up in the emergency room with a broken wrist.

12. Sigrid Undset, a Norwegian novelist, won the Nobel Prize in 1928.

13. James Joyce, on the other hand, never won the Nobel Prize in literature.

14. Joyce, Ireland's best-known novelist, lived most of his life outside the country.

15. Ben went to visit his cousins in Highland Park, a town outside Chicago.

16. Anyone ⌿ playing around with her food ⌿ is likely to make a mess.

17. The word *smorgasbord* ⌿ came into the English language from Swedish.

18. Well, I don't think there's anything more we can do about it now.

19. Along the sheer, rocky cliff hanging over the crashing waves, she crept along carefully, never daring to look down.

20. The actor's favorite speech was in Shakespeare's *Much Ado About Nothing*, Act IV, Scene ii.

21. In order to be considered healthy, foods should not be too high in fat or sugar.

22. You're not serious about it, are you?

23. Could I have your schedule form, please?

24. Randall will have to study harder, or he'll be in danger of losing his B average.

25. Can't you try one more time to reach her?

26. Hey, wait a minute!

27. Learning to downhill ski is not as hard as you might think.

28. To create a sound that offers good stereo, speakers should be placed at least eight feet apart.

29. To become a member of the band had been her goal for three years.

30. Sarah, did you mail a package to 522 Van Buren Street, Richmond, Indiana 47374?

31. Oh, I didn't realize this was your magazine.

32. I can't remember the last time I read such an exciting, electrifying novel!

33. Could you tell me how to get to the city attorney's office?

34. The group of weary explorers trudged on through the jungle, yet many had already given up hope of ever being found.

35. Breathing a sigh of relief, the coach shook hands with his assistant.

36. Ladysmith Black Mombazo, a famous choir from South Africa, has recorded many albums of religious and traditional music.

37. She won't go along with our plan, nor will she try to think of a better one.

38. Anyone who wants to go to the Spanish play should sign up in advance with the club advisor.

39. That girl reading the newspaper by the cafeteria door just moved here from Seattle.

40. Kristy missed the penalty kick, I'm sorry to say.

41. With this software program you don't need to save your work every few minutes.

42. Chad was looking for the office of Janet Montgomery, M.D.

43. You are requested to appear in court on Thursday, August 18, 2002, to give testimony on the case.

44. Inside the tumbledown and ramshackle old mansion, we found the evidence we were looking for.

45. You might still be able to sign up for the trip, if you hurry.

Mechanics

Lesson 84
Dashes to Signal Change and to Emphasize

Use a **dash** to set off an abrupt break or change in thought within a sentence.

The owl's excellent sight—a valuable complement to its astounding ability to turn its head 270 degrees—makes it a master hunter, even at night.

Dashes may also be used to set off and emphasize supplemental information or parenthetical comments.

Melanie finished reading the book—the best she had ever read.

When Melanie finished reading the book—the best she had ever read—she had tears in her eyes.

▶ **Exercise 1** **Insert dashes where necessary. If the sentence is correct as written, write *C* on the blank.**

_____ Born in Wapakoneta a small western Ohio city Neil Armstrong became the first man to set foot on the moon.

_____ **1.** The slight woman she smiled shyly and curtsied was Nelly Sachs.

_____ **2.** Nelly Sachs the story of her life reads like a modern fairy tale was awarded the Nobel Prize for literature.

_____ **3.** Born in 1891 in Berlin the capital and leading city of Germany Nelly Sachs was the daughter of a well-to-do manufacturer.

___C___ **4.** The Sachses lived in the most fashionable neighborhood in Berlin; who could have imagined what horrors this city would experience over the next half-century?

_____ **5.** The Sachses like many other middle-class and well-to-do Germans of the early twentieth century were Jewish.

_____ **6.** As a teenager, Nelly decided to try to develop her talent for writing abandoning her early interest in dance and began to compose stories and poems.

_____ **7.** Her first poems based on her observations of nature and on her reading Nelly collected in a book.

___C___ **8.** In the 1920s Berlin was a cultural capital of Europe; many artists, writers, and musicians called it home.

_____ **9.** The Sachs family unaware of the violent storm building in their homeland lived a quiet, respectable life.

Mechanics

_____ **10.** Looking out the windows of her home, Nelly might have seen organizers for a new

political party the National Socialists, or Nazis.

_____ **11.** In 1929 the economy of Germany and of all the industrialized world fell apart.

_____ **12.** This period of economic hardship it was known as the Great Depression frightened

people all over the world.

_____ **13.** In Germany, many people believed that the leader of the Nazi party he was an Austrian

who believed that power and might were Germany's rightful future had the answers to

Germany's devastating economic problems.

__C___ **14.** The confusion, fear, and economic hardships of the German people led many to become

followers of the Nazis and their leader, Adolf Hitler.

_____ **15.** Hitler had a simple explanation for all of the country's problems "The Jews," he

claimed, "are poisoning Germany."

__C___ **16.** Like poison, Hitler's beliefs spread through German society, and in 1934 the Nazi leader

became the country's ruler.

_____ **17.** The Nazis they now had total control of the country were prepared to enforce their

will by imprisoning or murdering those who opposed them.

_____ **18.** A series of laws they were known as the Nuremberg Laws and decreed that Jews were

no longer citizens gradually eliminated the rights of Germans who were Jewish.

__C___ **19.** A brutal secret police force known as the Gestapo enforced the laws against Jews.

__C___ **20.** As the campaign became more intense, Nazi police prevented people from dealing with

Jewish doctors, lawyers, or retailers; Jews understood that the situation would only

grow worse.

__C___ **21.** Thousands of Jews left Germany, although thousands more remained.

_____ **22.** In the meantime, Nelly Sachs's poetry because of its rhyme and subject matter had

begun to be published.

_____ **23.** As the Nazis moved closer to the Jews who remained many of whom were still loyal to

their country Nelly and her mother were forced to move from their home.

__C___ **24.** Taking only a few of their possessions, they moved to a poorer neighborhood of Berlin.

__C___ **25.** In spite of the reduced circumstances she found herself in, Nelly tried to continue with

her writing and other parts of her old life.

Mechanics

Lesson 85
Parentheses

Use **parentheses** to set off material that is not important enough to be considered part of the main statement.

The Dead Sea, at 397 meters (1,302 feet) below sea level, is the lowest spot on the earth's land surface.

A complete sentence within parentheses is not capitalized and needs no period if it is contained within another sentence. If a sentence in parentheses is not contained within another sentence, both a capital letter and a period are needed.

In 1940 Nelly Sachs (she was almost fifty years old) was forced to flee Nazi Germany.

If a comma, a semicolon, or a colon is required, place it *after* the closing parenthesis.

During the year of Grandma's birth (1939), many important historical events took place.

Place a necessary question mark or exclamation point inside the parentheses if it is part of the parenthetical expression.

I saw your brother Tim (or was it Tom?) at the game.

▶ **Exercise 1 Rewrite the sentences in the space provided, adding parentheses and punctuation where necessary. If a sentence is correct, write *correct* on the line.**

Mr. Fox my biology teacher needs three volunteers to help with the field trip.

Mr. Fox (my biology teacher) needs three volunteers to help with the field trip.

1. If my cousin comes to visit I really hope he does, I'm sure he'll bring his banjo.

   If my cousin comes to visit (I really hope he does!), I'm sure he'll bring his banjo.

2. Peugeot and Renault neither is sold in the United States are both French automobiles.

   Peugeot and Renault (neither is sold in the United States) are both French automobiles.

3. The TV show will air at 9:00 P.M. Eastern Standard Time 8:00 P.M. Central.

   The TV show will air at 9:00 P.M. Eastern Standard Time (8:00 P.M. Central).

4. Giuseppe Verdi the Italian composer became popular during Italy's drive for independence.

   Giuseppe Verdi (the Italian composer) became popular during Italy's drive for independence.

5. Can you imagine close your eyes and try staying at a hotel that doesn't have electricity?

   Can you imagine (close your eyes and try) staying at a hotel that doesn't have electricity?

Mechanics

6. If you like that idea, then LeConte Lodge in Tennessee is for you!

correct

7. Racing bicycles yes, I know you have a mountain bike are very efficient machines.

Racing bicycles (yes, I know you have a mountain bike!) are very efficient machines.

8. Gina told me you lost her denim jacket.

correct

9. A person should eat two to four servings from another food group fruit is a good one.

A person should eat two to four servings from another food group (fruit is a good one).

10. One source of ascorbic acid Vitamin C is orange juice.

One source of ascorbic acid (Vitamin C) is orange juice.

11. Peter Gabriel he was once in the band Genesis has performed solo for almost twenty years.

Peter Gabriel (he was once in the band Genesis) has performed solo for almost twenty years.

12. When you get a letter from your pen pal I hope you get it soon, let me know right away.

When you get a letter from your pen pal (I hope you get it soon), let me know right away.

13. I'm applying for a pen pal myself.

correct

14. It sounds like fun to write to someone in a foreign country.

correct

15. Birds flying south migrating is one unmistakable sign of fall.

Birds flying south (migrating) is one unmistakable sign of fall.

16. My grandfather always talks about his favorite baseball player, Stan the Man Musial.

My grandfather always talks about his favorite baseball player, Stan (the Man) Musial.

17. African elephants they're rightly feared by many people differ from Asian elephants.

African elephants (they're rightly feared by many people) differ from Asian elephants.

18. At birth a typical Asian elephant weighs about 260 pounds about 118 kilograms!

At birth a typical Asian elephant weighs about 260 pounds (about 118 kilograms)!

19. His parents left on a tour of Scandinavia Norway, Finland, Sweden, and Denmark.

His parents left on a tour of Scandinavia (Norway, Finland, Sweden, and Denmark).

20. Did you hear that Luis he's my brother's friend was accepted at Harvard?

Did you hear that Luis (he's my brother's friend) was accepted at Harvard?

Lesson 86
Quotation Marks for Direct Quotations

Use **quotation marks** to enclose a direct quotation. Separate introductory or explanatory remarks from the quotation with a comma.

The man looked at Angie and said, "I believe you are to blame for this."

Do not use a comma after a quotation that ends with an exclamation point or a question mark.

"What are you doing here?" the police officer asked.

When a quotation is interrupted by explanatory words such as *she said*, use two sets of quotation marks.

"An aged man is but a paltry thing," wrote the Irish poet William Butler Yeats, "a tattered coat upon a stick."

Do not use quotation marks in an indirect quotation.

Father said the train was running late.

Use single quotation marks around a quotation within a quotation.

"I heard the announcer say, 'You win a new car,'" he explained excitedly.

In writing dialogue, begin a new paragraph and use a new set of quotation marks every time the speaker changes.

Little Crow asked quietly, "Are you ready for the ceremony?"
"I don't know," White Wing replied, not daring to look at the older man.

▶ **Exercise 1** Rewrite the sentences in the space provided, adding or deleting quotation marks and other punctuation where necessary. Some sentences may be correct.

"Fools need advice most" Ben Franklin wrote, but wise men only are the better for it.

"Fools need advice most," Ben Franklin wrote, "but wise men only are the better for it."

1. The poster read, It's 11:00. Do you know where your kids are

   The poster read, "It's 11:00. Do you know where your kids are?"

2. My reply he explained, was I would never do that   "My reply," he explained, "was 'I would never do that!'"

3. Rehearsals start on Monday announced the director. I hope everyone will be on time

   "Rehearsals start on Monday," announced the director. "I hope everyone will be on time."

4. Everybody get down the woman screamed when the car exploded.

   "Everybody get down!" the woman screamed when the car exploded.

5. The scarecrow told Dorothy that some folks went this way and others went that way.

   correct

6. The school nurse asked Charlie, Are you feeling better now?

   The school nurse asked Charlie, "Are you feeling better now?"

7. Ms. Wallinchek assigned Patrick Henry's speech" said Annie.

   "Ms. Wallinchek assigned Patrick Henry's speech," said Annie.

8. The one in which he says Give me liberty or give me death asked Tonya.

   "The one in which he says, 'Give me liberty or give me death'?" asked Tonya.

9. May I help you asked the girl behind the counter.

   "May I help you?" asked the girl behind the counter.

10. We got our history tests back yesterday, Matt explained."

    "We got our history tests back yesterday," Matt explained.

11. I got a B plus he added proudly.   "I got a B plus," he added proudly.

12. The woman walked up to my mother and asked Do you know me

    The woman walked up to my mother and asked, "Do you know me?"

13. William boasted "that he had read *The Scarlet Letter* in one night."

    William boasted that he had read *The Scarlet Letter* in one night.

14. We have a problem said Grandpa with a worried look a big problem

    "We have a problem," said Grandpa with a worried look, "a big problem."

15. The forecast for tonight said the meteorologist is snow

    "The forecast for tonight," said the meteorologist, "is snow."

16. Christina Rossetti is my favorite poet declared Megan.

    "Christina Rossetti is my favorite poet," declared Megan.

17. The clerk explained how the radio worked.   correct

18. Lincoln warned "that a house divided against itself could not stand."

    Lincoln warned that a house divided against itself could not stand.

19. Did the announcement say, Only sophomores need report at 3:30

    Did the announcement say, "Only sophomores need report at 3:30"?

20. When Jose mentioned "that he might be going to the chess club meeting," I asked Do you mind if I come along

    When Jose mentioned that he might be going to the chess club meeting, I asked, "Do you mind if I come

    along?"

Lesson 87
Quotation Marks with Titles of Short Works, Unusual Expressions, and Other Marks of Punctuation

Use **quotation marks** to enclose titles of short works, such as stories, poems, essays, newspaper and magazine articles, book chapters, and songs.

"The Tell-Tale Heart" (short story)
"Self-Reliance" (essay)

Use quotation marks to enclose unfamiliar slang and unusual expressions.

Jamal explained that in football a "pick" is a pass interception.

Place commas and periods inside closing quotation marks.

"I Like to See It Lap the Miles," a poem by Emily Dickinson, is about a train.

Place a colon or semicolon outside closing quotation marks.

This is my opinion of Emily Dickinson's "Because I Could Not Stop for Death": it's one of the greatest poems ever written.

Place a question mark or an exclamation point outside the closing quotation marks when it is part of the entire sentence but inside if it refers only to the quoted matter.

Did the caller say, "Drop the ransom money behind the big oak tree"?
Suzi asked, "What is your favorite poem?"

▶ **Exercise 1** **Rewrite the sentences in the space provided, adding quotation marks where necessary. If a sentence is correct, write** *correct.*

The Necklace is a famous story by Guy de Maupassant.

"The Necklace" is a famous story by Guy de Maupassant.

1. Ouch! yelled Clarissa.

   "Ouch!" yelled Clarissa.

2. Mom likes to listen to Michael Feinstein sing Isn't It Romantic?

   Mom likes to listen to Michael Feinstein sing "Isn't It Romantic?"

3. In tennis a score of zero is called love.

   In tennis a score of zero is called "love."

Mechanics

4. Which of these poems by Edgar Allan Poe do you prefer—The Bells or The Raven?

Which of these poems by Edgar Allan Poe do you prefer—"The Bells" or "The Raven"?

5. I'm going to call my essay How to Proceed to Succeed.

I'm going to call my essay "How to Proceed to Succeed."

6. Never, shouted Morgan, will I agree to such terms!

"Never," shouted Morgan, "will I agree to such terms!"

7. Am I Blue? was a popular song in my great-grandmother's youth.

"Am I Blue?" was a popular song in my great-grandmother's youth.

8. Did Stephen Crane write a short story called The Open Boat?

Did Stephen Crane write a short story called "The Open Boat"?

9. For my report I read an article titled Unidentified Flying Objects—Fact or Fiction?

For my report I read an article titled "Unidentified Flying Objects—Fact or Fiction?"

10. Can you quote the first line of the patriotic poem Concord Hymn?

Can you quote the first line of the patriotic peom "Concord Hymn"?

11. For homework Ms. Ruiz assigned Chapter 22, The Great Depression.

For homework Ms. Ruiz assigned Chapter 22, "The Great Depression."

12. Do you know what a gofer is?

Do you know what a "gofer" is?

13. Do you know who wrote the nonsense poem Jabberwocky?

Do you know who wrote the nonsense poem "Jabberwocky"?

14. The Bear is probably William Faulkner's most famous short story.

"The Bear" is probably William Faulkner's most famous short story.

Mechanics

Lesson 88
Italics

Titles of books, long poems, plays, films, television series, works of art, and long musical compositions are printed in italic type. Names of newspapers, magazines, ships, trains, airplanes, and spacecraft are also printed in italics. It is common practice not to italicize the article preceding the title of a newspaper or a magazine. In handwriting, use underlining to indicate italics.

the ***Washington Post*** (newspaper)   ***The Marriage of Figaro*** (musical work)

Italicize (underline) foreign words and expressions that are not used frequently in English.

In Italy, we spent a lot of time at the ***stazione ferroviaria,*** or train station.

Italicize (underline) words and letters used to represent themselves.

The word *carols* comes from the Greek word *choraules.*

▶ **Exercise 1   Underline each word or phrase that should be italicized. Not every sentence has words that should be italicized.**

Tamara will read <u>The Return of the Native</u> for her book report.

1. Selma Lagerlof's best-known novel is <u>The Story of Gosta Berling</u>.

2. Lagerlof was the first woman to win the Nobel Prize in literature.

3. There is an article in <u>National Geographic</u> about Lagerlof's homeland.

4. The music club went to see a production of the opera <u>Billy Budd</u>.

5. The opera is based on a story by Herman Melville, author of the novel <u>Moby-Dick</u>.

6. <u>Semper paratus</u>—"Always prepared"—is the motto of the U.S. Coast Guard.

7. Sarah's dad made us a delicious dinner with <u>bulgogi</u> and <u>kimchee</u>.

8. My sister hung in her room a poster of Edward Hopper's painting <u>Nighthawks</u>.

9. <u>Ich dien</u> is the motto of the Prince of Wales.

10. Lianna didn't have any idea how often she said the word <u>whatever</u>.

11. Matt felt proud that he had earned all <u>A</u>'s and <u>B</u>'s.

12. We read the early edition of the <u>Cleveland Plain Dealer</u>.

13. One of the best places to get a <u>galette</u> is Rennes, France.

14. He was suffering from <u>weltschmerz</u>, a German word for "world-weariness."

15. My mom's favorite album of all time is the Police's <u>Ghost in the Machine</u>.

Mechanics

16. However, her favorite song is Aretha Franklin's "Respect."

17. The drama club is presenting Thornton Wilder's play <u>Our Town</u> next weekend.

18. Which movie did you like better: <u>Home Alone</u> or <u>Home Alone II</u>?

19. The word <u>smee</u> plays an important role in A.M. Burrage's story of the same name.

20. Whenever it's my turn to cook a meal for the family, I always make spaghetti.

21. It's fun to look through old <u>Life</u> and <u>Look</u> magazines.

22. Mahpiua-luta was a famous chief of the Dakota people.

23. The Broadway musical <u>My Fair Lady</u> is based on <u>Pygmalion</u>, a play by George Bernard Shaw.

24. My grandparents sent me a postcard of Michelangelo's statue <u>David</u>.

25. "The sequels to <u>Gone with the Wind</u> aren't as good as the original movie," she said.

26. The <u>h</u> on his computer keyboard didn't work.

27. My favorite story in the book <u>Twice-Told Tales</u> is "The Gray Champion."

28. We rode aboard the <u>Delta Queen</u>, a remodeled steamboat.

29. Roberto made a delicious Puerto Rican dish called <u>monfongo con caldo</u>.

30. Jennifer's mom, a carpenter, appeared on the television series <u>This Old House</u>.

31. Whitman was in tune with the <u>zeitgeist</u>, or "spirit of the times," of the 1850s.

32. Bach's <u>Mass in B Minor</u> is a great choral work.

33. Achilles, the great warrior, is a main character in the poem.

34. We traveled on the <u>Highland Belle</u> through northern Scotland.

35. I looked at the poster and realized I'd left out the <u>c</u> in <u>dance</u>!

36. You can make Ethiopian <u>injera</u> bread with wheat flour.

37. Our film club rented the movies <u>Citizen Kane</u> and <u>Ben-Hur</u>.

38. Rachel read the novel <u>Pride and Prejudice</u> in two days.

39. Dad christened his new boat <u>Daybreak</u>.

40. One of my favorite paintings is called <u>Luncheon of the Boating Party</u>.

41. My little sister is dancing to selections from <u>The Nutcracker Suite</u>.

42. Arthur says watching <u>Sesame Street</u> helped him learn to read.

43. Jerome's grandmother suggested that he mind his <u>p</u>'s and <u>q</u>'s.

44. Jazz great Charlie Parker was nicknamed "Bird."

Lesson 89
The Apostrophe

Use an apostrophe and -*s* to form the possessive of a singular noun, even one that ends in -*s*. Use an apostrophe alone to form the possessive of a plural noun that ends in -*s*. Use an apostrophe and -*s* to form the possessive of a plural noun that does not end in -*s*.

Doris's car   **boys'** bicycles   the children**'s** room

Put only the last word of a compound noun in the possessive form.

the secretary of state**'s** home   her brother-in-law**'s** car

If two or more partners possess something jointly, use the possessive form for the last partner named. If two or more partners possess something individually, put each one's name in the possessive form.

Laurel and Hardy**'s** comedies   Boeing**'s** and Lockheed**'s** airplanes

Use an apostrophe in place of letters omitted in contractions. Common contractions combine a subject and a verb or a verb and an adverb.

he**'s** (he is, he has)   won**'t** (will not)   it**'s** (it is, it has)

Use an apostrophe in place of the omitted numerals of a particular year.

the class of **'97**   the **'96** election

▶ **Exercise 1   Add an apostrophe where necessary. Delete (⸉) apostrophes used incorrectly.**

Cara's ski club is borrowing our⸉ room for their meeting.

1. Among Nobel Prize winners, Barbara McClintock's name stands out in many ways.

2. For example, this world-famous scientist doesn't own a telephone, so when she won the Nobel

   Prize in medicine in 1983, the Nobel committee couldn't call her!

3. She's not a teacher as so many other winner⸉s of the award have been.

4. Barbara's childhood was unusual.

5. Barbara's father, a doctor, insisted that his children not be given any homework.

6. He wanted them to have free time to enjoy the wood⸉s and outdoor activities.

7. Barbara chose to study at New York's Cornell University.

8. At Cornell Barbara made many friend⸉s and was elected president of the women's freshman

   class.

9. Although she worked hard on her⸉ studies, she was able to find time to play the banjo in a

   student jazz band.

10. At Cornell Barbara became interested in genetics and the study of heredity—the passing on of a parent's characteristics to his or her offspring.

11. Genetic's as a science was still in it's youth when Barbara began to study it.

12. The pioneer in genetics' research was an Austrian monk named Gregor Mendel.

13. Mendel experimented with plants in his monastery's garden.

14. Mendel's discoveries' about how the plants passed on certain characteristics to their offspring became the foundation of modern genetics.

15. However, it took scientists several decades to accept Mendel's theories.

16. By the time Barbara McClintock was studying genetics at Cornell, scientists had confirmed the existence of genes, heredity's building blocks.

17. Genes, which transmit organisms' messages to their offspring, are carried on chromosome's, tiny rods present in the cells of all living things.

18. You'd be surprised to learn about the methods of pioneers in the study of genetics.

19. Mendel studied pea plants while other's studied fruit flies.

20. Barbara McClintock's favorite organism was a type of corn called maize.

21. Maize is the multicolored corn you'd use as a decoration in the fall.

22. The colors of the kernels indicate the genetic makeup of the corn's chromosomes.

23. The early scientists' research was difficult because of the small size of chromosome's.

24. The future Nobel Prize winner's first major breakthrough was the identification of a corn kernel's individual chromosomes.

25. During her year's at Cornell, Barbara met many other's interested in genetics.

26. In later years they would benefit greatly from each other's research.

27. Barbara and another young scientist, Harriet Creighton, discovered that a cell's chromosomal message's are exchanged during meiosis.

28. Meiosis is the process of a cell's reproduction by division.

29. After several years at Cornell, Barbara accepted the National Research Council's offer of a fellowship to study and teach.

30. Over the next forty years, Barbara made many discoveries' about the nature of chromosomes, genes, and heredity.

Lesson 90
The Hyphen

Use a **hyphen** after any prefix joined to a proper noun or proper adjective (see Lesson 2, pp. 49-50, and Lesson 8, pp. 61-62). Use a hyphen after the prefixes *all-, ex-,* and *self-* joined to any noun or adjective. Use a hyphen after the prefix *anti-* joined to a word beginning with a vowel, and use a hyphen after the prefix *vice-,* except in *vice president.*

trans-Africa   all-state   anti-inflation

Use a hyphen in a compound adjective that precedes a noun. Do not use a hyphen if one of the words is an adverb ending in *-ly.*

a twelve-year-old boy *but* The boy is twelve years old.   softly spoken words

Hyphenate any spelled-out cardinal or ordinal compound number up to *ninety-nine* or *ninety-ninth.* Hyphenate a fraction used as an adjective.

twenty-two   one-half tablespoon *but* one half of a tablespoon

Words are generally hyphenated at the ends of lines between syllables. In general, if a word contains two consonants occurring between two vowels, divide the word between the two consonants. If a suffix has been added to a complete word that ends in two consonants, divide the word after the two consonants. Use a dictionary when in doubt.

moun-tain   ask-ing

▶ **Exercise 1 Add hyphens where necessary. Delete (Ɣ) unnecessary hyphens. Some sentences may be correct.**

The seasoned reporter removed a well-worn suitcase from the trunk of her car.

1. Ashok finished twenty-first out of ninety-seven runners.

2. When Torrie found out she had made the all-conference team, she was ecstatic.

3. Babies are certainly tiny when they're threeƔweeksƔold.

4. Oscar Robertson is one of basketball's all-time greats.

5. Use one-fourth teaspoon of cinnamon in this recipe.

6. The evening sky was an unbelievable shade of darkƔblue.

7. Our ex-babysitter's photograph was in the paper because she won an award.

8. Of all the teachers in our school, Ms. Sanchez is probably the mostƔpopular.

9. The horse had to run the race with a sixteen-pound weight on his saddle.

10. The concerto was well performed.

11. Sean's self-confidence rose when he won second prize in the art show.

12. The teacher said she could tell our report was thoroughly researched.

13. Excuse me, but are these tulips the late-blooming variety?

14. The members of the anti-poverty group were meeting in the auditorium.

15. The recipe called for three-quarters of a pound of butter or margarine.

16. This is definitely a mouth-watering dish.

17. Steven eats only well-done hamburgers.

18. Virginia's blue-green outfit did not look good with her bluish-purple hat.

19. Congratulations to the fifty-ninth graduating class of Roosevelt High.

20. That was a back-breaking job.

▶ **Exercise 2** **Show where each word would be hyphenated at the end of a line by drawing a vertical line (|) at the spot.**

sum|mer

1. think|ing

2. chick|en

3. high|est

4. ban|quet

5. spokes|per|son

6. stomp|ing

7. mil|lion

8. thought|less

9. mis|take

10. long|est

11. hol|low

12. doc|tor

13. an|nounce

14. sal|vage

15. thank|ful

16. pos|sess|ive

17. foot|ball

18. other|wise

19. bal|loon

20. friend|ship

▶ **Writing Link** **Write a paragraph describing an outfit you might wear to a costume party. Use at least two compound adjectives and two prefixes in your description.**

_____

_____

_____

_____

_____

_____

Mechanics

Lesson 91
Abbreviations

Use all capital letters and no periods for **abbreviations** that are pronounced letter by letter or as words. Exceptions are U.S. and Washington, D.C., which do use periods.

NBC   PIN   AMA   NASA   NAACP   AIDS   NATO

In ordinary prose, spell out state names and words that refer to streets, such as *Street, Road,* and *Boulevard*. On envelopes only, use the postal abbreviations for state names. Also on envelopes only, you may abbreviate words that refer to streets, such as *Street, Road,* and *Boulevard*.

AL Alabama   **MI** Michigan   **IL** Illinois
St. Street   **Rd.** Road   **Blvd.** Boulevard

Use the abbreviations A.M. (*ante meridiem,* "before noon") and P.M. (*post meridiem,* "after noon") for exact times. For dates, use B.C. (before Christ) and, sometimes, A.D. (*anno Domini,* "in the year of the Lord," after Christ.)

9:12 A.M.   11:20 P.M.   A.D. 1200   10,000 B.C.

Personal titles, such as *Mrs.* and *Jr.,* are almost always abbreviated. Titles of government and military officials and of clergy members are often abbreviated when used before the full name. This kind of abbreviation always ends with a period.

Ken Griffey **Jr.**   **Gen.** Dwight Eisenhower   **Sen.** Bruce Johnson

Units of measure are abbreviated when used with numerals in technical or scientific writing but are not abbreviated in ordinary sentences. The abbreviation is the same for both plural and singular units. Metric abbreviations do not take periods.

ENGLISH SYSTEM   METRIC SYSTEM
ft. foot   **cm** centimeter

▶ **Exercise 1 Choose the word or abbreviation in the parentheses that correctly completes each sentence and write it on the blank.**

Tomorrow I will run one ____kilometer____ farther than I ran today. (km, kilometer)

1. Marlene missed her goal shot by two _____feet_____. (feet, ft.)

2. _____Sen._____ Ted Kennedy was the name on the office door. (Sen., Sen)

3. Saudi Arabia is one of the members of _____OPEC_____. (OPEC, O.P.E.C.)

Mechanics

4. Martin Luther King _____Jr._____ was born in January. (Junior, Jr.)

5. At 11:45 _____A.M._____ the balloon touched down behind the school. (A.M., *ante meridiem*)

6. _____ABC_____ is one of the major television networks. (A.B.C., ABC)

7. _____Gen._____ Robert E. Lee led the South during the Civil War. (Gen., GEN.)

8. Three _____yards_____ of the fabric cost $5.40. (yd., yards)

9. Around 8000 _____B.C._____ the wooly mammoth died out. (B.C., before Christ)

10. When we toured the Space Center, a _____NASA_____ official was our guide. (N.A.S.A., NASA)

11. The steak weighed about two _____pounds_____ on the butcher's scale. (lb., pounds)

12. In ____A.D.____ 476 the Roman Empire finally came to an end. (A.D., *anno Domini*)

13. Step 4 of the lab instructions says, "Cut a segment 3 _____cm_____ long." (cm., cm)

14. Did the bus arrive before or after 4:00 _____P.M._____? (*post meridiem*, P.M.)

15. My friend Spencer lives in Long Branch, _____New Jersey_____. (NJ, New Jersey)

16. Mom sent me to the grocery store to buy one _____pound_____ of bacon. (lb., pound)

17. The tire pressure measured thirty-five _____cubic centimeters_____. (cc, cubic centimeters)

18. The story's main character is a lovable giant who is nine _____feet_____ tall. (ft., feet)

19. The _____doctor_____ will see you tomorrow at noon. (Dr., doctor)

20. _____NATO_____ is the abbreviation for the North Atlantic Treaty Organization. (N.A.T.O., NATO)

▶ **Exercise 2** **Rewrite the following addresses as if they would appear on envelopes, using the acceptable abbreviations.**

Maria Lopez	Maria Lopez
1557 Westchester Boulevard	1557 Westchester Blvd.
Detroit, Michigan 13799	Detroit, MI 13799
Rachel Goldberg	Rachel Goldberg
375 Andrews Street	375 Andrews St.
Huntsville, Alabama 10227	Huntsville, AL 10227
Michael Lee	Michael Lee
879 Meander Road	879 Meander Rd.
Chicago, Illinois 11337	Chicago, IL 11337

Mechanics

Lesson 92
Numbers and Numerals

Use **numerals** in charts and tables. In sentences, spell numbers that begin a sentence or that can be written in one or two words. Use numerals for those requiring more than two words.

An acre equals **43,560** square feet.
Five hundred fifty-five students attended the exhibit.
Mitch was the **twenty-second** person in the long ticket line.

Use numerals to express decimals, percentages, and amounts of money involving both dollars and cents. Write out amounts of money that can be written in one or two words.

2.2 liters   70 percent $17.95   seventy-five cents

Use numerals to express the year and day in a date and to express the precise time with the abbreviations A.M. and P.M. Spell out expressions of time that are approximate or that do not use A.M. or P.M.

November 11, 1918   8:15 A.M.   eight o'clock

Use numerals for numbered streets and avenues over ten and for all house, apartment, and room numbers.

202 East 44th Street   Apartment 34B   305 First Avenue

Use numerals to express page, line, act, and scene numbers.

page 101   lines 4-20 of the poem   Act 2, Scene 3, *or* Act II, Scene iii

▶ **Exercise 1** Write in the blank the expression shown in parentheses that correctly completes the sentence.

The candidate collected _____ one thousand _____ signatures. (1,000; one thousand)

1. On page _____ 42 _____ I found information about the Crusades. (42, forty-two)

2. On November _____ 27 _____ , 1095, Pope Urban II gave a speech that launched the Crusades. (27, twenty-seventh)

3. The Crusades occurred between 1096 and _____ 1270 _____ . (twelve hundred seventy, 1270)

4. About _____ thirty thousand _____ crusaders fought in the First Crusade. (thirty thousand; 30,000)

5. _____ Four thousand _____ of these crusaders were knights. (4,000; Four thousand)

6. The store at 349 West _____ 47th _____ Street has many books about history. (47th, forty-seventh)

7. There I purchased a biography of Franklin D. Roosevelt for _____ $16.95 _____ . (sixteen dollars and ninety-five cents, $16.95)

8. The store also has a large table of bargain books that are priced from _____**twenty-five**_____ cents to three dollars. (25, twenty-five)

9. The library sells used books for _____**one dollar**_____ each. ($1.00, one dollar)

10. More than _____**70**_____ percent of all library users check out videos. (seventy, 70)

11. The average number of books checked out by each user is _____**5.5**_____ per visit. (five point five, 5.5)

12. Jane lives on _____**Tenth**_____ Avenue between Ninth Street and 11th Street. (10th, Tenth)

13. At _____**26,600**_____ feet, Nanga Parbat is one of the highest peaks in the Himalayas. (twenty-six thousand six hundred, 26,600)

14. The country of Sweden covers _____**170,250**_____ square miles. (170,250; one hundred seventy thousand two hundred fifty)

15. Chapter 3 begins on page _____**76**_____ . (76, seventy-six)

16. The meeting will be held Tuesday at _____**8:15**_____ P.M. (eight fifteen, 8:15)

17. More than _____**five hundred**_____ people attended the rally. (500, five hundred)

18. In Act 1, Scene _____**1**_____, a farmer and his wife are discussing how they will make ends meet after a drought has destroyed their crops. (1, one)

19. In lines _____**66–72**_____ of the scene, the oldest daughter explains why she has decided to leave the farm. (66–72, sixty-six to seventy-two)

20. The daughter, one of _____**four**_____ children, longs for a job in the city. (4, four)

21. The whale-watching boat leaves from this dock at _____**six**_____ o'clock. (six, 6)

22. The _____**forty-ninth**_____ state to join the United States was Alaska. (49th, forty-ninth)

23. Arnette was one of _____**twelve**_____ students who were recognized for outstanding effort in cleaning up the park. (twelve, 12)

24. _____**Eighty-five**_____ percent of our students graduate from high school. (Eighty-five, 85)

25. The judge fined the company _____**$30,500**_____ a day until they stopped releasing chemicals into the lake. ($30,500; thirty thousand five hundred dollars)

26. The art museum is at 600 _____**Second**_____ Avenue. (Second, 2nd)

27. The university library owns more than _____**9,339,560**_____ books. (nine million three hundred thirty-nine thousand five hundred sixty; 9,339,560)

28. On election day the polls will open at _____**7:00**_____ A.M. (7:00, seven)

29. Jana knocked on the door of Apartment _____**3**_____. (3, three)

30. He was the _____**twenty-fifth**_____ player chosen in the draft. (25th, twenty-fifth)

Mechanics

☑ Unit 12 **Review**

▶ **Exercise** **Add all necessary punctuation marks. Underline words or phrases that should be in italics.**

Jane Austen, who wrote the novel <u>Emma</u>, is one of my favorite authors.

1. Among authors who have won the Nobel Prize for literature is Gabriela Mistral, the Chilean poet who wrote the collection <u>Sonnets of Death</u>.

2. Her haunting early poems often reflect the sadness of her childhood and youth, which she spent as a schoolteacher in the Chilean countryside.

3. Her later poems are concerned with the joys of motherhood, social justice, and the plight of the poor campesinos, rural people of Latin America.

4. What prizewinning author is known for her portrayals of life in the Middle Ages?

5. Sigrid Undset, who won the Nobel Prize in literature in 1928, is the author of <u>Kristin Lavransdatter</u>, an epic story of life and love in medieval Norway.

6. The winner of the 1938 Nobel Prize in literature was American Pearl Buck, whose famous novel <u>The Good Earth</u> is based on her experiences living in China.

7. <u>The Good Earth</u>, which tells the story of Chinese peasants very much like the ones Pearl Buck lived with in the 1920s and 1930s, has been translated into at least sixty-five different languages.

8. Another American winner of the Nobel Prize in literature is Toni Morrison; her rich, absorbing novels, such as <u>The Bluest Eye</u>, reveal both beauties and tragedies of African American life.

9. In the category of peace one, indeed, in which women have won a large number of Nobel Prizes two American women have been honored.

10. Perhaps best known as the founder of Hull House, a famous community center in Chicago, Jane Addams won the Nobel Peace Prize in 1931.

11. The name of Emily Balch, unlike Jane Addams's, is not familiar to most Americans.

12. Throughout her ninety-four years, Emily Balch was a tireless worker for the rights of women and for international peace.

13. Her efforts were rewarded in 1946 with the Nobel committee's decision to award her the Nobel Peace Prize.

Mechanics

Cumulative Review: Units 1–12

► **Exercise 1** Label each adjective clause *adj. clause* and each adverb clause *adv. clause*. Write the kind of sentence in the blank using these abbreviations: *dec.* (declarative), *imp.* (imperative), *int.* (interrogative), or *exc.* (exclamatory).

	adj. clause
_____dec._____	The player who scores the most points will win a prize.
_____int._____	1. Did you leave your skates in the garage?
	adv. clause
_____dec._____	2. After Katie joined the soccer team, she gave us tickets to the first game.
exc. and imp.	3. Look how high that skier jumped!
	adj. clause
_____dec._____	4. Ivan's family still lives in the house that his grandfather built.
	adv. clause
_____dec._____	5. Because he did not practice, Jake did not make the team.
	adj. clause
_____imp._____	6. Don't break the antique glasses that Aunt Emily gave me.
	adj. clause
_____int._____	7. Where is the map that shows the best route to take?
	adv. clause
_____dec._____	8. Brigitta joined us as soon as she could.
_____exc._____	9. What an incredible story we heard!
	adj. clause
_____dec._____	10. Our coach, who usually walks to practice, drove her car today.
	adj. clause
_____imp._____	11. Bring me the letter that the mail carrier delivered.
	adj. clause
_____int._____	12. Who wants to claim the hat that was left on the chair?
	adv. clause
_____dec._____	13. Although we both shopped for an hour, Claire visited twice as many stores as I did.
	adv. clause
_____dec._____	14. I will wait until Suzy is finished painting the fence.
	adv. clause
_____dec._____	15. Cora will play the melody while An Li plays the harmony.
	adv. clause
_____int._____	16. Why did the puppy hide when Sebastian appeared?
	adj. clause
_____imp._____	17. Look for the person who is in charge of volunteers.
_____exc._____	18. Those special effects were fantastic!
	adv. clause
_____int._____	19. Who ate the dessert before I served dinner?
	adj. clause
_____dec._____	20. She chose a time when the park was deserted for our picnic.
	adj. clause
_____dec._____	21. The car which Kurt purchased can travel thirty miles on a single gallon of gas.
	adj. clause
_____imp._____	22. Help me hang the portrait that Linda painted.

Mechanics

▶ **Exercise 2** Complete each sentence by writing the form of the verb listed in parentheses. Cross out each pronoun that does not agree with its antecedent and write the correct pronoun above it.

their
Angela and Tim _____worked_____ on ~~its~~ science fair project. (past tense of *work*)

1. Karla _____wants_____ to give ~~their~~ old clothes to charity. (present tense of *want*)

her

2. Steve and Lauren _____drove_____ ~~its~~ car to Dallas. (past tense of *drive*)

their

3. The team _____will wait_____ for next year; ~~she~~ starts practice again next week. (future tense of *wait*)

it

4. Ms. Sanchez _____prepared_____ all the food in ~~his~~ own kitchen. (past tense of *prepare*)

her

5. The thunderstorm _____left_____ ~~her~~ mark on the small town. (past tense of *leave*)

its

6. The astronauts _____board_____ the space shuttle in five minutes. (present tense of *board*)

7. I _____have gone_____ to the store for milk and will be home soon. (present perfect tense of *go*)

8. These books can be checked out, so _____give_____ ~~it~~ to Sabrina to place on the shelves. (present tense of *give*)

them

9. This department store _____sells_____ both men's and women's fragrances, though

its
~~his~~ selection is rather limited. (present tense of *sell*)

10. The artist _____painted_____ ~~their~~ canvas in bold strokes of red and blue. (past tense of *paint*)

his or her

11. Michael _____sailed_____ the boat into the lake, then ~~she~~ photographed the swans. (past tense of *sail*)

he

12. The mirror might break if we _____drop_____ ~~him~~. (present tense of *drop*)

it

13. Wildflowers _____are_____ prettiest when growing in ~~its~~ natural habitat. (present tense of *be*)

their

14. Before leaving for practice, Jennifer _____grabbed_____ her ball and glove. (past tense of *grab*)

15. Several tourists _____are hoping_____ to visit the museum, and ~~he~~ hope to see the new

they

monument as well. (present progressive tense of *hope*)

16. Aunt Sylvia _____will meet_____ us at the fabric store when ~~they~~ finishes talking to Darla. (future tense of *meet*)

she

Mechanics

Name _____ Class _____ Date _____

17. Uncle Antonio _____took_____ us bowling last Tuesday. (past tense of *take*)

18. The mysterious castle _____kept_____ ~~his~~ **its** secrets locked inside. (past tense of *keep*)

19. Claude _____climbed_____ the hill quickly, but Lawrence took ~~its~~ **his** time. (past tense of *climb*)

20. We _____will have walked_____ six miles when we reach ~~their~~ **our** destination. (future perfect tense of *walk*)

21. George _____had invited_____ Susan before remembering ~~they~~ **she** was out of town. (past perfect tense of *invite*)

22. Kyle _____makes_____ jewelry out of everyday objects and gives it to his friends. (present tense of *make*)

▶ **Exercise 3** Draw three lines under each letter that should be capitalized. Add the correct end mark to each sentence. Delete (✀) each unnecessary comma, semicolon, or colon.

george is traveling to Connecticut, for thanksgiving.

1. When is the independence day celebration going to start?

2. The following, plays were written by William shakespeare: *Romeo and Juliet, Twelfth Night,* and *othello.*

3. Two chemistry students will be selected; to participate in the demonstration.

4. look at those; incredible acrobats.

5. Leave your books on the table next to the letters, and the box of stamps.

6. My american history class will take a field trip to ford's theater next week.

7. Why, do you look so confused, kristen?

8. That television show was fantastic!

9. kimberly, jerome, and juanita will sing selections from; *Grease.*

10. My friend and i want to learn; how to play lacrosse.

11. mr. bennet, who collects antique clocks, can tell you how much grandfather's present is worth.

12. Do you know, how to get to Chelton street?

13. Open the kitchen window, victor.

14. wave to Susie, from the train.

15. Two of the contestants arrived early; however, jack arrived late because his car had a flat tire.

16. Tabitha's grocery list included, bread, milk, eggs, and apples.

288   *Grammar and Language Workbook, Grade 9*

Vocabulary and Spelling

Unit 13: Vocabulary and Spelling

Lesson 93

Building Vocabulary: Learning from Context

Clues to the meaning of an unfamiliar word can be found in its context, the other words and sentences surrounding it. As a reader, you can analyze a passage both for specific clues and for general context.

CLUE WORDS

that	like	also	but	because
in other words	for example	likewise	on the other hand	since
or	such as	similarly	on the contrary	therefore
also known as	for instance	resembling	unlike	as a result
which means	including	identical	however	consequently

INTERPRETING CLUE WORDS

Type of Context Clue

Definition: The meaning of the unfamiliar word is stated in the sentence.
Meteorology, or the science of weather forecasting, has become Todd's favorite subject.

Example: The meaning of the unfamiliar word is explained through one familiar case.
Fran loves to study mammals such as kangaroos.

Comparison: The unfamiliar word is similar to a familiar word or phrase.
Dissension closely resembles disagreement.

Contrast: The unfamiliar word is the opposite of a familiar word or phrase.
Constructive criticism can be helpful; however, criticism without foundation can be harmful.

Cause and effect: The unfamiliar word describes a cause in a sentence in which the effect is understood.
Garret had to fly stand-by; therefore, he was not sure he would get a seat on the five o'clock flight.

▶ **Exercise 1** Underline the specific clue word or words. Using the context of the italicized word, define the word.

Unlike Michiko, who always wore colorful and fashionable clothing, Myra dressed in a *nondescript* manner.   lacking distinctive or interesting qualities

1. The story is an *allegory* like the tale of the tortoise and the hare.   a symbolic representation

Vocabulary and Spelling

2. Though both of the senators were opposed to the bill, one seemed willing to reconsider but the

other was *adamant*. _unshakable or unmovable, especially in opposition_____

3. Although he delayed his research for a week, Miguel finally started to work seriously when he

realized his group might get an "incomplete" for the project as a result of his *dilatory* practices.

_tending or intended to cause delay_____

4. The *itinerant* farmers were concerned their children would not have the advantage of a good

education because they changed schools with each move. _traveling from place to place_____

5. The fashion museum was filled with styles that were the *vogue* during different eras.

For example, mini-skirts and knee-high boots from the sixties were on display.

_something in fashion at a particular period of time_____

6. Jackie usually talks only when she has something important to say. Armand, on the other hand,

is often rather *garrulous*. _pointlessly or annoyingly talkative_____

7. David had been fascinated with insects since he was a child. Consequently, no one was

surprised when he chose *entomology* as his major in college.

_the science that deals with insects_____

8. Since the project involves much detail, we need a very *meticulous* person to manage it.

_extremely or excessively careful in handling details_____

9. The *facade* of the building is very ornate, unlike the interior which is almost austere.

_the front of a building_____

10. Jeannie felt challenged by *profound* ideas such as the meaning of existence and the origin of

the universe. _very serious or highly abstract_____

11. Sam really is a *flamboyant* dresser; likewise, Judy enjoys wearing bright colors and unusual

styles. _given to showy display_____

12. Harriet is *zealous* in her efforts to preserve the environment. However, she finds few people

who share her enthusiasm. _strongly, even fanatically, interested in or devoted to_____

13. My diagnosis as *hypertensive,* which means my blood pressure is higher than it should be, was

all I needed to control my diet. _having abnormally high blood pressure_____

14. I expected my classmates to have a *plethora* of ideas for community service projects.

Therefore, I was surprised when only a few offered suggestions. _an excess_____

Vocabulary and
Spelling

Lesson 94
Building Vocabulary: Word Roots

The main part of a word is its **root**. When this is a complete word, it is called a **base word**. A root is often combined with a prefix (a part attached to the beginning), a suffix (a part attached to the end), or another root. Prefixes and suffixes often change the direction of a word's meaning. The chart below lists some word roots and their meanings.

Roots	Meanings
arch	rule, govern
ben	good
ced	go
dic, dict	say, speak
fac, fact	make
gen	class, start
hydr	water
man	hand
port	carry
sci	know
string, strict	bind
trac	draw, pull
viv	live, alive

▶ **Exercise 1** Underline the root of each word. Using a dictionary when needed, define each word. If there is more than one definition, use one that emphasizes the meaning of the root.

gen<u>eric</u> __characteristic of a whole group__

1. mon<u>arch</u> __the single or sole ruler of state__

2. matri<u>arch</u>y __government by women__

3. hier<u>arch</u>y __a classification of people according to a specific standard__

4. <u>ben</u>efit __help__

5. <u>ben</u>efactor __a person who gives help__

6. <u>ben</u>evolence __an inclination to do good__

7. pro<u>ced</u>ure __a particular course of action, a way to proceed__

8. pre<u>ced</u>e __to be, come, or go before in time, place, order, rank, or importance__

9. ante<u>ced</u>ent __going or coming before in time, order, or logic__

10. <u>dict</u>ate __to say or read something out loud to be written by another__

11. pre<u>dict</u>able __able to be foreseen; able to say in advance__

12. syndicate _to sell for publication in many newspapers_

13. valedictory _a farewell speech, usually given at graduation_

14. manufacture _to make something by hand or by machinery_

15. fact _that which is done or made_

16. genesis _the way in which something comes to be; the beginning_

17. generation _all the people born and living at the same time_

18. homogeneous _composed of similar or identical elements or parts; uniform_

19. hydraulic _operated by the movement and force of liquid_

20. anhydrous _without water_

21. rehydration _the restoration of water or other liquid to_

22. manacles _handcuffs; fetters or shackles for the hands_

23. manicure _the care of the hands, especially a trimming or polishing of the fingernails_

24. portage _a carrying of boats and supplies overland from one lake or river to another, as during a canoe trip_

25. portfolio _a flat, portable case for carrying loose sheets of paper, manuscripts, or drawings_

26. transport _to carry from one place to another, especially over long distances_

27. conscious _knowing or feeling_

28. conscientious _governed by, or made or done according to, what one knows is right_

29. prescient _apparently aware of things before they happen or come into being_

30. constrict _to make smaller or narrower, especially at one place, by binding, squeezing, or shrinking_

31. restrict _to keep within certain limits_

32. astringent _that which contracts body tissue and checks secretions_

33. tractor _a vehicle with heavy tires or a chain of continuous metal tracks used to pull heavy loads over rough ground_

34. distract _to draw away in another direction_

35. survive _to live longer than; to live through_

36. vivid _full of life_

Lesson 95
Building Vocabulary: Prefixes and Suffixes

Prefixes are syllables attached before a root to alter or enhance its meaning. For example, the prefix *un-* gives the opposite meaning to any word to which it is attached.

PREFIX	MEANING	PREFIX	MEANING
circum-	around, about	*il-, im-, in-,* and *ir-*	not
de-	from, down	*mis-*	do badly, hate
dis-	not	*pre-*	before
hyper-	excessive	*sub-*	beneath, less than

Suffixes can be added to root words to create new words with new meanings. Suffixes also have grammatical functions and can change, for example, an adjective like *deaf* into a noun like *deafness* with the addition of a suffix like *-ness.* Note that the spelling of the root can change when a suffix is added.

SUFFIXES	MEANING	PART OF SPEECH FORMED
-able, -ible	capable of, able to be	adjective
-ant, -ent	one who does an action	concrete noun
-en	to become	verb
-hood	condition, state	abstract noun
-ist	one who	concrete noun
-ly	in the manner or way of	adverb
-ous	full of	adjective
-sion, -tion	the state of being something	abstract noun

▶ **Exercise 1** Underline the prefix in items 1 through 10 and the suffix in items 11 through 20. Using the meanings of the prefixes and suffixes listed above, write the meaning of the word. Check your answers in a dictionary.

illegal _not legal_

1. devaluate _take value from_

2. misrepresent _represent badly_

3. circumnavigate _navigate around_

4. disrespectful _not respectful_

5. hyperactive _overly active_

6. subtotal _less than total_

7. illogical _not logical_

8. improper _not proper_

9. prehistoric _before history_

10. irregular _not regular_

11. exportable _able to be exported_

12. student _one who studies_

13. likelihood _condition of being likely_

14. servant _one who serves_

15. normally _in a normal way_

16. confusion _state of being confused_

17. famous _full of fame_

18. humorist _one who makes humor_

19. tough<u>en</u> __to become tough_____

20. flex<u>ible</u> __able to be flexed_____

▶ **Exercise 2** Underline at least one prefix or suffix in each word. Write the meaning of the word.
Check your answers in a dictionary.

    <u>im</u>proper __not proper_____

1. <u>dis</u>agree<u>able</u> __not able to agree_____

2. descend<u>ant</u> __one who descends_____

3. <u>sub</u>committee __a lesser committee_____

4. mother<u>hood</u> __the state of being a mother_____

5. art<u>ist</u> __one who makes art_____

6. <u>im</u>balanced __not balanced_____

7. <u>circum</u>scribe __to mark off or draw a line around_____

8. <u>de</u>congestant __something that removes congestion_____

9. <u>hyper</u>critical __overly critical_____

10. sensitive<u>ly</u> __in a sensitive manner_____

11. <u>dis</u>advantage __not an advantage_____

12. cancer<u>ous</u> __full of cancer_____

13. absorp<u>tion</u> __the fact or state of being absorbed_____

14. <u>pre</u>operative __before an operation_____

15. adop<u>tion</u> __state of being adopted_____

16. <u>un</u>popular __not popular_____

17. stiff<u>en</u> __to make or become stiff_____

18. <u>mis</u>behave __to behave badly_____

19. ten<u>sion</u> __state of being tense_____

20. <u>in</u>compress<u>ible</u> __not able to be compressed_____

Lesson 96
Basic Spelling Rules I

SPELLING *IE* AND *EI*

The *i* comes before the *e*, except when both letters follow *c* or when both letters are pronounced together as an $\bar{a}$ sound. However, many exceptions to this rule exist.

ach**ie**ve (*i* before *e*)   rec**ei**ve (*ei* after *c*)   sl**ei**gh (*a* sound)   s**ei**ze (exception)

SPELLING *-CEDE, -CEED,* AND *-SEDE*

The $s\bar{e}d$ sound at the end of a word is usually spelled -cede. *Supersede, succeed, proceed,* and *exceed* are exceptions.

ac**cede**   con**cede**   inter**cede**   pre**cede**

SPELLING UNSTRESSED VOWELS

An unstressed vowel is a vowel sound that is not emphasized when the word is pronounced. For example, in *or-i-gin* the second syllable, *i,* is unstressed. To determine how an unstressed syllable is spelled, think of a related word in which the syllable containing that vowel sound is stressed. For *origin* think of *original.*

▶ **Exercise 1** **Write each word, adding *ie* or *ei* where necessary. Items 1 through 15 follow the rules; items 16 through 20 are exceptions to the rules.**

ch—f *chief* _____

1. f—nd *fiend* _____
2. s—ge *siege* _____
3. br—f *brief* _____
4. pr—st *priest* _____
5. repr—ve *reprieve* _____
6. r—gn *reign* _____
7. sl—gh *sleigh* _____
8. b—ge *beige* _____
9. v—n *vein* _____
10. h—nous *heinous* _____

11. dec—t *deceit* _____
12. rec—pt *receipt* _____
13. perc—ve *perceive* _____
14. misconc—ve *misconceive* _____
15. imperc—vable *imperceivable* _____
16. d—ty *deity* _____
17. h—r *heir* _____
18. effic—nt *efficient* _____
19. kal—doscope *kaleidoscope* _____
20. h—fer *heifer* _____

Vocabulary and Spelling

Name _____ Class _____ Date _____

▶ **Exercise 2** Fill in the missing letter or letters in each word.

trag___e___ dy

1. succe___ed___   11. re___cede___

2. interce___de___   12. se___cede___

3. pre___ce___de   13. ex___ceed___

4. proc___ee___d   14. con___cede___

5. super___se___de   15. ac___cede___

6. med___i___cine   16. com___a___tose

7. fall___a___cy   17. com___e___dy

8. col___o___ny   18. magn___e___tize

9. sed___a___tive   19. comb___i___nation

10. dram___a___tist   20. crit___i___cism

SUFFIXES AND THE SILENT *E*

When adding a suffix that begins with a consonant to a word that ends in silent *e*, keep the *e*. When adding a suffix that begins with a vowel or *y* to a word that ends in silent *e*, drop the *e*. When adding a suffix that begins with *a* or *o* to a word that ends in *ce* or *ge*, keep the *e* so the word will retain the soft *c* or *g* sound. When adding a suffix that begins with a vowel to a word that ends in *ee* or *oe*, keep the *e*.

plac**ement** (*e* + suffix)   excit**able** (drop *e*, add suffix)
chang**eable** (*e* + suffix)   se**eing** (*e* + suffix)

When adding a suffix to a word that ends in a consonant + *y*, change the *y* to *i*. Do not change the *y* to *i* when the suffix begins with *i*. When adding a suffix to a word that ends in a vowel + *y*, keep the *y*.

tr**ied** (*y* changed to *i* + suffix)   cop**ying** (*y* + suffix)   jo**yous** (*y* + suffix)

▶ **Exercise 3** Use the spelling rules in this lesson to spell the words indicated.

reuse + -able reusable

1. dose + -age dosage   6. notice + -able noticeable

2. degrade + -able degradable   7. courage + -ous courageous

3. guide + -ance guidance   8. foresee + -able foreseeable

4. replace + -able replaceable   9. tiptoe + -ing tiptoeing

5. salvage + -able salvageable   10. accompany + -ed accompanied

Lesson 97
Basic Spelling Rules II

DOUBLING THE FINAL CONSONANT

Double the final consonant before adding a suffix that begins with a vowel to a word that ends in a single consonant preceded by a single vowel.

tip**ping**   submi**tting**   rese**tting**

ADDING -*LY* AND -*NESS*

When adding -*ly* to a word that ends in a single *l*, keep the *l*. If a word ends in a double *l*, drop one *l*. If a word ends in a consonant +*le*, drop the *le*. When adding -*ness* to a word that ends in *n*, keep the *n*.

real**ly**   hil**ly**   horri**bly**   mea**nness**

FORMING COMPOUND WORDS

When joining a word that ends in a consonant to a word that begins with a consonant, keep both consonants.

da**yb**reak   su**ns**et

▶ **Exercise 1** Use the spelling rules in this lesson to spell the words indicated.

drop + -ing __dropping__

1. sled + -ing __sledding__
2. numerical + -ly __numerically__
3. slip + -age __slippage__
4. modern + -ness __modernness__
5. clan + -ish __clannish__
6. rebel + -ion __rebellion__
7. book + keeper __bookkeeper__
8. offset + -ing __offsetting__
9. full + -ly __fully__
10. camp + site __campsite__
11. dismal + -ly __dismally__
12. agreeable + -ly __agreeably__

13. underbid + -ing __underbidding__
14. shrill + -ly __shrilly__
15. card + board __cardboard__
16. lean + -ness __leanness__
17. prefer + -ing __preferring__
18. ear + ring __earring__
19. humble + -ly __humbly__
20. critical + -ly __critically__
21. knot + -ed __knotted__
22. chill + -ly __chilly__
23. able + -ly __ably__
24. night + time __nighttime__

25. stern + -ness _sternness_

26. broken + -ness _brokenness_

27. especial + -ly _especially_

28. lamp + post _lamppost_

29. admirable + -ly _admirably_

30. near + -by _nearby_

GENERAL RULES FOR FORMING PLURALS

Most nouns form their plurals by adding -s or -es. However, nouns that end in -ch, -s, -sh, -x, or -z form their plurals by adding -es. If the noun ends in a consonant +y, change y to i and add -es. If the noun ends in -lf, change the f to a v and add -es. If the noun ends in -fe, change the f to a v and add -s.

books   lun**ches**   fol**lies**   shel**ves**   li**ves**

SPECIAL RULES FOR PLURALS

To form the plural of proper names and one-word compound nouns, follow the general rules for plurals. To form the plural of hyphenated compound nouns or compound nouns of more than one word, make the most important word plural.

D'Albertos   Jones**es**   blueber**ries**   mother**s**-in-law

Some nouns have the same singular and plural forms.

series   deer

▶ **Exercise 2** **Write the plural of each word.**

mess _messes_

1. church _churches_

2. patio _patios_

3. donkey _donkeys_

4. self _selves_

5. desk _desks_

6. city _cities_

7. proof _proofs_

8. cuff _cuffs_

9. fox _foxes_

10. Gomez _Gomezes_

11. waltz _waltzes_

12. lieutenant governor _lieutenant governors_

13. all-star _all-stars_

14. thrush _thrushes_

15. sheep _sheep_

16. festival _festivals_

17. basketball _basketballs_

18. wife _wives_

19. business _businesses_

20. teammate _teammates_

21. calf _calves_

22. bunch _bunches_

23. Chin _Chins_

24. knife _knives_

Vocabulary and Spelling

☑ Review: Building Vocabulary

Nowadays the term "Creole cuisine," a relatively recent American food interest, *conjures up* images of blackened fish and overbearing spices. *Natives* of southern Louisiana, who have enjoyed Creole delights at their dinner tables for generations, know their *culinary tradition* is rich and complex. It is a popular *misconception* to consider the terms "Creole" and "Cajun" *interchangeable.* While there are similarities, the two styles are *distinctly* different. The *inhabitants* of New Orleans created Creole *cuisine* over many years with the *influence* of many cultures. The French, Spanish, Africans, Native Americans, Cajuns, Chinese, and Germans all contributed to the *genuine* Creole cuisine enjoyed in homes in southern Louisiana. The Cajuns, who *emigrated* from Nova Scotia in the eighteenth century and settled in the more *remote* areas of the Louisiana countryside, *improvised* with ingredients readily available in the swamps and bayous. While Cajun cooking *features* the fresh food that the wetlands *bountifully* provide, Creole cuisine *developed* over the centuries, changing to accommodate the needs and tastes of each new group that came to Louisiana to settle.

▶ **Exercise 1** **Fill in the blank with the letter of the word or phrase that best defines each italicized word in the above passage.**

___c___   images
       a. eras   **c.** concepts
       b. dreams   **d.** formulas

___b___ **1.** nowadays
       a. soon   **c.** rarely
       b. at the present time   **d.** occasionally

___a___ **2.** conjures up
       a. calls to mind   **c.** confuses
       b. performs magic   **d.** brings together

___a___ **3.** natives
       a. people born in the area   **c.** inborn
       b. senior citizens   **d.** visitors

___d___ **4.** culinary
       a. holiday   **c.** community
       b. char-broiled   **d.** of cooking

___b___ **5.** tradition
       a. beliefs   **c.** vocabulary
       b. customs   **d.** subjects

_____a_____ **6.** misconception
    a. mistaken idea   **c.** belief
    b. understanding   **d.** pregnancy

_____c_____ **7.** interchangeable
    a. the same size   **c.** having the same meaning
    b. from the same source   **d.** movable

_____b_____ **8.** distinctly
    a. vaguely   **c.** ordinarily
    b. definitely   **d.** separate

_____c_____ **9.** inhabitants
    a. visitors   **c.** people who live in a place
    b. people who have moved to the city   **d.** original settlers of a place

_____b_____ **10.** cuisine
    a. kitchen appliances   **c.** decor
    b. style of cooking   **d.** stored food

_____c_____ **11.** influence
    a. authority   **c.** effect
    b. bias   **d.** motivate

_____a_____ **12.** genuine
    a. real   **c.** counterfeit
    b. sincere   **d.** recent

_____a_____ **13.** emigrated
    a. moved from   **c.** descended from
    b. cared about   **d.** changed names

_____c_____ **14.** remote
    a. pointless   **c.** outlying
    b. public   **d.** private

_____a_____ **15.** improvised
    a. made do   **c.** made better
    b. fake   **d.** wrong

_____b_____ **16.** features
    a. qualities   **c.** portrays
    b. highlights   **d.** fastens

_____b_____ **17.** bountifully
    a. charitably   **c.** meagerly
    b. abundantly   **d.** reluctantly

_____c_____ **18.** developed
    a. became stronger   **c.** evolved
    b. became more available   **d.** faded away

Vocabulary and Spelling

☑ Review: Basic Spelling Rules

▶ **Exercise 1 Underline the word that is spelled correctly.**

1. In medieval warfare, castles were put under (siege, seige) for many months.

2. Truly, I can not (percieve, perceive) any difference.

3. Queen Victoria was the (reigning, riegning) monarch of England for sixty-four years from 1837 to 1901.

4. South Carolina was the first state to (sesede, secede, seceed) from the nation in 1860.

5. The highway patrol mounted a campaign urging motorists not to (exsede, excede, exceed) the speed limits.

6. Jacob couldn't remember the (combination, combenation) to his lock.

7. The wrappings on this package are all (biodegradeable, biodegradable).

8. Anne's scar is hardly (noticeable, noticable) now.

9. (Providing, Provideing) child care in the workplace has significantly reduced the absenteeism among parents of young children.

10. This order is wrong. I know I (specifyed, specified) the color as blue.

11. We can't decamp yet. The tent is still (driing, drying) in the sun.

12. Even though I was (annoyed, annoid), I remained calm and collected.

13. Miguel hasn't yet decided what courses he will take to meet the language (requirement, requirment) for college admission.

14. Wong enjoys (struming, strumming) his guitar while thinking about other things.

15. The racquetball (rocketed, rocketted) off both walls before Ian could hit it again.

16. I am already (regreting, regretting) my decision.

17. The detectives were (investigateing, investigating) the mysterious disappearance of the mayor.

18. The school is (scheduling, scheduleing) parent-teacher conferences for Tuesday.

19. The (preferred, prefered) dress code for ushers is white shirts and black slacks.

20. I wouldn't mind (repeatting, repeating) if I thought you had listened the first time.

21. To reduce the fat content of your diet, look for (leaness, leanness) in the cuts of meat you buy.

22. Ryan was really excited to have Geoffry as a (teammate, teamate).

23. Stacey didn't enjoy the movie even though it was (<u>critically</u>, criticaly) acclaimed.

24. A sixty-degree temperature in August seems (chily, <u>chilly</u>).

25. Mrs. Reed (<u>humbly</u>, humblely) accepted the award.

▶ **Exercise 2 Write the plural form of each noun.**

bike <u>bikes</u>

1. bench <u>benches</u>
2. video <u>videos</u>
3. turkey <u>turkeys</u>
4. bookshelf <u>bookshelves</u>
5. sister-in-law <u>sisters-in-law</u>
6. activity <u>activities</u>
7. belief <u>beliefs</u>
8. staff <u>staffs</u>
9. duplex <u>duplexes</u>
10. topaz <u>topazes</u>

11. Gonzalez <u>Gonzalezes</u>
12. Rand <u>Rands</u>
13. kickoff <u>kickoffs</u>
14. brush <u>brushes</u>
15. leaf <u>leaves</u>
16. library <u>libraries</u>
17. monkey <u>monkeys</u>
18. life <u>lives</u>
19. bus <u>buses</u>
20. holiday <u>holidays</u>

Composition

Unit 14: Composition

Lesson 98

The Writing Process: Prewriting

Before you begin writing anything, there are several factors that you must determine about what you are going to write. The **topic** is the subject about which you will write. You can determine the topic by *freewriting,* writing anything that comes to mind; *collecting,* gathering information from various sources; *making lists* about one key word or idea; and *asking general questions.* After a topic is chosen, determine the **purpose,** which is the reason for writing. One piece can have more than one purpose. The purpose is a narrowed form of the topic. Finally, you must determine the **audience,** or who is intended to read the piece. The overall nature of the piece will be different if it is intended for your best friend as opposed to the President. Knowing your audience will tell you how much they know about the topic, what writing style is needed, and what level of vocabulary is necessary. All of these factors will color your writing differently. Basically, you will determine *what* you want to say (topic), *how* you want to say it (purpose), and *to whom* you want to say it (audience).

▶ **Exercise 1** **Spend 10 minutes prewriting, using any of the techniques listed above.**

_____

_____

_____

_____

_____

_____

_____

_____

_____

_____

_____

_____

_____

_____

_____

_____

_____

_____

_____

▶ **Exercise 2** **Choose five specific topics that can be found in your prewriting from the previous exercise.**

_____

_____

▶ **Exercise 3** **Identify the purpose and topic of each topic sentence given below.**

Has the food in the cafeteria ever tasted worse? _topic: cafeteria food; purpose: to persuade_

the reader that the cafeteria food is bad

1. Currently, legislators are debating whether or not to increase the legal driving age. _topic: driving_

   age; purpose: to inform reader of current legislation

2. Annette is clearly the best candidate for mayor. _topic: Annette's mayoral campaign; purpose: to_

   persuade reader to vote for Annette

3. The violins began the piece the orchestra played. _topic: the orchestra's piece; purpose: to narrate the_

   orchestra's playing of the piece

4. This town has a ten o'clock curfew. _topic: the curfew; purpose: to inform the reader of the curfew_

   _____

5. Did you hear the one about the three-legged dog? _topic: a joke; purpose: to amuse the reader_

6. The earth is in grave danger from our constant pollution. _topic: pollution; purpose: to inform_

   and persuade the reader about environmental concerns

7. The locker, standing as tall as I, is painted red. _topic: locker; purpose: to describe the locker to_

   the reader

8. If you have not tried fly-fishing, you are really missing out on some great fun.

   topic: fly fishing; purpose: to persuade the reader that fly-fishing is fun

9. The television show began with a fade-in before the credits. _topic: a television show; purpose: to_

describe the format of the show _____

10. Many endangered species could become extinct within our lifetime.

topic: extinction; purpose: to inform and possibly persuade the reader concerning endangered species

and their possible extinction _____

▶ **Exercise 4 Write a sentence that conveys both the topic and the purpose listed below.**

topic: books; purpose: to inform the reader of new titles available Twenty new books are now

displayed in the window of the bookstore.

1. topic: job; purpose: to persuade an employer to hire I possess the strong leadership qualities

needed to be successful at this job.

2. topic: fast food; purpose: to inform the reader of the different styles of fast food

Although often thought of as a business of burgers, fast food restaurants offer many styles of dining.

3. topic: movie; purpose: to amuse a friend with a funny scene from a film The scene in which the

piano rolls down the steps made my sides hurt from laughing.

4. topic: family; purpose: to describe your family to a stranger There is nothing more special than a

family, and mine is no exception to that rule.

5. topic: entertainment; purpose: to persuade a friend to join you with that entertainment

You do not know how much fun a rock concert can be unless you've been to one.

6. topic: the solution to a mystery; purpose: to describe the events of the case By piecing together

the separate clues, the answer becomes obvious.

7. topic: money; purpose: to inform a manufacturer that you want a cash refund The product I

purchased was faulty, and I would like my money back.

8. topic: sporting event; purpose: to narrate a commentary of the event The quarterback takes the

snap and is flushed out of the pocket.

9. topic: military action; purpose: to inform a soldier of the next mission Your mission will take you

into the Middle East.

10. topic: clothes; purpose: to persuade someone to buy you an article of clothing as a present

That pair of jeans would look very nice on me.

Composition

▶ **Exercise 5** **Write a brief paragraph about the controversy for each audience listed.**

Controversy: Whether or not to put a soda pop vending machine in the cafeteria.

1. audience: the student body

_____
_____
_____
_____
_____
_____

2. audience: the office

_____
_____
_____
_____
_____
_____

3. audience: parents

_____
_____
_____
_____
_____
_____

4. audience: the custodial staff

_____
_____
_____
_____
_____
_____

Lesson 99
The Writing Process: Drafting

After prewriting, you can begin drafting, or writing the piece in paragraph form. From the topic and the purpose you can develop a theme, the point the piece is trying to make. This theme should be stated in a thesis statement in the first paragraph. A paragraph consists of a topic sentence, which states a main idea related to the theme, and related sentences that support the main idea with details. Depending on the audience, theme, and purpose, you may choose to adopt a different style or voice, which gives the writing its "feel."

▶ **Exercise 1** State a theme that is consistent with the topic and the purpose given. Use a complete sentence.

topic: glaciers; purpose: inform Glaciers are slow-moving blocks of ice travelling over our planet.

1. topic: castles; purpose: describe Castles are often characterized by a majestic atmosphere.

2. topic: basketball; purpose: narrate The home team won its championship game.

3. topic: airplanes; purpose: inform Jet engines have a very complex design.

4. topic: smoking; purpose: inform Some have suggested that inhaling second-hand smoke can be worse than smoking.

5. topic: cars; purpose: persuade The Porsche is the best-designed sports car.

6. topic: languages; purpose: describe The French language is characterized by syllables run together with soft sounds.

7. topic: the Vietnam War; purpose: narrate The Vietnam conflict began with no formal declaration of war.

8. topic: painting; purpose: describe My friend's paintings flow across the canvas.

9. topic: politics; purpose: persuade There are many reasons to vote for Akira Chan in November.

10. topic: AIDS; purpose: inform AIDS occurs as a result of the human immunodeficiency virus.

11. topic: fashion; purpose: describe The flowing silk contributes to the fluid nature of the dress.

12. topic: singing; purpose: amuse That spoof on the latest pop song contains several hilarious lyrics.

13. topic: computers; purpose: describe The large memory on my hard drive allows me to perform a variety of tasks.

14. topic: weddings; purpose: narrate The bride and groom gave their vows to each other.

Composition

15. topic: giraffes; purpose: amuse _Seeing a giraffe bend down for a drink of water can really make you_ laugh.

16. topic: apartments; purpose: describe _Several flights of stairs led to my uncle's apartment._

17. topic: school; purpose: amuse _My most embarrassing moment at school was when I tripped in the play._

18. topic: celebrities; purpose: persuade _The Academy Awards is the most important event in Hollywood._

19. topic: situation comedies; purpose: narrate _The show began with a lot of slapstick._

20. topic: math; purpose: inform _Most story problems can be solved using a series of simple steps._

▶ Exercise 2 **Write a complete thesis statement from the theme given below.**

theme: the danger of being an astronaut _Although being an astronaut can be exciting, much danger is involved._

1. theme: the significance of the invention of the telephone _The invention of the telephone pioneered the ever-expanding business of telecommunications._

2. theme: the beauty of wintertime _The light snow on the ground is just one of many beauties of the winter months._

3. theme: the exhilaration of horseback riding _Riding a horse can make your heart pound with excitement._

4. theme: the impact of photography on journalism _Photography provided the public with real images of world events._

5. theme: the excitement of skiing _Nothing can beat the feeling of racing down a ski slope!_

6. theme: the unique quality of rap music _Rap music offers a variety of styles, presentations, and artists._

7. theme: the plight of Native Americans _Many Native Americans died during the early years of America._

8. theme: the high-quality acting in a play _The performers' style was tremendous._

9. theme: the hardships of the American frontier _Many people braved specific dangers to settle in this country._

10. theme: the variety of events in track and field _The sport of track and field offers many different events._

11. theme: the joys of woodworking _Woodworking can be relaxing and fun._

12. theme: the events leading the world into World War II _No one single event started World War II._

13. theme: the humor found in reading certain comic strips _The comics in the paper always make me laugh._

Composition

14. theme: the vastness of the oceans A majority of our planet is covered by the oceans.

15. theme: the accomplishments of the Aztecs The Aztecs developed some practices and techniques that pre-dated Western civilization.

16. theme: the health benefits of dancing Dancing can offer a good, healthy aerobic workout.

17. theme: the importance of rain forests for new medicines Many medicines can be derived from rain forest plants.

18. theme: the suspected causes of cancer There is much speculation as to the cause of cancer.

19. theme: the chain of command below the President. A direct chain of command leads from the President.

20. theme: the many different species of birds Birds have a tremendous variety of species.

▶ **Exercise 3 Write four related sentences that provide details to support the topic sentence below.**

1. Martin Luther King Jr. accomplished much for the American civil rights movement.

_____

_____

_____

_____

2. Japanese culture seems exotic and mysterious to some. _____

_____

_____

_____

3. A variety of career opportunities await me after I finish school. _____

_____

_____

_____

4. Different families celebrate holidays differently. _____

_____

_____

_____

Composition

5. Finding the right hairstyle requires a little thought. _____

_____

_____

_____

_____

▶ **Exercise 4** **Draft a brief one-paragraph piece concerning the following theme. Be sure to incorporate a proper voice and style.**

1. theme: thanking a friend for a gift   _The style and voice should be informal and friendly._

_____

_____

_____

2. theme: urging a politician to vote a certain way on an issue _The style and voice should be formal._

_____

_____

_____

3. theme: requesting a day off from your employer _The style and voice should be formal and_

businesslike.

_____

_____

_____

4. theme: demanding a formal apology for a public insult _The style and voice should be somewhat_

formal and firm.

_____

_____

_____

5. theme: informing your family about your vacation _The style and voice should be informal and_

relaxed.

_____

_____

_____

Composition

Lesson 100
The Writing Process: Revising

Revise, or improve, your writing after completing a draft. Revising a paper allows you to improve the quality of the sentences and paragraphs. As you revise, check for three things. First, check for meaning. Make sure the piece is stating the intended theme. Then, check for unity. Make sure the organization is logical and the necessary details support the topics. Finally, check for coherence. Make sure the writing flows and the communication is clear.

▶ **Exercise 1** **Reorganize each paragraph for meaning, unity, and coherence.**

1. Earvin "Magic" Johnson played professional basketball for the Los Angeles Lakers. He went to Michigan State to play college basketball. Earvin Johnson was born in 1959. Recently, he contracted HIV and retired from playing professional basketball. He was nicknamed "Magic" because of a spectacular basketball game he played in high school.   Earvin Johnson was born in

1959. He was nicknamed "Magic" because of a spectacular basketball game he played in high school. He went

to Michigan State to play college basketball. Earvin "Magic" Johnson played professional basketball for the Los

Angeles Lakers. Recently, he contracted HIV and retired from playing professional basketball.

_____

_____

_____

_____

2. The Battle of the Bulge included an unsuccessful attempt by the Germans to make the Allies retreat. It was one of the next major military steps after D-Day in July 1944. The Battle of the Bulge, also called the Battle of the Ardennes, raged from December 16, 1944 to January 16, 1945. It got its name from Winston Churchill, who said that the Germans drove a "bulge," or wedge, into the Allied lines.

The Battle of the Bulge, also called the Battle of the Ardennes, raged from December 16, 1944, to January 16,

1945. It got its name from Winston Churchill, who said that the Germans drove a "bulge," or wedge, into the

Allied lines. The Battle of the Bulge included an unsuccessful attempt by the Germans to make the Allies

retreat. It was one of the next major military steps after D-Day in July 1944.

_____

_____

_____

_____

Composition

3. Clearly, pronghorns are built for blazing speed. They are similar to deer and antelope. Pronghorns, the fastest of all American mammals, can easily outrun their enemies. Their huge windpipes, lungs, and hearts accommodate sudden bursts of energy. <u>Pronghorns, the fastest of all American mammals, can easily outrun their enemies. They are similar to deer and antelope. Their huge windpipes, lungs, and hearts accommodate sudden bursts of energy. Clearly, pronghorns are built for blazing speed.</u>

_____

_____

_____

▶ **Exercise 2 Revise and rewrite the paragraph below.**

1. The idea of a computer has been around for a very long time. Microprocessors make modern computers very fast. Much faster than early computers like ENIAC. I have a computer at home. In 1944, Howard Aiken of Harvard built an early digital computer. It was Mark I. In 1642, Blaise Pascal of France built a calculating machine. It used rotating toothed wheels. In 1946, J. Presper Eckert Jr. and John W. Mauchly built ENIAC (*Electronic Numerical Integrator And Computer*). It was 1,000 times faster than Mark I. In 1930, Vannevar Bush made a "differential analyzer," a machine to perform calculus. Transistors made computers faster and smaller. So did integrated circuits. <u>The idea of the computer dates back to France in 1642, when Blaise Pascal built the first calculating machine. This machine used rotating toothed wheels to perform calculations. Almost three hundred years later, in 1930, Vannevar Bush built what he called a "differential analyzer" to perform calculus. The first digital computer, called Mark I, was invented by Howard Aiken in 1944. But it was not long before J. Presper Eckert Jr. and John W. Mauchly built a machine that ran over one thousand times faster than Mark I. This computer was known as ENIAC (*Electronic Numerical Integrator And Computer*). Inventions such as transistors, integrated circuits, and microprocessors have made computers much smaller and faster.</u>

_____

_____

_____

_____

_____

Lesson 101
The Writing Process: Editing

After revising your work, you can **edit** and clarify your ideas in writing. While you edit, look for the following items: correct word usage, subject-verb agreement, correct verb tenses, clear pronoun references, run-on sentences, and sentence fragments. When editing, cross out words and write new words in margins and spaces. **Proofreading** entails checking for spelling, punctuation, and capitalization errors. Use the following proofreading marks:

MARK	MEANING	EXAMPLE
^ (caret)	insert	sould
ϒ (dele)	delete	thje
#	insert space	hockeypuck
‿	close up space	over use
≡	capitalize	texas
/	make lowercase	Mine
⬭ sp	check spelling	recieve sp
∼	switch order	you me or
¶	new paragraph	...how I felt. Just then....

▶ **Exercise 1** Edit the sentence for clarity and correct grammar.

The best football guy, he be it.   *is* ^player

1. She are the starling of the team.   *is*

2. Gary asked Ken why he should do that.   *, Ken,*

3. Boy did we work for Over five hours!   *!* *ed*

4. My brother run to the store yesterday.   *ran*

5. I bought some bread came home quickly.   *and*

6. Looking at the *Lone Ranger* movie are fun.   *Watching* *is*

7. Dogs and cats makes great pets.

8. The coach not know why I left practice.   *does*

9. Two friends of mine Kenji and Jose.   *are*

10. That instructor reallyknows the Subject.   *#*

▶ **Exercise 2** **Edit the paragraph for clarity and correct grammar.**

Yesterday, I ~~had to~~ give my first ~~aural~~(oral) report ever ~~since~~. I don't know how I did it ~~I was so~~
~~nervous~~. I was so nervous that the back of my knee caps ~~was~~(were) sweating. But I ~~did it I'll never know~~(gave the report successfully). I
guess I could ~~of did~~(have done) as ~~good~~(well) without worrying as much as I had. (It)Went great(!). This ~~is the kinda~~(of)
report ~~where you speak~~(is spoken, not written).

▶ **Exercise 3** **Proofread each sentence for spelling, punctuation, and capitalization errors.**

I was (nervus)[sp] when I moved from ontario,canada.

1. he returned from (scalling)[sp] the mountains;

2. Ana saw a pod of (dolfins)[sp] (swiming)[sp] off the florida coast.

3. Jack considered mr. Han, his Algebra teacher,among his personal (heros)[sp]

4. My bike (roored)[sp] over the hill.

5. Struggling,the (majician)[sp] freed (hisself)[sp]

6. Because this Bandage keeps falling off,this cut will never (heel)[sp]

7. I bought the new (albumn)[sp] at zany's, that new record store.

8. They visited the great (Smoky) Mountains.

9. space (travve)[sp] is (dream a of) the future.

10. Jane and leanne (wattered)[sp] the (poinsetas)[sp]

▶ **Exercise 3** **Proofread the paragraph for spelling, punctuation, and capitalization errors.**

The Special Effects in motion (pitures)[sp] (ofen)[sp] add[#]to the (realisium)[sp] of a film. Some times movies
are mad[e] (simply)[sp] to show[#]off, some (effects special)[#] This part of[#]the movie-making (prosess)[sp] has often
(contribeuted)[sp] to (enormus)[sp] budgets for certain[#]films. With new technology,in Computer Animation,
movie makers can bring The Impossible to Life. A process known[#]as "morphing" can visually
change one image to[#]another. who knows the limit of this (technolgy)[sp]?

Composition

Lesson 102
The Writing Process: Presenting

After completing a piece of writing, you may want to **present**, or share your work with others. The idea of presentation can come as early as the prewriting stage. Knowing the audience often defines the market for your work. Many times, the nature of the material also defines the market. Several different outlets exist for writing composed by ninth graders. Some markets include school forums, which include school newspapers and classroom presentations; community forums, which include community groups and local community papers; contests, which are often offered by magazines; and open-market forums, which include professional magazines and periodicals. Carefully examine your writing and determine the audience. Then search for a market that serves that audience. You may find the *Market Guide for Young Writers,* available at libraries, very useful. Some outlets, like classroom presentations, exchange groups, and community productions, offer a chance for an oral presentation. In this case, prepare visual aids to add to your presentation.

▶ **Exercise 1** **Suggest a market for the writing described below.**

an essay on model-making __a hobby magazine or newsletter or a school assignment__

1. a short romance story __a romance fiction magazine__

2. an original song composition __a local band or a radio station__

3. a review of a movie or play __the school newspaper or community newspaper__

4. an anecdotal essay about your childhood __a literary journal or an exchange forum__

5. an opinion piece concerning the school's curriculum __the school newspaper or the community newspaper__

6. a brief biography of your favorite actor or actress __any school forum or a community group__

7. a humorous year in review of your freshman class __the school yearbook__

8. a poem about nature __a poetry magazine, literary journal, or school publication__

9. a report on a recent scientific development __school newspaper or science magazine__

10. an analysis of one of Shakespeare's plays __a literary journal or school publication__

▶ **Exercise 2** **Suggest two visual aids to increase the effectiveness of the writing piece listed.**

a speech about the ozone layer __photos of the ozone hole and models of the chemicals involved__

1. a research paper on economics __a graph of economic trends and a chart explaining economic terms__

2. a short play __costumes for the actors and props for the set design__

Name _____ Class _____ Date _____

3. a music composition _costumes for musicians and dancers_

4. a review of a film or television show _photo stills from the film or television show and a chart of_ ratings

5. an informative speech about history _posters of historical sites and artifacts or antiques from that time_

6. a poem about nature _photos and hand sketches of the nature described_

7. an anecdotal speech about your vacation _slides and souvenirs from your vacation_

8. an explanation of the sports teams in your school _photos of the teams and programs from the_ sporting events

9. a speech to the student body about your running for student council _a list of your activities_ and a propaganda picture

10. a plea to the community to donate to a wildlife fund _pictures of the wildlife in need and photos of_ the community

▶ **Exercise 3** **Prewrite on any topic desired. Write a short piece with a specific audience in mind. Then, explain how and to whom you might present this piece.**

Students should follow established prewriting steps and drafting procedures.

_____
_____
_____
_____
_____
_____
_____
_____
_____
_____
_____
_____
_____

Composition

Lesson 103
Outlining

Outlining is a method used to organize the information in a piece of writing. Because prewriting can often be a jumble of words and phrases, it makes sense to organize that information before starting the drafting process. One method of constructing an outline is to put all your prewriting information on index cards. These cards can then be arranged by main topics and the details supporting that topic. To write your outline, indicate your main topics with Roman numerals. Put supporting details, or subtopics, beneath each topic with capital letters. These subtopics can have subdivisions as regular numbers. However, if you subdivide a topic or subtopic, at least two subdivisions must be named. For example, an outline of an audition for the school play might look like this:

I. Trying Out for the School Play
   A. First time trying out
      1. I was nervous and excited
      2. I did not think that I would remember my lines
      3. I had to audition for Ms. Hendrix, the drama teacher

   B. The role I wanted
      1. Hero of a romantic comedy
      2. Character is handsome and charming
      3. I had pictured myself in a role like this
II. Performing In the School Play

▶ **Exercise 1 Evaluate the outline below.**
   I. Jets
      A. Effects on warfare
         1. Non-stop bombing flights
      B. Helicopters used in Korean and Vietnam Wars
   II. Balloons
      A. Used to observe troop movements
      B. Blimps
         1. Hindenburg was one
         2. Filled with hot air or gas
   III. Airplanes

First, *Blimps* should have a separate main topic heading because it is not a subtopic of

Balloons. Helicopters should also have its own heading because it is different from *Jets.*

Section I.A. should not be subdivided into only one section. Finally, the order of the outline should be

changed to follow a logical sequence.

_____

_____

_____

_____

▶ Exercise 2 **Organize the following topics and details into an outline of the biography of Howard Hughes.**

Became a millionaire; Born 1905 in Houston, TX; Business Life; Companies controlled; Controller of Trans World Airlines; Died in 1976; Dropped out of society in the 1950s; Early Life; Father died in 1924; Hughes Aircraft Company; Inherited Hughes Tool Company upon father's death; Later Life; Never seen in public; Refused to be photographed; RKO Pictures Corporation

I. **Early Life** _____

   A. **Born 1905 in Houston, TX** _____

   B. **Father died in 1924** _____

II. **Business Life** _____

   A. **Became a millionaire** _____

   B. **Companies controlled** _____

      1. **Inherited Hughes Tool Company upon father's death** _____

      2. **Hughes Aircraft Company** _____

      3. **RKO Pictures Corporation** _____

      4. **Controller of Trans World Airlines** _____

III. **Later Life** _____

   A. **Dropped out of society in the 1950s** _____

      1. **Never seen in public** _____

      2. **Refused to be photographed** _____

   B. **Died in 1976** _____

▶ Exercise 3 **Prewrite on any topic desired. Then, construct an organized outline about that topic.**

Outlines should follow correct format and logic. _____

_____

_____

_____

_____

_____

_____

_____

Lesson 104
Writing Effective Sentences

When you tell a story out loud, you can raise or lower your voice to emphasize a passage. You can also control how fast you read, slowing down if you want to be solemn and speeding up if you want to show quick action. When you write, sentences do the work of your voice.

The hardest working sentence in a paragraph is the topic sentence. A **topic sentence** states the main idea of a paragraph. Write a clear, strong topic sentence. Use **supporting details** to develop the main idea. Supporting details prove, clarify, or give more information about the main idea. Emphasis and pace are determined by where you place the supporting details in the sentence and by the number of details you choose to include. Long sentences have a slower pace than short sentences. Change the pattern of a topic sentence to add emphasis to a word or group of words.

You can draw attention to the subject by moving it to the end of the sentence. For example, "Over the horizon rose a ship's mast." This sentence would also be correct with the subject stated first: "A ship's mast rose over the horizon." Notice that whether the subject comes first or last, its verb remains the same.

The action verb is in the **active voice** when the subject of a sentence performs the action. When the action is performed on the subject, the action verb is in the **passive voice**. Use the passive voice when you do not want to emphasize the subject or when you do not know who is performing the action.

▶ **Exercise 1** **Combine the four sentences into an effective topic sentence, or write a topic sentence accompanied by one or more supporting details.**

   a. Many youngsters go without food.
   b. This happens every day.
   c. We should help them.
   d. They are very needy.

Because many youngsters go without food each day, we should help feed needy children.
_____

1. a. We will perform the play on Friday.
   b. We need more rehearsals.
   c. It will be a huge hit if we rehearse.
   d. People will talk about it for weeks afterwards.

The play we are to perform on Friday will be a huge hit if we have more rehearsals. People will

talk about it for weeks afterwards.
_____

Composition

2. **a.** Elephants are enormous.
   b. They are also very gentle.
   c. They will pluck a peanut right from your hand.
   d. The elephants at the zoo fascinate me.

Elephants are enormous, yet they will gently pluck a peanut from your hand. Those at the zoo fascinate

me.

3. **a.** My favorite skater took the ice.
   b. She had an excellent routine.
   c. The jumps were amazing.
   d. I was excited.

My heart beat with excitement as my favorite skater took the ice with an excellent routine filled with amazing

jumps.

4. **a.** You are very negative.
   b. That behavior is unpleasant.
   c. You may lose friends over this.
   d. Stop being negative.

You may lose some friends if you do not stop being so unpleasant and negative.

_____

5. **a.** Ernie sells hot dogs.
   b. He is weird, yet lovable.
   c. Everyone in town knows and likes him.
   d. He is part of what makes our town interesting.

Everyone agrees that weird and lovable Ernie the hot dog man is part of what makes our town interesting.

_____

6. **a.** The night was hot.
   b. The night was wet.
   c. Our air conditioner broke.
   d. We were miserable that night.

We were miserable during that hot, wet night when our air conditioner broke.

_____

7. **a.** The balls fly.
   b. The players stumble.
   c. The pace of volleyball is very fast.
   d. Volleyball is very exciting.

The fast pace of a volleyball game, with balls flying and players stumbling, is tremendously exciting.

_____

Composition

Name _____ Class _____ Date _____

8. a. Jules Verne lived in the nineteenth century.
   b. He wrote *20,000 Leagues Under the Sea.*
   c. The book has sold well to this day.
   d. It predicted the use of submarines.

Written in the nineteenth century by Jules Verne, *20,000 Leagues Under the Sea* has sold well to this day. It

predicted the use of submarines.

9. a. I went to the football game.
   b. The home team won.
   c. The score was close.
   d. The game went into overtime.

I went to the football game to see the home team win by a close score in overtime.

10. a. Tyrannosaurus rex was the largest meat-eating dinosaur.
   b. It stood eighteen feet tall.
   c. It lived during the Cretaceous period.
   d. Only a small number of Tyrannosaurus fossils have been found.

Living during the Cretaceous period and standing eighteen feet tall, Tyrannosaurus rex was the largest

meat-eating dinosaur. Only a small number of Tyrannosaurus fossils have been found.

▶ **Exercise 2** **Explain whether the verb voice used in the sentence is the best choice. If the verb voice needs to be changed, rewrite the sentence.**

The pie was eaten by Chen. _Chen ate the pie._

1. The dance contest was won by Sabrina. _Sabrina won the dance contest._

2. The money was stolen from the register. _Okay. We don't know who stole the money._

3. The rival teams were evenly matched. _Okay. Emphasis is on the teams._

4. The actors were given scripts by the director. _The director gave scripts to the actors._

5. The actors auditioned for the director. _Okay. Sentence uses active voice._

6. This ticket must be presented at the door. _Okay. Emphasis is on the ticket._

7. The dog was covered with mud. _Okay. Emphasis is on the dog._

8. The dog frolicked in the mud. _Okay. Sentence uses active voice._

9. That portrait was painted by Koto. _Koto painted that portrait._

10. The design was approved by Ana. _Ana approved the design._

▶ **Exercise 3** **Rewrite the paragraph below with effective sentences.**

I am amazed at the sight of the enormous roller coaster. The group waiting to board the roller coaster is joined by me. I watch the bright red cars grind to a halt. The riders seem exhausted but happy. The riders spring out of their seats. The riders head for the next ride. I sit in one of the cars when my turn comes. I buckle myself in. I take a deep breath. The roller coaster starts to move. It moves at a deceptively slow pace. It moves with more force up a steep incline. It reaches the top of the steel hill. At this time I can see the entire park. The park is spread out before me like a colorful quilt. The roller coaster suddenly begins to move downward. Whoosh! I feel like I'm plummeting to the ground! But I am not plummeting to the ground. I am safely inside a car. The car is following a track. The track is carefully placed. The ground is never reached by me. Instead, I am led up another steel hill. This hill is taller. But this time I am prepared. Here I go!

Amazed at the sight of the enormous roller coaster, I join the group waiting to board it. I watch the bright red cars grind to a halt. Exhausted but happy riders spring out of their seats and head for the next ride. When my turn comes, I sit in one of the cars, buckle myself in, and take a deep breath. The roller coaster starts to move at a deceptively slow pace. Then it moves with more force up a steep incline. As it reaches the top of the steel hill, I can see the entire park spread before me like a colorful quilt. Suddenly the roller coaster begins moving downward. Whoosh! I feel like I'm plummeting to the ground! But I am safely inside a car following a carefully placed track. I never reach the ground. Instead, I am led up another steel hill. This one is taller, but this time I am prepared. Here I go!

_____

_____

_____

_____

_____

_____

_____

_____

_____

_____

_____

_____

_____

_____

Composition

Lesson 105
Building Paragraphs

The supporting details in a paragraph can be arranged in different ways. Chronological order places events in the order that they happened. Spatial order is the way objects appear. Compare/contrast order shows similarities and differences.

For example, this note from a friend makes use of compare/contrast order in the first paragraph, spatial order in the second, and chronological order in the third.

You must try the East Side Grill! It is bigger and better than the restaurant we went to last week. The servers and hosts at the East Side Grill are much friendlier. Also, the bill at the East Side Grill was a lot less expensive!

When you walk into the East Side Grill, you might think the place is run-down and old. But the dark hallway opens into a bright, modern dining room with windows on the ceilings. There is a jukebox against one wall and a grand piano against another.

The food at the East Side Grill is great! First, we had huge salads filled with crisp vegetables. Then we had thick, hot soups. Next, we had main courses of roast beef and potatoes. We finished our meals with slices of homemade pie for dessert.

▶ **Exercise 1** **Number the following sentences in chronological order.**

__6__ Then I cut two slices from a tomato.

__7__ I place the tomato slices atop the cheese and ham.

__1__ I always make my favorite sandwich a certain way.

__8__ To complete my creation, I put the mustard-covered slice of bread atop the loaded slice of bread.

__2__ First, I place two slices of whole wheat bread on a plate.

__5__ Next, I put one slice of Swiss cheese on top of the ham.

__9__ Finally, I enjoy!

__3__ I put mayonnaise on one slice of bread and mustard on the other.

__4__ Then I lay three pieces of ham on the mayonnaise-covered slice.

Composition

▶ **Exercise 2 Revise the following paragraph in chronological order, then rewrite the paragraph.**

First we hiked up a steep grade, but the trail was clear and easy to follow. We had to climb over nearly a dozen felled trees to get to the halfway point. Our six-mile hike to the river thoroughly exhausted us. We began our hike from Pine Grove Park early in the morning. At the two-mile mark, we spotted a family of deer. We found the stream that marked the end of the fifth mile and followed it to the river. We got lost, wandered in a circle, and ended up doing the fourth mile twice! Finally, we fell asleep under a giant tree.

We began our hike from Pine Grove Park early in the morning. First we hiked up a steep grade, but the trail was clear and easy to follow. At the two-mile mark, we spotted a family of deer. Then we had to climb over nearly a dozen felled trees to get to the halfway point. After that, we got lost, wandered in a circle, and ended up doing the fourth mile twice! We found the stream that marked the end of the fifth mile and followed it to the river. Finally, we fell asleep under a giant tree. Our six-mile hike had thoroughly exhausted us.

Composition

▶ **Exercise 3 Write the following paragraph in spatial order.**

At the stop sign, a boy and a girl jumped rope. Across the street from the Garzas' house, a mail carrier made a delivery. At the Wittenauers' house across the street from ours, sprinklers noisily sprayed water onto the grass. From my front step, I looked from one end of the street to the other. The mail carrier moved to the next house, where Mrs. Meyer and her two sons were playing basketball. In the driveway of the first house on the right, Mr. Garza washed his car. Our street was buzzing with activity on Saturday morning. At the end of our street, my friend Jerry was trying to teach his puppy to sit.

Our street was buzzing with activity on Saturday morning. From my front step, I looked from one end of the street to the other. At the stop sign, a boy and girl jumped rope. In the driveway of the first house on the right, Mr. Garza washed his car. Across the street from the Garzas' house, a mail carrier made a delivery. The mail carrier moved to the next house, where Mrs. Meyer and her two sons were playing basketball. At the Wittenauers' house across the street from ours, sprinklers noisily sprayed water onto the grass. At the end of our street, my friend Jerry was trying to teach his puppy to sit.

_____

_____

_____

_____

_____

_____

_____

_____

_____

_____

_____

_____

_____

_____

▶ **Exercise 3 Use compare/contrast order to write a paragraph about one of the following topics:**

your best friend

what has made this school year interesting

the way your bedroom looks

_____

_____

_____

_____

_____

_____

_____

_____

_____

_____

_____

_____

_____

_____

_____

_____

_____

_____

_____

_____

_____

_____

_____

_____

_____

Composition

Lesson 106
Paragraph Ordering

Revising a first draft includes checking the **unity** and **coherence** of paragraphs. You need to make sure that each paragraph is unified; that is, it opens with a topic sentence (a sentence that states the main idea of the paragraph) and the supporting details are related to that topic sentence. To make sure the comparisons are clear, or coherent, you must check chronological, spatial, and compare/contrast details. (See Lesson 105.) Finally, you need to make sure that ideas are properly linked by transitions.

▶ **Exercise 1 Revise the following paragraphs for unity and coherence.**

I had been watching and admiring the ragged puppy from my porch for about an hour. My dog Emma was a stray when I found her. Her "home" was the cold concrete under a car in front of my house. She was thinner and dirtier, but what made me fall in love with her were her ears, of all things. I could just tell that beneath all that grime was the pet I'd always wanted.

I had to figure out a way to get her. She would venture out from under the car only when she was sure no humans were near. As soon as I approached her, she would scurry back under the car. She would creep up to the sidewalk and give me a look that seemed to say that she wanted to be friends. One ear pointed straight up, and the other flopped down. When I looked under the car, she whimpered. I could tell that she needed me as much.

I had an idea, and I was glad that my mother wasn't home so I could put my plan into action. I went into our house and got my mother's leftover beef stew. I brought out a big bowl and placed it beside the car so the dog would have to come out to eat.

Slowly, she inched toward the bowl. I could hear her sniffing, so I knew that she was smelling a better meal. She stuck her head out from under the car and looked up at me with those big brown eyes. I didn't grab her when she began eating. I stroked her head slowly, to let her know I was her pal. When she was finished, I picked her up and carried her home. She couldn't have weighed more than ten or fifteen pounds. I've had her ever since. I had to bathe her three times to get the engine oil off her.

▶ **Exercise 2** **Rewrite the paragraphs, based on your revisions.**

Students' revision notes for Exercise 1 will differ. Here is an example of a revised draft:

My dog Emma was a stray when I found her. Her " home" was the cold concrete under a car in front of my house. I had been watching and admiring the ragged puppy from my porch for about an hour. She was thinner and dirtier than any dog I had ever seen, but what made me fall in love with her were her ears, of all things. One ear pointed straight up, and the other flopped down. I could just tell that beneath all that grime was the pet I'd always wanted.

However, she would venture out from under the car only when she was sure no humans were near. She would creep up to the sidewalk and give me a look that seemed to say that she wanted to be friends, but as soon as I approached her, she would scurry back under the car. When I would look under the car, she would whimper, and I could tell that she needed me as much as I needed her. I had to figure out a way to get her.

Then I had an idea, and I was glad my mother wasn't home so I could put my plan into action. I went into our house and got my mother's leftover beef stew. I brought out a big bowl and placed it beside the car so the dog would have to come out to eat. The pup began sniffing, so I knew that she was smelling a better meal than she had ever had. Slowly, she inched toward the bowl. Finally, she stuck her head out from under the car and looked up at me with big, brown eyes.

I didn't grab her when she began eating. Instead, I stroked her head slowly, to let her know I was her pal. When she was finished, I picked her up and carried her home; she couldn't have weighed more than ten or fifteen pounds. Then I had to bathe her three times to get the engine oil off her. I've had her ever since.

Lesson 107
Personal Letters

A **personal letter** is often a letter to a friend or relative. In a personal letter, you describe recent events in your life and ask the recipient questions about his or her life. A personal letter can also be an invitation or a thank-you note.

These letters are usually written in indented form. Each paragraph is indented, as well as each line in the heading and the signature (see Handbook page 20).

▶ **Exercise 1** **Read the following personal letter. Answer each question.**

> 951 Pleasantville Drive
> Sunnydale, Illinois 60000
> May 15, 1996

Dear Chris,

  You won't believe what a great month I've had! I couldn't wait to write you. First of all, I finally made the swim team. All that extra practice has paid off. My first meet is Monday. I'm a little nervous, but I'll be all right once I get in the water.

  The time I've spent mowing lawns and cleaning garages is paying off, too. I'm using the money I've earned to buy the mountain bike I told you about in my last letter. The next time you come for a visit, you can try it out.

  Did you buy the bike you had your eye on? Write soon and tell me all about it. Tell me what else you've been doing, too. I miss you.

> Your friend,
> *Taylor*

1. Who is Chris? __a friend of Taylor's__

2. Why is Taylor writing to Chris? __He or she has news to convey to Chris.__

3. How is this a good example of a personal letter? __It is written from one friend to another in an informal tone. It includes news of what the writer is doing and asks for news in return. It is written in the form of a personal letter.__

4. What might Chris include in a response to Taylor's letter? __Chris will most likely respond to Taylor's question about whether he or she bought the bike Taylor mentions. Chris will also describe what he or she has been doing since the last time he or she wrote to Taylor and may have questions for Taylor.__

▶ **Exercise 2 Write a personal letter to a friend.**

Students' letters should be informal in tone and written in indented form. The letters should include information about recent events in the students' lives and should ask questions about events in the recipients' lives.

_____

_____

_____

_____

_____

_____

_____

_____

_____

_____

_____

_____

_____

_____

_____

_____

_____

_____

_____

_____

_____

_____

_____

_____

_____

_____

Composition

Different situations call for different kinds of personal letters. You would probably use a different tone and style in writing to an adult relative than you would in writing to your best friend. Your letter to your relative would probably be more formal, while you might make use of secret code words and slang in your letter to your friend.

You would also write differently to an author you admire than you would to a friend who has just performed in a play. While you would certainly be gracious in both letters, your letter to the author might express stronger feelings about how art affects life.

▶ **Exercise 3** **Write a letter thanking an adult relative for a gift or discussing a recent visit. On the last three lines of the answer space, explain why you chose the style you used.**

Letter should be semi-formal. The writer wants the letter to sound natural and not forced. Avoid slang.

_____

_____

_____

_____

_____

_____

_____

_____

_____

_____

_____

_____

_____

_____

_____

_____

_____

_____

_____

▶ **Exercise 4** Write a letter to an author or performer you admire. On the last three lines of the answer space, explain why you chose the style you used.

Letter should be semi-formal. The writer should explain how the performer's work has affected the writer's life, school, career choices, etc.

_____

_____

_____

_____

_____

_____

_____

_____

_____

_____

_____

_____

_____

_____

_____

_____

_____

_____

_____

_____

_____

_____

_____

_____

Composition

Lesson 108
Business Letters: Letters of Request or Complaint

A **letter of request** is a letter that asks for information or service. When writing a letter of request, you should be clear and courteous. Explain what information you need and why you need it. Include any information the receiver may need to answer your request.

Business letters are usually written in block form or semiblock form. In block form, everything is lined up with the left margin. In semiblock form, the heading, complimentary close, and signature are placed on the right-hand side of the page (see Handbook, pages 19-20).

▶ **Exercise 1** Read the following letter. Is this a good example of a letter of request? Why or why not?

This is not a particularly good example of a letter of request. It is rather brief and not very courteous.

Also, Paul should have written sooner and given Ms. Ling time to respond.

Dear Ms. Ling:
I am a freshman at Polk High School. I am currently working on a science-fair project concerning methods of weather forecasting. Since I am planning to be in New York next week, I was wondering if I could tour your meteorological facility and ask you some questions. I hope so.

Sincerely,

Paul Thornton

▶ **Exercise 2** Think of a situation in which you would need to ask someone for information. Perhaps there is a certain camp you are interested in attending or a service program you would like to join. Write some ideas for your letter on the lines below. Then write your letter on a separate piece of paper and send it to the person who can answer your questions. Be sure to use proper business-letter format.

Students should write ideas for a letter of request, including the person and place the letter will be addressed to

and some questions the students would like to ask. Letters of request should follow the guidelines provided in this

lesson.

Composition

A **letter of complaint** is a letter informing someone of a problem or concern and sometimes a request for action. It should be clear, concise, and rational. Never let your anger get the best of you. Begin your letter by stating the problem and telling how it happened. Then use supporting details as evidence of your problem. End your letter by explaining what you want done. Be reasonable, and avoid insults and threats.

▶ **Exercise 1** **Describe any problems that exist in the letter of complaint below. Suggest how to correct any errors.**

Dear Customer relations manager,
    You're umbrellas stink! I just bought one and it fell apart as soon as I walked out the door. First of all it leaked then it ripped when the wind blew. Dont you know umbrelas are supposed to protect us from things like that. I got soaked when I walked home and its all you're stupid fault! I don't want another of you're lousy umbrellas, all I want is my money back now. If you dont give me a full refund I promise, you will be sorry!

Angrily,
Bill Higgins

First of all, the letter is insulting. Be courteous and rational. Also, several grammatical and spelling errors exist in

the letter. The letter does not contain proper business letter courtesy or format. Do not threaten the recipient of the

letter. Also, make a formal and realistic request.

_____

_____

_____

_____

▶ **Exercise 2** **Revise and rewrite the letter of complaint above.**

Dear Customer Relations Manager:

    I recently bought one of your umbrellas and, much to my surprise, it fell apart the first

time I used it. First of all, it began leaking almost as soon as I stepped out in the rain. Then it

ripped due to the wind.

    Enclosed is a copy of my sales receipt. I would appreciate either a new umbrella or a

full refund. I hope to hear from you soon.

    Sincerely,

    Bill Higgins

Lesson 109
Business Letters: Résumés and Cover Letters

A **résumé** is a summary of your work experience, school experience, talents, and interests. It is used in applying for a job or for admittance into a school or academic program.

You want your résumé to be clear, concise, and expressive. In describing your accomplishments, use action verbs (*won* the award, *taught* the children). Because a résumé is a summary, it is not necessary to use complete sentences. However, you do want to use a consistent format, as in the following example:

Frank Garcia
2210 Victory Parkway
Cincinnati, Ohio 45210
(513) 555–5555

Objective:	Admission into the Future Teachers of America Young Scholars Program
Education:	Central High School, September 1994–present. 4.0 grade-point average
	Eastern Junior High School, September 1989–June 1992. 4.0 grade-point average.
Work Experience:	Camp counselor, Camp Lookout, Cincinnati, Ohio, June–August 1994.
Responsibilities:	Tutored third graders in math and English.
References:	John McGraw, teacher, Central High School (513) 555–5555
	Marla Quincy, manager, Camp Lookout (513) 555–5555

▶ **Exercise 1 Answer the following questions about Frank Garcia's résumé.**

1. How might the headings (Objective, Education, etc.) of his résumé be ordered if Frank were applying for a job? Why? <u>Work experience would come first, because recent work experience would be</u> <u>important to potential employers.</u>

_____

_____

2. In what order should entries for education and experience be listed? <u>in chronological order, with</u> <u>most recent experience first</u>

_____

_____

3. The headings Frank used are not the only ones you can use on a résumé. Name at least two other

appropriate headings. __Activities, Awards, Interests_____

_____

_____

_____

4. Whom should you use for references? Why should you get their permission first?

Use authority figures who know you and your abilities well as references. Get their permission

first, so they are prepared to talk with potential employers.

_____

_____

_____

▶ **Exercise 2** **You are applying for one of the following:**

• a summer job as a camp counselor

• a job teaching a musical instrument to children

• a job coaching a children's sports team

• an academic honors society

Freewrite for ten minutes about the information you want in your résumé.

_____

_____

_____

_____

_____

_____

_____

_____

_____

_____

_____

_____

Composition

▶ **Exercise 3 Write your résumé. Pay close attention to structure.**

Should follow structure of sample _____

_____

_____

_____

_____

_____

_____

_____

_____

_____

_____

_____

_____

_____

_____

_____

_____

_____

_____

_____

_____

_____

_____

A **cover letter** is a brief letter of introduction that usually accompanies a résumé. A cover letter states what you are applying for and where you can be contacted, and it refers the reader to your résumé for additional information. It may also briefly state why you feel you are well-suited for the position.

The following is an example of a well-formatted, concise cover letter. Note that the letter follows business letter style rules and that it is directed to a specific person.

Frank Garcia
2210 Victory Parkway
Cincinnati, Ohio 45210

Future Teachers of America
Young Scholars Program
c/o Barbara Jeffers
106 Vine Street
Cincinnati, Ohio 45216

Dear Ms. Jeffers:
As a hard-working honors student at Central High School, I am interested in becoming a member of the Young Scholars Program. My dedication to education makes me a worthy candidate for membership in your organization.

Enclosed is a copy of my résumé. I hope you will find that I am a well-qualified student. Please feel free to contact me if you have any questions. I hope to hear from you soon.

Sincerely,
Frank Garcia
Frank Garcia

▶ **Exercise 1 Write a cover letter based on the position you applied for in the résumé activity.**

Letter should follow structure of sample.

_____

_____

_____

_____

_____

_____

_____

_____

_____

_____

*I*ndex

· ·

Index

A

A, an (usage), 10, 219
A, an, the (articles), 4, 10, 61
Abbreviations, correct use of, 17, 281
Absolute phrases, 7
Abstract nouns, defined, 2, 50
Accept, except, 11, 219
Action verbs, defined, 3, 55
Active voice, explained, 4, 155, 323
   in writing, 155, 323
Adapt, adopt, 11
Adjective clauses, 7, 42, 107, 255
   essential, 107
   nonessential, 42, 107, 255
Adjective phrases
   as infinitive phrases, 7, 95
   as participial phrases, 7, 91
   as prepositional phrases, 6, 89
Adjectives, defined, 4–5, 61
   articles as, 4, 10, 61
   comparative forms of, 9–10, 199, 201
     avoiding errors in, 10, 203
   coordinate, 15, 44, 253
   demonstrative, 227
   hyphen in compound, 16, 279
   kinds of, 4–5, 61
   object complement, 5, 6, 86
   predicate, 6, 85
   proper, 5, 14, 61, 239
Adopt, adapt, 11
Adverb clauses, 7, 111, 259
   elliptical, 111
Adverb phrases
   infinitive phrases, 7, 95
   prepositional phrases, 6, 89
Adverbs, defined, 5, 63
   comparative forms of, 9–10, 67, 199, 201
   conjunctive, 5
   negative words as, 10, 63
   standard usage of rules for, 9–10, 63
Advice, advise, 11
Affect, effect, 11, 219
Agreement
   pronoun-antecedent, 9, 30–34, 187, 189, 191, 193
   subject-verb, 8, 26–29, 161, 163, 165, 167, 169, 171, 173, 175
Ain't, avoiding, 11, 219
All ready, already, 11, 220
All right, not *alright,* 11, 220
All the farther, all the faster,
   avoiding, 220

All together, altogether, 11, 220
Allusion, illusion, 11
A lot, not *alot,* 10, 219
Already, all ready, 11, 220
Altogether, all together, 11, 220
Among, between, 11, 221
Amount, number, 221
Antecedents, defined, 3, 9, 187
   agreement of pronouns with, 9, 30–31, 187, 189, 191
   clear pronoun reference, 32–33, 193
Anyways, anywheres, avoiding, 11
Apostrophes, rules for using, 16, 277
   in contractions, 16, 277
   in possessive nouns and pronouns, 16, 277
   in special plurals, 16, 277
Appositive phrases, 6, 43, 94
Appositives, defined, 6, 43, 94, 183
Articles, 4, 10, 61
As, like, 12–13, 225
Audience, 18, 307
Auxiliary verbs, defined, 3, 59
   list, 59
A while, awhile, 10, 219

B

Bad, badly, 11, 205, 221
Being as, being that, avoiding, 11, 221
Beside, besides, 11, 221
Between, among, 11, 221
Block form for letters, 19, 337
Borrow, lend, loan, 11, 222
Bring, take, 11, 222
Business letters, 19–20, 337–339, 342
   block and semiblock forms, 19, 337
   cover letters, 20, 342
   letters of complaint, 20, 338
   letters of request, 20, 337
   opinion letters, 20
   résumés, 20, 339
But
   preposition, 5, 69
   coordinating conjunction, 71

C

Can, may, 11, 222
Can't hardly, can't scarcely,
   avoiding, 11, 222
Capitalization, rules for, 13–14, 235, 237, 239

   in direct quotations, 13, 235
   in family names and titles of persons, 13, 237
   of first words of sentences, 13, 235
   of proper adjectives, 5, 14, 239
   of proper nouns, 2, 13–14, 237
   of sections of country, 14, 237
Case of pronouns, 2, 8–9, 181, 183
Chronological order, 18, 327
Clauses, defined, 7, 101
   See also Adjective clauses, Adverb clauses, Dependent clauses, Independent clauses, Main clauses, Noun clauses, Subordinate clauses
Clue words, 17, 291
Collective nouns, defined, 2, 47
   agreement of verb with, 2, 27, 169
Colons, rules, 14, 16, 247
Commas, rules, 15–16, 42–44, 251, 253, 255, 257, 259, 261, 263
   with addresses, 15, 261
   and adverb clauses, 259
   and antithetical phrases, 259
   with appositives, 43, 94
   and compound sentences, 15, 251
   between coordinate adjectives, 15, 44, 253
   in direct address, 15, 263
   in direct quotations, 15, 16, 271
   and introductory phrases, 257
   with nonessential elements, 42–43, 255
   with numbers, 15, 261, 283
   for parenthetical elements, 15, 43
   in references, 15
   after salutations and closings in letters, 15, 263
   in series, 15, 44, 253
   in tag questions, 263
   with titles, 261
Common nouns, defined, 2, 49
Comparative form, modifiers, 9–10, 67, 199, 201
Compare/contrast order, 18, 327
Comparison
   of adjectives, 9–10, 199, 201
   of adverbs, 9–10, 67, 199, 201
   double and incomplete, 10, 203
   irregular, 10, 201
Complements, 5–6, 83–86
   direct objects, 6, 83
   indirect objects, 6, 84
   object, 5, 6, 86

S

Said, says, 13, 227

Scarcely, in double negatives, 11, 222

Semiblock form of letters, 19, 337

Semicolons, 14–15, 16, 249, 273
    to correct run-on sentences, 24–25, 125

Sentence fragments, 22–23, 123

Sentence patterns, explained, 5–6, 8, 81, 167

Sentence structure
    complex, 7, 105
    compound, 7, 103
    compound-complex, 7, 105
    simple, 7, 103

Sentences, effective, 323
    active voice, 155, 323
    interruption, 323
    parallelism, 323
    unusual patterns, 323
    varied length, 18, 323
    varied structure, 18, 323

Sentences, kinds of
    declarative, 8, 119
    exclamatory, 8, 121
    imperative, 8, 119
    interrogative, 8, 121

Sentences, run-on, 24–25, 125

Series, commas in, 15, 44, 253
    colon before, 247

Set, sit, 13, 227

Simple predicates, defined, 6, 75

Simple sentences, defined, 7, 103

Simple subjects, defined, 5, 75

Singular nouns, 2, 47

Sit, set, 13, 227

Spatial order, 18, 327

Spelling
    adding -*ly* and -*ness,* 18, 299
    doubling the final consonant, 18, 299
    forming compound words, 16, 18, 279, 299
    of -*cede,* -*ceed,* and -*sede,* 17, 297
    of *ie* and *ei,* 17, 297
    of plural nouns, 18, 300
    of suffixes, 17, 18, 298
    of unstressed vowels, 297

Subject complements, 6, 85

Subject-verb agreement, 8, 26–29, 161, 163, 165, 167, 169, 171, 173, 175
    in adjective clauses, 8
    and collective nouns, 27, 169

and compound subjects, 8, 28–29, 171

and indefinite pronouns, 8, 29, 175

and intervening expressions, 8, 29, 173

and intervening prepositional phrases, 8, 26, 163

in inverted sentences, 8, 26–27, 167

and linking verbs, 26, 165, 167, 169

and predicate nominatives, 26, 165

and special subjects, 8, 169

with titles, 8

Subjects
    agreement of verb with, 8, 26–29, 161, 163, 165, 167, 169, 171, 173, 175
    complete, 6, 77
    compound, 5, 79, 103, 171
    gerunds and infinitives as, 7, 93, 97
    noun clauses as, 7, 115
    simple, 5, 75

Subjunctive mood, verbs, 4

Subordinate (dependent) clauses, 7, 101, 259

Subordinating conjunctions, 5, 71, 101

Suffixes, 17, 18, 295, 297, 298

Superlative form, 9–10, 67, 199, 201

T

Take, bring, 11, 222

Teach, learn, 12, 225

Tenses, defined, 3, 145
    future, 3, 145
    future perfect, 3, 147
    incorrect, 36–37
    past, 3, 145
    past perfect, 3, 147
    present, 3, 145
    present perfect, 3, 147
    shifts in, avoiding, 35, 153

Than, then, 13, 227

That there, this here, avoiding, 13, 227

Theme, writing, 18, 311

Then, than, 13, 227

Thesis statement, writing, 18, 311

This here, that there, avoiding, 13, 227

This kind, these kinds, 225

Topic sentences, 311, 323, 331

Transitive verbs, defined, 3, 55

U

Understood subject, 119

V

Verb phrases, defined, 3, 6, 59

Verbal phrases, 7, 93, 97

Verbals, defined, 7, 93, 95, 97
    See also Gerunds, Infinitives, Participles

Verbs, defined, 3, 55
    action verbs, 3, 55
        intransitive, 3, 55
        transitive, 3, 55
    agreement with subjects, rules, 8, 26–29, 161, 163, 165, 167, 169, 171, 173, 175
    auxiliary (helping), 3, 59
    emphatic, 4, 152
    intransitive, 3, 55
    irregular, regular, 3–4, 141, 143
    linking, 3, 57
    list, 3–4, 59, 141, 143
    moods of, 4
    principal parts of irregular, 3–4, 143
    principal parts of regular, 141
    progressive, 4, 151
    tenses of, 3, 35–37, 145, 147, 149, 151–152
        compatibility, 153
        shifts in, avoiding, 35
        See also Tenses
    transitive, 3, 55
    voice of, active and passive, 4, 155, 323

Vocabulary building, 17–18, 291, 293, 295
    from context, 17, 291
    prefixes and suffixes, 17–18, 295
    word roots, base words, 17, 293

Voice of verbs, defined, 4, 155, 323
    active, 4, 155, 323
    effective use of, 155, 323
    passive, 4, 155, 323

W

Well, good, 12, 205, 224

Where at, avoiding, 227

Who, whom, 13, 185

Writing process. *See specific steps.*

Writing letters, 19–20, 333, 335, 337–339, 342

Writing paragraphs, 18, 327

Y

You, as understood subject, 119

Unit 1 Test: Parts of Speech

• •

▶ **Subtest 1** **Write in the blank the part of speech of each italicized word.**

_____ 1. Jamaal's little *brother* always waves good-bye.

_____ 2. The basketball team *rapidly* improved after the loss.

_____ 3. *Wow!* I can't believe Lilla invited me!

_____ 4. On the first day of school, Kenji wandered *around* the halls looking for his locker.

_____ 5. Judy *ran* to school to beat the tardy bell.

_____ 6. Keiko sat on the dock watching the boats as *they* sailed toward the bay.

_____ 7. Jon wore a wrinkled shirt *because* he had no time to iron.

_____ 8. Apple trees bear *white* blossoms in the spring.

_____ 9. Rabi *and* Zina marched down the stairs.

_____ 10. A herd of sheep roamed *through* the pasture.

_____ 11. *Boy,* your painting looks great hanging in the lobby!

_____ 12. The rock *concert* was sold out.

_____ 13. It is important to take *pride* in your school.

_____ 14. *One* of the most heavily populated areas in the world is the Nile River Valley in Egypt.

_____ 15. The plot of the mystery novel *thoroughly* baffled me.

_____ 16. When Evelyn's family went camping, they *hiked* along the Appalachian National Scenic Trail.

_____ 17. When my cousin had an *acute* attack of appendicitis, we rushed him to the hospital.

_____ 18. *Those* are the most unusual earrings I've ever seen!

▶ **Subtest 2** **Read the following paragraph. Underline each noun once, each verb twice, and each adverb three times.**

Alaska is the largest state in the United States, but it has a relatively small population. Alaska

became a state in 1959, the first new state in forty-seven years. Alaska produces valuable resources,

such as oil, fish, minerals, and timber. It is a majestically beautiful state with mountains and

unspoiled wilderness.

▶ **Subtest 3** **Identify the type of noun in italics. In the blank, write** *con.* **if it is concrete,** *abs.* **if it is abstract,** *col.* **if it is both collective and concrete, or** *prop.* **if it is both proper and concrete.**

_____ 1. Playing sports is a source of *enjoyment* as well as a way to stay physically fit.

_____ 2. The *crowd* cheered when the home team scored the winning run.

_____ 3. Maria's new *puppy* follows her everywhere.

_____ 4. *Juan* tiptoed out the door so he wouldn't wake his grandfather.

_____ 5. The *reason* I did so well on the test was that I studied for three hours.

_____ 6. Going to the science museum was a great *idea*.

_____ 7. The *class* surprised the teacher by handing in their reports early.

_____ 8. Han and Mika walked to the *park* to feed the pigeons.

▶ **Subtest 4** **Identify the type of pronoun in italics. In the blank, write** *pers.* **for personal,** *pos.* **for possessive,** *ref.* **for reflexive,** *in.* **for intensive,** *inter.* **for interrogative,** *rel.* **for relative,** *dem.* **for demonstrative, or** *ind.* **for indefinite.**

_____ 1. *What* is your favorite Friday night television show?

_____ 2. We discovered *those* on the beach this morning.

_____ 3. Please tell *me* how to get to the mall.

_____ 4. Tricia painted a portrait of *herself* in her Halloween costume.

_____ 5. Emilio is excited about getting *his* driver's license next year.

_____ 6. Is there *anybody* here who can help me with my math homework?

_____ 7. Yuji *himself* was able to change the flat tire on his car.

_____ 8. Maya Lin was the architecture student *who* designed the Vietnam Veterans Memorial.

▶ **Subtest 5** **Identify the type of verb in italics. In the blank, write** *tran.* **for transitive,** *intran.* **for intransitive,** *link.* **for linking, and** *aux.* **for auxiliary.**

_____ 1. The mayor *invited* our class to attend a city council meeting.

_____ 2. It *snowed* all night, and school was canceled this morning.

_____ 3. Jill and Tammy *are* walking to their aerobics class after school.

_____ 4. When Keshia *cut* the grapefruit, it squirted in her eye.

_____ 5. *Would* you please help me weed the garden?

_____ 6. The New York Knicks *are* my brother's favorite basketball team.

_____ 7. The balloon *disappeared* silently into the clouds above.

_____ 8. Environmental pollution *is* a serious problem.

Unit 2 Test: Parts of the Sentence

••

▶ **Subtest 1** Draw one line under the simple subject. Draw two lines under the simple predicate.

1. The Quobonga brothers operate a bus service in southern Africa.

2. Captain Dlamini's automobile lost power after striking a small rock.

3. During the cyclone persistent rains caused massive flooding.

4. Malangeni advised me on the problems with the poultry project.

5. In the alley, dogs are barking.

6. Before every science exam Harriet studied her notes for two or three hours.

7. Yesterday our basketball team defeated a team from Pennsylvania.

8. During the summer Suki purchases avocados from the Tsela family.

9. Johnny's birthday falls on the day after his parents' anniversary.

10. Chip's strong play contributed to the Bearcats' victory.

▶ **Subtest 2** Draw a vertical line between the complete subject and the complete predicate. Label each direct object *d.o.* and each indirect object *i.o.*

1. The patrolman gave us advice.

2. Bill and Vicki have friends in Stillwater, Oklahoma.

3. Dale chopped wood for a fire.

4. Martha showed Dr. Medlin her science project about caffeine.

5. Andrew pedaled his bicycle toward Glasgow.

6. A salt spray covered the green pickup truck near the ocean.

7. Abbey paddled the canoe toward the snow-covered mountain.

8. The tropical fish in the aquarium provided us hours of enjoyment.

9. Philip's wife and her mother share the same name.

10. Tonya bought Carla a magazine about popular music.

11. Ryan's parents will visit him in the future.

12. Bending his knees, Remo lifted the stone into place.

13. An unpleasant phone call canceled Patrick's travel plans.

14. Tina made us two delicious pies.

15. The Shoshone and the Crow groups left the upper Yellowstone in 1872.

▶ **Subtest 3** Label each predicate nominative *p.n.*, each predicate adjective *p.a.*, and each object complement *o.c.*

1. Sweet corn can be yellow or white.

2. Without Lazelle, the team's chances are slim.

3. The can of oatcakes is a gift from a Scottish friend.

4. My younger brother found the program interesting.

5. These bananas are too green for me.

6. Bob and Virginia found the road rough and narrow.

7. The nearby slaughterhouse makes the area unattractive.

8. Sources of Vitamin C are grapefruits, oranges, and lemons.

9. The delay was unavoidable and unwelcome.

10. Two important editorial skills are accuracy and consistency.

11. Greg considered Brad's acting impressive and captivating.

12. Kirsten's costume looks funny on her.

13. The sun must be a star of medium size.

14. The unidentified object is a yellow chicken.

15. The speech by Joanna's hero seemed brief.

Unit 3 Test: Phrases

• •

▶ **Subtest 1** Circle each prepositional phrase. Draw an arrow from the phrase to the word it modifies.

1. Amad's pet cat always dozes on the television set.

2. My science book is the one with the red cover.

3. Algebra is easy for Susan.

4. For years I have wanted a ticket to the Super Bowl game.

5. Kenji brought his new pet turtle to the beach.

6. Unfortunately for me the post office had already closed.

7. Our trip to Colorado was my favorite vacation.

8. Before the movie Tasha bought a large box of popcorn and a soda.

9. The bakery on Elm Street has the best bagels.

10. The Knights of the Round Table were known for their heroism and chivalry.

▶ **Subtest 2** Circle the participle or participial phrase in each sentence below, and draw an arrow to the word it modifies.

1. Coming home, Scott dreamed of being a world-famous athlete.

2. Jenny considered her father a discriminating traveler.

3. I love to watch the sun rising from beneath the horizon.

4. Nothing has been the same since a stranger named Shane came to the little town.

5. Moving from guest to guest, the hostess spoke to everyone at the party.

6. Julio, excited about the spring break trip, packed his bags in record time.

7. Erosion can result from running water.

8. The wood burning in the fireplace quickly warmed the cabin.

9. Knowing the right answer, Keshia raised her hand.

10. Enjoying Tom's company, Joel watched the entire movie.

▶ **Subtest 3 Underline the gerund or gerund phrase in each sentence.**

1. Speaking to large audiences was one of Martin Luther King's strong points.

2. I really enjoy reading a good book.

3. Waiting in a long line can be very frustrating.

4. Signing autographs was a thrill for the young champion.

5. Burning fossil fuels provides energy for many tasks.

6. Mr. Kim cannot stand eating beets.

7. Galilahi enjoyed reading Native American legends.

8. After a trip lasting the entire summer, returning home pleased Benito.

9. Finishing the race gave Carlos self-confidence.

10. Dancing is a popular pastime.

▶ **Subtest 4 Underline the appositive or appositive phrase in each sentence.**

1. Miss Diaz, our new physical education teacher, used to play professional golf.

2. My new neighbor, that old man in the blue hat, has been in the apartment since last Tuesday.

3. Press the clutch, the pedal on the left, to switch gears.

4. *Star Wars,* my favorite movie, is going to be on television next Sunday.

5. A former president of the United States, Ronald Reagan, visited our town.

6. Have you ever been to Reykjavík, the capital of Iceland?

7. The Galápagos tortoise, the oldest land animal, is also one of the slowest.

8. Gaelic, the Celtic language of Scotland, is still spoken in some areas of the British Isles.

9. Thomas Jefferson, the author of the Declaration of Independence, held the office of president from 1801 through 1809.

10. That movie was directed by John Huston, an Academy Award winner.

Name _____ Class _____ Date _____

▶ **Subtest 5** Underline the infinitive in each sentence. Above each infinitive, write *n.* if it is used as a noun, *adj.* if it is used as an adjective, and *adv.* if it is used as an adverb.

1. Using a computer is a quick and easy way to complete assignments.

2. The costume that Jeanne wore to the party will not be easy to forget.

3. To finish the season undefeated was the wrestling team's main goal.

4. To remain calm in a panic situation is difficult, but necessary.

5. To avoid splashing is the aim of many contestants in a diving competition.

6. Now is the time to invest in your future.

7. Many students choose to join the armed forces when they graduate.

8. His decision in a tight moment was to play the fool.

9. William of Normandy's army continued to fight throughout the Battle of Hastings.

10. Telephone numbers are hard for me to remember.

▶ **Subtest 6** In the blank, write *participial, gerund,* or *appositive* to identify the type of phrase in italics.

_____ 1. Waterskiing is vastly different from *skiing on snow.*

_____ 2. *Breaking the record* was the only thing on Akia's mind.

_____ 3. Spike Lee's epic film *Malcolm X* told the story of the famous African American civil rights leader.

_____ 4. The rainbow, *seeming to end just over the horizon,* is actually an optical illusion.

_____ 5. *Playing guitar in my own band* is a dream of mine.

_____ 6. Mr. Rice, *the principal of our school,* is friendly to everyone he sees in the hall.

_____ 7. For our vacation my family visited Rio de Janeiro, *the famous city in Brazil.*

_____ 8. *Returning home from school,* Hiroshi found the house empty; his father had gone shopping.

_____ 9. The sousaphone, *a kind of tuba,* can easily be carried by a band member.

_____ 10. My younger brother prefers *watching cartoons* over anything else.

_____ **11.** The book, *written by a young Jewish girl during her family's persecution in Nazi Germany,* is now widely read.

_____ **12.** My eyes, *burning from the chlorine,* continued to weep hours after I had left the pool.

_____ **13.** The Boston Celtic *Larry Bird* was one of the most respected basketball players of all time.

_____ **14.** My dog *named Penny* has been learning to sit, heel, and stay.

_____ **15.** *Slipping on a wet floor* can cause a serious injury.

▶ **Subtest 7** **In the blank, write *prepositional* or *infinitive* to identify the phrase in italics.**

_____ **1.** My brother loves *to ride roller coasters.*

_____ **2.** *To diagnose diseases* requires years of practice for interns.

_____ **3.** Sumi returned *to the campground* the following year.

_____ **4.** Jeff never fails *to inform us.*

_____ **5.** Will you be going *to the hockey game* on Thursday night?

_____ **6.** I'm sure we can find a solution *to the problem.*

_____ **7.** *To Jane and Michael Banks,* Mary Poppins was an amazing person.

_____ **8.** Karen was overjoyed *to receive her first paycheck.*

_____ **9.** It has never been easy for Manuel *to switch brands.*

_____ **10.** Cholena's letter *to the editor* stimulated serious conversations among the students and teachers.

_____ **11.** My goal for the semester is *to complete my term paper.*

_____ **12.** Movies based on superheroes from comic books attract viewers *to the theaters.*

_____ **13.** Scientists hope to bring relief *to sufferers of the disease.*

_____ **14.** *To arrive at first period on time,* Min ran all of the way to school.

_____ **15.** *To Gene's dismay* Leslie refused his invitation to the dance.

Unit 4 Test: Clauses and Sentence Structure

• •

▶ **Subtest 1** Label each sentence *dec.* for declarative, *imp.* for imperative, *int.* for interrogative, or *exc.* for exclamatory.

_____ **1.** There is nothing new I could give you.

_____ **2.** Do you believe Keith's story about the image on the ceiling of his room?

_____ **3.** You lied to us!

_____ **4.** All of Mrs. Howell's silver sits on a shelf beside the finely carved wood.

_____ **5.** Do the task now because tomorrow will be too late.

_____ **6.** That news sounds too good to be true!

_____ **7.** The firefighter likes to keep the fire engine clean.

_____ **8.** Take Shin Jie on a tour of the southern mountains before Thursday.

_____ **9.** Will milk remain fresh without refrigeration?

_____ **10.** The flannel shirt was made in the Philippines.

_____ **11.** Be sure to buy plenty of food before they arrive.

_____ **12.** Was that thunder I heard?

_____ **13.** Please unload all the packages in the next thirty minutes.

_____ **14.** Joe is likely to have another occupation next year.

_____ **15.** This lunch is my favorite!

▶ **Subtest 2** Tell whether you would add a subject (*subj.*), a verb (*v.*), or a main clause (*main*) to form a complete sentence.

_____ **1.** hot chili peppers in the blistering sun

_____ **2.** traveled Lincoln County Road 524

_____ **3.** with silver bracelets on Clara's wrists and flowers in her hair

_____ **4.** from the cradle to the grave

_____ **5.** married Claudette in Buenos Aires last January

_____ **6.** began on an uneventful morning

_____ **7.** an extreme change in the weather

_____ **8.** among the countless thousands walking to school

_____ **9.** these words of simple truth

_____ **10.** in a way they did not know

_____ **11.** planned a new roadway through the wilderness

_____ **12.** the music loud and clear

_____ **13.** was proven beyond the shadow of a doubt

_____ **14.** only one doe among the twelve deer

_____ **15.** the rain falling on his shoes

▶ **Subtest 3** Add a comma, period, or a semicolon to punctuate each sentence correctly. **Capitalize where necessary.**

1. You have to guess where you are most street signs are gone.

2. The evacuation procedure saved lives but urban planners fear a problem in future emergencies.

3. I could hear birds singing there was no sound of traffic.

4. Crocodiles are immensely powerful but they tire quickly.

5. Smiley visited Lithuania he had always wanted to go there.

6. A few insects are pests most give humans few problems.

7. Liam stayed in Denver for a few weeks he left when his job was finished.

8. Fred has lived in Pelican Rapids for several years duck hunting is popular around Pelican Rapids.

9. The car was a station wagon and Maria waved as it passed the restaurant we were surprised to see her.

10. The performer intended the song to be humorous many in the audience failed to laugh.

11. Mr. Grandstaff arrived at the gymnasium and there were no volleyballs; accordingly, he decided to play football.

12. Julia may go swimming she hopes Angelica will go also.

13. The details were unclear but the accident happened late last night.

14. Glenn was talented and dependable and his friends needed his assistance.

15. Michelle welcomed the woman from Lafayette her arrival was later than Michelle expected.

Unit 5 Test: Diagraming Sentences

● ●

▶ **Subtest 1 Diagram the following sentences.**

1. Ling opened the window.

2. My father served spicy ham, scalloped potatoes, and tossed salad.

3. Open this door, and let me in!

4. Being on the jury was a thrill for Caroline.

5. Winter vacation is a time for my family to travel.

6. The firefighter emerged carrying a tiny infant.

7. Is that beautifully elaborate building a cathedral or a museum?

8. America, Canada, and Mexico signed a trade agreement.

9. Capturing tremendous wind power, hurricanes usually occur over oceans.

10. At midnight on New Year's Eve, the ball in Times Square drops.

11. Mrs. Bernárdez, the new English teacher, enjoys tutoring after school.

12. Whatever you eventually buy is your decision.

13. Stopping, dropping, and rolling can extinguish a fire on your clothing.

14. Because he had sprained his ankle, Rafael needed crutches.

15. The place where I would like to work is the New York Stock Exchange.

16. The night that we met is etched indelibly in my mind.

Unit 6 Test: Verb Tenses and Voice

• •

▶ **Subtest 1** Fill in the blank with the correct form of the verb: base form, simple past, or past participle.

1. jump, _____ , jumped

2. know, knew, _____

3. fly, _____, flown

4. _____, caught, caught

5. _____, won, won

6. do, did, _____

7. write, _____, written

8. _____, went, gone

9. come, _____, come

10. sing, sang, _____

11. grow, grew, _____

12. lose, _____, lost

13. ring, rang, _____

14. put, _____, put

15. freeze, froze, _____

▶ **Subtest 2** Write the tense or form of the verb in italics.

_____ 1. We *shivered* in the cold wind while we were waiting for the bus.

_____ 2. Many types of turtles *will become* extinct if conservation methods are not taken.

_____ 3. By 1877 tennis *had replaced* croquet as the most popular outdoor sport in England.

_____ 4. The school psychologist *has helped* many students.

_____ 5. Shana always *explores* her grandmother's attic when she visits her during the summer.

_____ 6. Andre *will have taken* five guitar lessons by the end of the holidays.

_____ 7. In science class yesterday, we *were watching* a snake swallow a mouse when the fire alarm went off.

_____ 8. Marcos saw many adobe houses when his family *vacationed* in the Southwest.

_____ **9.** Jamaal's mother *is having* trouble with her new car.

_____ **10.** I *do want* to learn to play chess, but the game seems complicated.

_____ **11.** If you arrive late, your sister *will have* already *sung* her solo.

_____ **12.** I *will* never *forget* the wonderful time we had at the class picnic!

_____ **13.** By Friday we *had finished* painting the bedroom.

_____ **14.** The movie *will be starting* in an hour.

_____ **15.** I *did hear* the question, but I wasn't sure of the answer.

_____ **16.** Smelling that pepper *will make* me sneeze.

_____ **17.** Harriet Tubman *helped* hundreds of slaves escape to freedom.

_____ **18.** Walt Disney World in Florida *has been* a popular vacation spot since it opened in 1971.

_____ **19.** What time *will we be leaving* for the theater?

_____ **20.** Neal *had been playing* tennis for two hours when his calves began to ache.

▶ **Subtest 3 Complete each sentence with the correct form of the verb in parentheses.**

1. Alyson _____ a quarter in the pop machine yesterday. (lose)

2. Mr. Diaz _____ his flag every July fourth since 1975. (fly)

3. I _____ continually to hoist the sail, but I never succeeded. (try)

4. Last Wednesday the band _____ the band director with a cake for her birthday. (surprise)

5. Oh, no, I _____ my new sweater. (tear)

6. We have _____ all the orange juice that was in the refrigerator. (drink)

7. I am sure our soccer team _____ the opponent tomorrow. (defeat)

8. The two goldfish we won at the school fair have _____ us many hours of enjoyment. (give)

9. Juan has _____ his baseball card collection for five years. (have)

10. The telephone has _____ several times tonight. (ring)

▶ **Subtest 4 Complete each sentence with the verb form indicated in parentheses.**

1. If you are not careful, you _____ a mistake. (future of *make*)

2. We _____ that the weather would be better by now. (past perfect of *hope*)

3. The cashier at the grocery store _____ me too much change. (present perfect of *give*)

Name _____ Class _____ Date _____

4. We _____ in five minutes if we don't hurry inside the house. (future progressive of *freeze*)

5. Hiroshi _____ his dinner by the time the guests arrive. (future perfect of *eat*)

6. Tom Sawyer _____ to use his imagination. (past emphatic of *like*)

7. No one _____ the missing glove. (present perfect of *find*)

8. The police _____ the grounds for hidden evidence. (present progressive of *search*)

9. Koto _____ Mariko a map to show her the way. (past of *draw*)

10. I really _____ to play Monopoly. (present emphatic of *like*)

11. The firefighter _____ the ladder to rescue the scared child. (past of *climb*)

12. The Chinese table tennis champion _____ across the United States in several exciting exhibition matches. (present perfect progressive of *appear*)

▶ **Subtest 5** Underline the two verbs or verb phrases. If the tense of the second verb is incorrect, rewrite it. If it is correct, write *C*.

_____ 1. We watched the parade from the second-story window and have thrown confetti at the same time.

_____ 2. When Laura heard about the sale at the shoe store, she rushed there immediately.

_____ 3. The brisk November breeze blew our hair as we ride our bikes through the park.

_____ 4. Nikki put the pizza in the microwave and had set the timer for three minutes.

_____ 5. The tomatoes will be ripe in June, and the corn will be ready to eat in August.

_____ 6. By the time the movie was over, Naomi fell asleep.

_____ 7. I do my exercises because I had wanted to be healthy.

_____ 8. By the time you receive your report card, your parents had talked with your teachers.

_____ 9. Scientists have learned about a blood protein that plays an important role in Alzheimer's disease.

_____ 10. In his Wild West shows Will Rogers used the lassoing tricks he learns on his father's ranch as a boy.

▶ **Subtest 6** **Underline the verb or verb phrase. Write** *A* **above the verb if it is in the active voice,** *P* **if it is in the passive voice.**

1. A low-fat diet cuts one's risks of developing skin cancer.

2. Major companies are making clothes such as jackets, sweaters, underwear, and sneakers from recycled fabrics.

3. Entire shoes have been made from recycled products.

4. All ten bowling pins were knocked down by Rashida's zooming ball.

5. Taro and Mura rode the Ferris wheel at the county fair.

6. The door prizes will be donated by the booster club.

7. The mime imitated a child with a drippy ice-cream cone.

8. A fund-raising event is being planned by the student council.

9. The local newscasters report the news in an interesting, objective manner.

10. The squirrels will store their nuts for the winter.

Name _____ Class _____ Date _____

Unit 7 Test: Subject-Verb Agreement

▶ **Subtest 1** Underline the correct form of the verb in parentheses that agrees with the subject.

1. Alfonso (join, joins) the military academy.

2. Diet and exercise (stimulate, stimulates) weight loss.

3. The boxer shorts (was, were) good luck for George Foreman.

4. Many cable stations (change, changes) their programming schedules without notice.

5. Mario and his friends (were walking, was walking) to the theater.

6. The rubber band (snap, snaps) off the counselor's fingers.

7. All of the stars (burn, burns) far from Earth.

8. Robotics as a concept (was, were) originated by Isaac Asimov.

9. Someone (has broken, have broken) the valve on the water heater.

10. Some of the colonists (appear, appears) very tired in that painting.

11. The song's lyrics (bring, brings) tears to my eyes.

12. The marines (use, uses) rugged training and discipline.

13. Lobsters (taste, tastes) good dipped in butter sauce.

14. Jack and Jill (have encountered, has encountered) a hill.

15. The majestic lion (sleep, sleeps) most of the day.

16. Everything (seem, seems) lost for our heroes.

17. The wolf pack (were chasing, was chasing) the rabbit.

18. Turkey, stuffing, and gravy (is, are) my favorite holiday foods.

19. A tornado usually (destroy, destroys) much property if it touches the ground.

20. Eyedrops (relieve, relieves) the pain in irritated, red eyes.

21. Several senators (filibuster, filibusters) the bill in the Senate.

22. The jet engines (scream, screams) as the plane zooms overhead.

23. Four days (is, are) left until the spring trip to Mexico!

24. Everybody (has, have) a fear of some type of animal.

25. Neither the North nor the South (was, were) able to escape the Civil War unharmed.

26. Either my uncle or my grandparents (pick, picks) me up after school.

27. Nobody (know, knows) who the culprit is.

28. My cow (kick, kicks) her legs when she is being milked.

29. Most citizens over the age of eighteen (has, have) the right to vote.

30. My gloves (keep, keeps) my hands warm.

▶ **Subtest 2** Write in the blank the correct form of the verb in parentheses. Then draw an arrow from the verb to the subject of each sentence.

1. Heavy rain, accompanied by hail and ice, _____ in the forecast. (is, are)

2. Raccoons in the neighborhood _____ trash cans to get food. (dump, dumps)

3. The marathon _____ twenty-six miles long. (was, were)

4. Peggy, together with the rest of her family, _____ cranberry juice. (love, loves)

5. There _____ games to be won! (is, are)

6. A favorite pastime of many teenagers _____ listening to music. (is, are)

7. The school of fish _____ over the coral reef. (loom, looms)

8. Our sun _____ billions of years old. (are, is)

9. The sport of track and field _____ various foot races, in addition to the shot put and the javelin throw. (comprise, comprises)

10. Where _____ the constellation Cassiopeia among the stars? (are, is)

11. The teacher, with her students, _____ the historical museum. (is visiting, are visiting)

12. The hens in the henhouse _____ the fox. (see, sees)

13. Peter Gabriel, as well as Phil Collins, David Lee Roth, and Paul Simon, _____ as a soloist. (sing, sings)

14. The Great Pyramids at Giza, Egypt, _____ over the desert. (tower, towers)

15. The last of the Mohicans _____ called Hawkeye. (was, were)

16. The transcontinental flight _____ forty thousand feet above the ocean. (was, were)

17. There _____ termites in this building! (are, is)

18. The sheriff, accompanied by the ranchers, _____ across the porch. (mosey, moseys)

19. Butterflies in my stomach _____ whenever I am nervous. (appear, appears)

20. _____ the president agree with the bill? (Do, Does)

21. Producers, as well as actors and directors, _____ the event. (attend, attends)

22. All of these ingredients _____ a cake. (make, makes)

23. _____ Boris and Igal agree that we must get involved in saving the rain forests? (Do, Does)

24. _____ the press ever overstep its bounds? (Do, Does)

25. The modern school of thought _____ that the universe is expanding. (believe, believes)

26. The executive branch, together with Congress and the Supreme Court, _____ the federal government. (constitute, constitutes)

27. Each minute without air _____ brain cells. (endanger, endangers)

28. There _____ a small cabin in the forest. (are, is)

29. Around the thickets _____ the rabbit. (run, runs)

30. My relatives _____ supportive. (remain, remains)

▶ **Subtest 3** **Write in the blank the present-tense form of the verb in parentheses that agrees with the subject.**

1. The cost of these items, plus tax, _____ $17.45. (be)

2. The families in a neighborhood _____ a community. (make)

3. A few of the singers in the ensemble _____ laryngitis. (have)

4. Around the bends _____ the bobsled, accompanied by the four bobsledders. (roar)

5. Navy _____ Army! (beat)

6. The rights of the states and the responsibilities of the federal government _____ opposing forces. (balance)

7. All the workers on the job _____ to product quality. (contribute)

8. The castles of England, as well as those of Scotland and France, _____ the countryside. (decorate)

9. The boulders at the edge of the cliff _____ a danger to passing motorists. (be)

10. Each of the forests, together with the sky, _____ a gorgeous landscape. (produce)

11. Maine, Vermont, New Hampshire, Massachusetts, Rhode Island, and Connecticut

_____ New England states. (be)

12. George Washington, accompanied by other soldiers, _____ the Delaware. (cross)

13. The marching band and the swing choir _____ together. (perform)

14. No one among the computer technicians _____ the problem. (understand)

15. Bela, together with his whole family, _____ in the nearby neighborhoods for contributions for the homeless shelter. (ask)

16. _____ you use a hammer, a chisel, or a screwdriver? (do)

17. To the shore _____ ducks and driftwood. (float)

18. The patterns within patterns _____ a puzzle. (be)

19. In the tropics _____ pineapples and mangoes. (ripen)

20. "Duck!" _____ someone in the crowd. (shout)

Unit 8 Test: Using Pronouns Correctly

• •

▶ **Subtest 1** Underline the correct pronoun in parentheses.

1. The cheerleaders supported (their, theirs) football team.

2. Only the members, Mikail and (I, me), knew the secret code.

3. I am upset because (my, mine) favorite rock group will not be coming to town.

4. The principal, (who, whom) is also Deanna's father, knows me very well.

5. My grandfather, (who, whom) I love dearly, is very healthy.

6. The award was received by the team captains, Shoiban and (I, me).

7. Yori recognized that the sweater in the lost-and-found department belonged to (she, her).

8. When working on the community project, (we, us) volunteers always began before dawn.

9. Akikta liked the book so much that I gave it to (he, him) for his birthday.

10. (Who, Whom) will pick me up after choir practice?

11. The students elected Selam, (who, whom) many classmates admire.

12. Amy was glad she had run into (they, them), my friends from summer camp.

13. The students coordinating the project, Toni, Mika, and (I, me), met frequently to organize our data.

14. Because I borrowed Carolyn's class notes, I must return (they, them).

15. Cruz, (who, whom) was the captain of the debate team, became class president.

▶ **Subtest 2** Complete each sentence by adding a pronoun that agrees with the antecedent. Underline the antecedent.

1. Did everyone remember to bring _____ permission slip?

2. All of us signed a card for Yvonne because _____ birthday is today.

3. The cast of the play stayed up very late to watch _____ performances on videotape.

4. Several students gave some of _____ free time to volunteer in the community.

5. Many have voiced _____ concerns.

6. Louis moved to Utah after _____ grew up.

7. Glenn and Lisa were glad that _____ ran into me at the mall on Saturday.

8. No one knew what _____ should do in that situation.

9. My relatives were excited when _____ came for dinner.

10. We drove several hours just to see _____ team play.

▶ **Subtest 3** Label each italicized pronoun *nom.* (nominative), *obj.* (objective), or *pos.* (possessive) case.

1. Please ride *your* bike to the store to buy a loaf of bread.

2. Never before had *I* been so moved by a television show.

3. Vivian needed a radio, so I gave *her* my old one.

4. I like the Great Smoky Mountains because of *their* stunning scenery.

5. Abbot and Costello's most famous act is their "*Who's* on first?" routine.

6. Olivia got the job because *she* was the best candidate.

7. My puppy just loves to play with *its* squeaky toys.

8. To *whom* does this backpack belong?

9. The two politicians set aside *their* disagreements to solve a common problem.

10. The laws of *our* country must never conflict with the Constitution.

▶ **Subtest 4** Rewrite each sentence to eliminate any unclear pronoun reference.

1. Omar's family likes to visit exotic locations because they are exciting. _____

_____

_____

2. In this dictionary it says that *fax* comes from *facsimile*. _____

_____

_____

3. They claim that lightning never strikes the same place twice. _____

_____

_____

4. In 1946 you had ENIAC, the first all-purpose, all-electronic, digital computer.

_____

_____

Name _____ Class _____ Date _____

Unit 9 Test: Using Modifiers Correctly

• •

▶ **Subtest 1** Underline the correct form of the modifier in parentheses.

1. The colonists became (more unhappy, more unhappier) when the British taxed imported tea.

2. This year's wrestling team is (more good, better) than last year's team.

3. My headache was (worse, worser) in the afternoon than it had been in the morning.

4. The syrup ran (more fast, faster) after it was heated.

5. The ferocious bluefish fights (good, well) when it gets caught on a hook.

6. Which of the three dresses is the (most pretty, prettiest)?

7. The *Concorde* is the (quickest, most quick) way to fly across the ocean.

8. Do you like chocolate as (well, good) as I do?

9. Juanita has (littler, less) patience than Lina.

10. The lake is (more calm, calmer) at night when the winds die down.

▶ **Subtest 2** Complete each sentence with the correct form of the modifier in parentheses. Add *more* or *most* when necessary.

1. The monarch butterfly migrates the _____ of any butterfly. (far)

2. Today's football game was _____ than last weekend's game. (rough)

3. Ricky's aunt did the jigsaw puzzle _____ than she did the crossword puzzle. (easy)

4. These are the _____ mashed potatoes I have ever eaten! (good)

5. The sidewalk in front of my house is _____ than the one by the school. (icy)

6. Miguel wore the _____ costume of all. (scary)

7. Buttercup is the _____ of the two puppies. (small)

8. The field hockey team at our school is the _____ of all the girls' teams. (successful)

9. Unfortunately, this dress rehearsal is going _____ than expected. (bad)

10. Ruth rode the _____ of the two trains because she wanted to relax and enjoy the mountain scenery. (slow)

Unit 9, Test **371**

▶ **Subtest 3** Circle each misplaced modifier. Draw an arrow to its correct position.

 1. We learned about Grandma Jenny's escape from our visiting cousins.

 2. When his son was six years old, Mr. Kim taught his son to ride a bicycle.

 3. Singing enthusiastically, the audience listened attentively to the chorus.

 4. Shami only plays on the varsity volleyball team.

 5. I accepted the gift with great reluctance.

 6. A huge whale caught the eye of the jogger in the ocean.

 7. Kasem only bought one audiocassette because he hadn't saved enough money for two.

 8. Beth rode to her part-time job on the bus.

 9. Watching television, the couch collapsed from the weight of the family.

10. We were able to photograph the politician balancing on a high curb.

▶ **Subtest 4** Underline any double or incomplete comparisons. Write *C* in the blank if the sentence is correct.

_____ 1. Tara was the most nicest friend I ever knew.

_____ 2. Bastille Day, July 14, is the most celebrated holiday in France.

_____ 3. The wool gloves were more warmer than the nylon ones.

_____ 4. Sunee's bonsai tree was more perfectly formed than Tanya.

_____ 5. Pancake batter is thinner than a muffin.

▶ **Subtest 5** Underline the double negative in each sentence. Then write two ways to correct it.

1. The Harlem Globetrotters don't have no trouble mixing comedy with basketball.

   _____

2. I don't need no help with my homework. _____

3. Janet didn't tell nobody about the kitten she found in the garage. _____

4. Jerome hasn't built no snow fort this winter. _____

5. Mrs. McGraw wasn't getting nowhere with her knitting. _____

   _____

Unit 10 Test: Usage

• •

▶ **Subtest 1** Underline the correct word in each sentence.

1. I have a friend whose aunt (emigrated, immigrated) from Poland.

2. Because my younger brother does not know how to use a computer, I had to (learn, teach) him.

3. Gorillas are generally quite docile (accept, except) when they are threatened.

4. On the morning news the meteorologist (says, said) there will be snow on the slopes.

5. (This kind, These kinds) of used cars do not have safety air bags.

6. You cleaned that up very (good, well).

7. Everyone's body contains a large (amount, number) of individual cells.

8. Whenever I find myself in a challenging situation, I try to (affect, effect) one of the variables.

9. Janice told Clay to (sit, set) the computer equipment on the desk.

10. Khoa did not like to (leave, let) his dog alone for too long during the day.

11. The set of metal wind chimes (hanged, hung) on the porch.

12. Does anyone want to play a card game (beside, besides) euchre?

13. Although I am two years younger (than, then) my sister, many people think I am older.

14. Whenever I sleep, I (lay, lie) on my side.

15. The mysterious bird took off and soared away (in, into) the night.

16. Often, political races in the United States are (between, among) two political parties.

17. Chet had to (lend, loan) Gabrielle a pencil for the test.

18. A fancy dinner (preceded, proceeded) the homecoming dance.

19. (Can, May) I have a chance to be the goalie?

20. Before the ride began to move, Kanya removed her cap for fear she would (loose, lose) it.

▶ **Subtest 2** Correct the word in italics if it is incorrect. If the word is correct, write *C*.

_____ 1. In Japan it is traditional to bow *respectively* as a greeting.

_____ 2. The reason the dog nipped at the stranger is *because* it was protecting its owner.

_____ 3. Isra was named homecoming queen, *like* I was last year, in a ceremony at the football game.

_____ 4. I will continue to remain active *regardless* of my disability.

_____ **5.** I think it is amazing that we get along so well because my friends are different *than* your friends.

_____ **6.** If the archaeologists had dug a little longer, they could *of* had the find of the century.

_____ **7.** José handled the situation in the cabin very *badly.*

_____ **8.** Basir and I agreed that the superb acting, the excellent direction, and the spectacular special effects made the movie an *altogether* satisfying film.

_____ **9.** Please wait *a* hour before calling me.

_____ **10.** Yes, *that there* house was built completely by my family.

_____ **11.** On our flight to Minneapolis, we *past* over Chicago.

_____ **12.** Although shark attacks have been popularized in film, sharks generally *don't* attack people.

_____ **13.** *Being that* the president came to town, the police barricaded the streets.

_____ **14.** My friend Min likes to put *alot* of sugar in her iced tea.

_____ **15.** *Where* is the pep rally taking place?

_____ **16.** Just press that button to make the garage door *raise.*

_____ **17.** The humpback whales migrate *farther* than many marine animals.

_____ **18.** *Take* some biscuits to feed the neighbor's dogs at the fence.

_____ **19.** I waited for *awhile* outside the restaurant, but you never arrived.

_____ **20.** There are *less* unique comedians performing today than in the past.

_____ **21.** Some mornings I *can't hardly* find the energy to get out of bed.

_____ **22.** The sequel to the movie was *alright,* but it was not as good as the original.

_____ **23.** Those newspapers have *already* been folded.

_____ **24.** I could not remember if I *had of* used this razor yet.

_____ **25.** The speed of light is *all the faster* anything can travel.

Unit 11 Test: Capitalization

●●●

▶ **Subtest 1** Correct the capitalization in each sentence. Draw three lines under each lowercase letter that should be capitalized and a single slash (/) through any capitalized letters that should be lowercase.

1. The mount Vernon estate of George Washington is located on the Potomac river.

2. On july 28, 1982, a small airplane crashed near lindale, texas, when it failed to clear the Oak trees at the end of the Runway.

3. Next year Valerie plans to study geometry, Biology, and french II.

4. Then uncle Albert purchased a house located between Union middle school and st. Peter's elementary school.

5. The sergeant at arms resigned her position under pressure from judge Carlton Bass.

6. James was a shakespearean actor before gaining fame in Motion Pictures.

7. Christopher urged Paul to purchase the Videotape when he returns to scotland.

8. Very few students will participate in Baseball if coach Neal returns to his job as a National league umpire.

9. Hattie lived near the Waukegan boys' club and the King medical center.

10. My mother, Mildred, studied Nursing (her father encouraged her) after completing High School.

11. Young leaves and stems from the Pokeweed plant can be used to make a dish known as Poke Salad.

12. John r. Wooden was elected to the Naismith Memorial basketball hall of fame as both a Player and a Coach.

13. The somalis are the people of Somalia (A country in Africa located on the Indian ocean).

14. The holes in swiss cheese are made when Bacteria emit Carbon dioxide.

15. A portion of Sweden lies North of the arctic circle.

16. Two rare black Rhinos from zimbabwe reside at Fossil Rim wildlife center near Dallas, texas.

17. Mount shasta (a volcano in Northern California) has not erupted since the Eighteenth Century.

18. In 1979 the *Voyager I* Spacecraft relayed images that appeared to be Lightning from jupiter's atmosphere.

19. Vladivostok is a Russian Port on the sea of Japan.

20. The book *South light* by Michael Parfit describes life in antarctica.

21. during the month of april, Sandhill Cranes flock to the Platte river in southern nebraska.

22. After world war II, tensions between the governments of the U.s.A. and the U.s.s.R. led to nearly fifty years of conflict known as the cold war.

23. A widely used manual of writing style is *The Chicago manual of style,* published by the university of Chicago press.

24. The Southeastern conference includes many large Universities in the south.

25. The Nigerian diplomat saw a german shepherd at the U.S. department of agriculture on friday morning.

26. The milky way is a galaxy that includes our solar system.

27. Kristin did not talk to Feng Ying between memorial day and labor day.

28. After snacking on onion rings near the nile river, we boarded a toyota land rover for a visit to the Egyptian pyramids.

29. Guillermo requested a camera (either a canon or nikon) for christmas this year.

30. The management of General Motors corporation decided to build Saturn Automobiles in tennessee.

31. Ross spoke to Georgia before spanish class on Wednesday Afternoon.

32. from 1974 to 1976, america had an unelected presidential team in president Gerald Ford and vice president Nelson Rockefeller.

33. for most of the 1950s, the New York yankees dominated Major League baseball. (the team won five world series from 1949 to 1953.)

34. Chicago bulls fans were saddened by Michael Jordan's Retirement because he had led the Team to three consecutive championships; therefore, they were glad to welcome him back.

35. Amsterdam and Paris are european capitals that are popular Tourist Attractions.

Unit 12 Test: Punctuation, Abbreviations, and Numbers

▶ **Subtest 1** Complete each sentence by adding a period, an exclamation point, or a question mark as needed.

1. Every day before supper, Ann collects vegetables from her backyard garden

2. Does your mother ever mention any songs that were popular when she was in high school

3. What a clever idea that is

4. What time will the package arrive from Michigan

5. Evidently Brian spoke with Luisa on the telephone

6. Watch out for that car

7. Would you repeat the question for Jenny to hear

8. Arthur met Mr. Marola after leaving the Johnson residence

9. How handsome you look in that tuxedo, Ralph

10. The manager ordered him not to mention Juan's name in the evaluation

▶ **Subtest 2** Correct each sentence by adding a colon or a semicolon where necessary.

1. The list of groceries included the following ground beef, kidney beans, stewed tomatoes, crackers, celery, cheddar cheese, and spaghetti.

2. Our vacation took us to many states and left us exhausted however, everybody would gladly repeat the experience.

3. The interstate highway had long traffic delays due to construction subsequently, Eunice decided to try a country road.

4. Charles mentioned the following quotation from Gerald R. Ford, president of the United States from 1974 to 1977 "I am a Ford, not a Lincoln."

5. Hebrews 8 8–12 refers to Jeremiah 31 31–34.

6. The midnight bus to Moultrie will not arrive until 1210 A.M.

7. Luigi wants to officiate at soccer games he's learning the rules.

8. None of the Milwaukee Brewers had been to Botswana therefore, Vusi's interest in baseball surprised the ballplayers.

9. Jill asked the clerk to make sure the bouquet included the following flowers carnations, zinnias, chrysanthemums, and daffodils.

10. Attending the town meeting were Mrs. Nash, the librarian Mr. Wong, the florist and Miss Gonzales, the baker.

▶ **Subtest 3 Insert commas where necessary. Cross out commas used incorrectly by using the delete symbol [℣].**

1. Wilbur was both determined, and committed to becoming a veterinarian.

2. The next goal for the golf team is to perform well in the district competition and a good performance at the district level will give the team an opportunity to win a state championship.

3. Ignoring Roscoe's outburst Jeannie reported her solution to the algebra exercise.

4. The Witwatersrand complex, a mineral deposit containing gold lies beneath the Transvaal, and the Orange Free State in the Republic of South Africa making South Africa the world's largest producer of gold.

5. The community was sufficiently large to include a recreation center three swimming pools and three urban parks.

6. Much of eastern Brazil is covered by dense lush tropical rain forest.

7. The Red Sea unlike the Mediterranean Sea touches both Egypt, and the Sudan.

8. Josephine's mother, Rachel after she learned of Josephine's scholarship was ecstatic.

9. On September 11 1983 Dr. Avery Miles D.V.M. addressed a group of horse trainers gathered at the River Inn, at 3850 East Montague Avenue.

10. Before entering the city limits of Nashville Tennessee Regina looked at her watch.

11. Never, neglect to finish a project Sherman.

12. Abe sold everything that he owned counted his profit, and departed for Tallahassee, Florida.

13. Harold can you remember an enjoyable educational program on television, last week?

14. The choir if it is to be ready for the performance next weekend must add an extra practice Wednesday night.

15. All of the staff with the exception of Dr. Gloria Knight Ph.D., discussed the matter on Tuesday May 7.

▶ **Subtest 4** **Insert dashes, parentheses, or quotation marks where necessary. Cross out dashes, parentheses, or quotation marks used incorrectly by using a delete symbol [ ].**

1. Born in 1942 in Liverpool a British port and center of international commerce Paul McCartney was the son (of a cotton trader and a midwife).

2. The World Cup match between Brazil and Canada begins at precisely "3:00 P.M." Pacific Standard Time 6:00 P.M. Eastern Standard Time.

3. Miguel's poems about "birds" the one about "geese" is wonderful were written last year.

4. Due to the success of the "UCLA" basketball team, Coach John R. Wooden became known as the Wizard of Westwood.

5. Mr. Nash exclaimed, Your spotted mutt tried to bite my leg! (when Ernie arrived at the apartment.)

6. The Gleasons like many other families in East Orange, New Jersey were hospitable to strangers.

7. The splitting of atomic nuclei (fission) is used to generate electricity (in nuclear power plants.)

8. George Herman Babe Ruth hit 714 "home runs" during his baseball career.

9. The price of gasoline in certain "African" countries can be $0.50 per liter $1.89 per gallon more than the price of gasoline in the United States.

10. Gena and I enjoyed the documentary film on Canadian railroads Gordan Lightfoot's music was very appropriate that aired—on Channel 18—last week.

11. Omar did not say that "the plane would be on time."

12. (Glancing at the newsstand), her eyes focused on the headline, Many Still Missing after Bridge Collapses.

13. People can learn everything about me through my songs, if they know where to look, Bob Dylan stated (in a 1990 interview).

14. Research grants from the "American Cancer Society" have led to (significant) progress in understanding and treating cancer.

15. With the assistance of the mayor to whom the staff of Channel 21 had written for permission television cameras were allowed at the ceremony.

▶ **Subtest 5** **Insert all necessary punctuation marks. Underline words or phrases that should be in italics.**

1. In order to prevent canine distemper from infecting lions which are a big tourist attraction in Tanzanias Serengeti National Park the Veterinary Investigation Centre is planning to vaccinate some thirty thousand domestic dogs living near the park.

2. During a long and productive life of ninety three years Linus C Pauling Ph.D. worked to advance the human condition two Nobel Prizes are a testimony to Dr Paulings tireless efforts to improve human life.

3. One of two US presidents born in Vermont Chester A Arthur is the other Calvin Coolidge assumed the presidency after Warren G Hardings death in 1923.

4. Referring to the effect of acid rain on forest songbirds in the Netherlands ecologist Japp Graveland stated Right now the number of young per pair is half what it is in a normal forest.

5. Peter Jenkinss book A Walk Across America first appeared in the April 1977 issue of National Geographic magazine as an article titled A Walk Across America.

6. Sir Isaac Newtons discoveries from his investigations with gravity and motion were published in the book Philosophae Naturalis Principia Mathematica in 1687.

7. The 1992 93 Dallas Cowboys made the franchises thirty third season a memorable one by winning Super Bowl XXVII.

8. The school day for Carr Middle School begins precisely at 810 AM

9. The manufacturing plant near Loiss home estimated financial losses totaling ten thousand dollars resulting from the four hour power outage.

10. Two films made from John Steinbecks novels The Grapes of Wrath starring Henry Fonda and East of Eden starring James Dean greatly boosted Mr Fondas and Mr Deans acting careers.

Unit 13 Test: Vocabulary and Spelling

• •

▶ **Subtest 1** Underline the word in parentheses that correctly defines the italicized word. Determine its meaning from the context of the sentence.

1. The old stage lighting was so inadequate that the audience could see only a few *nebulous* outlines of the scenery. (vague, crooked)

2. Sonia, feeling extremely disappointed, had a *doleful* expression on her face when the coach told her she had not made the tennis team. (cheerful, sorrowful)

3. Pablo's excuse is hardly *plausible;* could his gerbil really have eaten his assignment? (dangerous, believable)

4. Because of the *halcyon* skies we decided to head for the beach. (threatening, peaceful)

5. Blooming crocuses are a *harbinger* of spring. (sign, study)

6. Wearing fur coats is *anathema* to animal-rights activists. (something detested, something analyzed)

7. Irene's speech was so long and *discursive* I couldn't understand what her point was. (concise, rambling)

8. Because the concert began late, police had to quiet the *raucous* crowd. (rowdy, pleasant)

9. Ajay was in a *quandary* when by mistake he invited two girls to a movie on the same Friday night. (predicament, building)

10. A wonderful *limpid* stream runs through my grandparents' farmland. (polluted, clear)

▶ **Subtest 2** Underline the correct meaning for the italicized root, prefix, or suffix in each pair of words. In the blank write *r* for root, *p* for prefix, or *s* for suffix.

_____ 1. *bio*logy, *bio*graphy (book, life)

_____ 2. *intra*mural, *intra*galactic (within, outside)

_____ 3. meaning*less,* effort*less* (inclined to, without)

_____ 4. *com*municate, *com*bination (away from, together)

_____ 5. *lev*er, *lev*itate (tool, raise)

_____ 6. occup*ant,* particip*ant* (person who, process of)

_____ 7. minusc*ule,* molec*ule* (unseen, little)

_____ **8.** *de*duction, *de*throne (from, around)

_____ **9.** in*doc*trinate, *doc*umentary (lead, teach)

_____ **10.** *ir*rational, *ir*relevant (before, not)

▶ **Subtest 3** Underline the word that is spelled correctly.

1. believe, beleive

2. nieghbor, neighbor

3. acheive, achieve

4. precede, presede

5. friend, freind

6. succede, succeed

7. defanition, definition

8. excede, exceed

9. combination, combunation

10. discipline, discapline

11. lampost, lamppost

12. courageous, couragous

▶ **Subtest 4** Spell each word as indicated.

1. thin + -ness _____

2. acquire + -ing _____

3. response + -ible _____

4. believe + -able _____

5. hum + -ed _____

6. practical + -ly _____

7. enforce + -ing _____

8. advertise + -ment _____

9. forget + -ing _____

10. dance + -able _____

▶ **Subtest 5** Write the plural of each word.

1. monkey _____

2. potato _____

3. sky _____

4. couch _____

5. leaf _____

6. sheep _____

7. Williams _____

8. sister-in-law _____

9. vice president _____

10. checkbook _____

Unit 14 Test: Composition

• •

▶ **Subtest 1 Edit the following piece of writing and rewrite it based on your editing marks.**

     Last fall my sister and me seen the Pacific Ocean for the first time either one of us can remember. We'd been invited by our cusins to stay with them in Oregon. My cousins are named Billy, Evelyn, and Dusty. The town they live in is called Florence and the Ocean is really close to the town.

     We woke up at on monday morning. all five of us left the house after breakfast to walk to the beach. There were a few trees, I could hear the Ocean for about 15 minutes before I seen it. Everyone including me walked along the beach in our bare feet. Evelyn spotted tracks in the sand. She also saw the tracks going in the water. Billy suggested the tracks were made by a bear of some kind. Maybe the bear was fishing he told us.

_____

_____

_____

_____

_____

_____

_____

_____

_____

_____

_____

_____

_____

_____

_____

_____

_____

_____

_____

▶ **Subtest 2** **Change each topic sentence to better attract a reader's attention. Be sure to use the correct verb voice and to add supporting detail.**

1. I heard the newborn baby. _____ _____

_____

2. A lot was on their minds. _____

_____

3. The train appeared to be on fire. _____

_____

4. The dogs kept me from entering the house. _____

_____

5. The sun rose at 6:00 A.M. _____

_____

_____

6. Bruce works very hard. _____

_____

_____

7. The rain came quickly last night. _____

_____

_____

8. Arthur's arrival has made the team better. _____

_____

_____

9. They remembered everything for the camping trip except a can opener. _____

_____

_____

_____

10. The church's steeple was visible for miles. _____

_____

_____

_____

▶ **Subtest 3** **Edit the following paragraphs for unity and coherence. Then rewrite the paragraphs based on your changes.**

My good friend, Doug Liddell, received a superior rating on his science fair project. He studied the use of vegetable oils in making fuel for automobiles. I thought he had the best project.

Our school, Schmidt Middle School, held a Science Fair last March. Only three students received a superior rating. Besides my good friend Doug Liddell, Tony Herrera did receive a superior rating for his project. He studied the effect of a magnetic field on how plants will grow.

Connie Robinson received a superior rating too. Her project was about weather balloons. She is in Mrs. Jenning's class like me. Doug took Mr. Middleton's class. Tony has Mrs. Ayala.

_____

_____

_____

_____

_____

_____

_____

_____

_____

_____

_____

_____

_____

_____

_____

_____

_____

_____

_____

_____

_____

_____

_____

_____

▶ **Subtest 4** **Respond to the considerations below and write an opinion letter on the educational value of class field trips.**

Opinion: _____

_____

_____

_____

_____

Audience: _____

_____

_____

_____

Attitude of audience: _____

_____

_____

_____

_____

What audience needs to know: _____

_____

_____

_____

_____

Supporting evidence: _____

_____

_____

_____

_____

Answer Key to Testing Program

Unit 1 Test: Parts of Speech

Subtest 1
1. noun
2. adverb
3. interjection
4. preposition
5. verb
6. pronoun
7. conjunction
8. adjective
9. conjunction
10. preposition
11. interjection
12. noun
13. noun
14. pronoun
15. adverb
16. verb
17. adjective
18. pronoun

Subtest 2
Nouns: Alaska, state, United States, population, Alaska, state, 1959, state, years, Alaska, resources, oil, fish, minerals, timber, state, mountains, wilderness
Verbs: is, has, became, produces, is
Adverbs: relatively, majestically

Subtest 3
1. abs.
2. col.
3. con.
4. prop.
5. abs.
6. abs.
7. col.
8. con.

Subtest 4
1. inter.
2. dem.
3. pers.
4. ref.
5. pos.
6. ind.
7. in.
8. rel.

Subtest 5
1. tran.
2. intran.
3. aux.
4. tran.
5. aux.
6. link.
7. intran.
8. link.

Unit 2 Test: Parts of the Sentence

Subtest 1 (subject; predicate)
1. brothers; operate
2. automobile; lost
3. rains; caused
4. Malangeni; advised
5. dogs; are barking
6. Harriet; studied
7. team; defeated
8. Suki; purchases
9. birthday; falls
10. play; contributed

Subtest 2 (last word of complete subject | first word of complete predicate, *indirect object,* **direct object**)
1. patrolman | gave *us* **advice**
2. Vicki | have **friends**
3. Dale | chopped **wood**
4. Martha | showed *Dr. Medlin* **project**
5. Andrew | pedaled **bicycle**
6. spray | covered **truck**
7. Abbey | paddled **canoe**
8. aquarium | provided *us* **hours**
9. mother | share **name**
10. Tonya | bought *Carla* **magazine**
11. parents | will **him**
12. Remo | lifted **stone**
13. call | cancelled **plans**
14. Tina | made *us* **pies**
15. groups | left **Yellowstone**

Subtest 3 (**predicate nominative,** predicate adjective, *object complement*)
1. yellow; white
2. slim
3. **gift**
4. *interesting*
5. green
6. *rough; narrow*
7. *unattractive*
8. **grapefruits; oranges; lemons**
9. unavoidable; unwelcome
10. **accuracy; consistency**
11. *impressive; captivating*
12. funny
13. **star**
14. **chicken**
15. brief

Unit 3 Test: Phrases

Subtest 1 (phrase; word modified)
1. on the television set; dozes
2. with the red cover; one
3. for Susan; easy
4. For years; have wanted/to the Super Bowl game; ticket
5. to the beach; brought
6. for me; Unfortunately
7. to Colorado; trip
8. Before the movie; bought/of popcorn; box
9. on Elm Street; bakery
10. of the Round Table; Knights/for their heroism and chivalry; were known

Subtest 2 (phrase; word modified)
1. Coming home; Scott
2. discriminating; traveler
3. rising from beneath the horizon; sun
4. named Shane; stranger
5. Moving from guest to guest; hostess
6. excited about the spring break trip; Julio
7. running; water
8. burning in the fireplace; wood
9. Knowing the right answer; Keshia
10. Enjoying Tom's company; Joel

Subtest 3
1. Speaking to large audiences
2. reading a good book
3. Waiting in a long line
4. Signing autographs
5. Burning fossil fuels
6. eating beets
7. reading Native American legends
8. returning home
9. Finishing the race
10. Dancing

Subtest 4
1. our new physical education teacher
2. that old man in the blue hat
3. the pedal on the left
4. my favorite movie
5. Ronald Reagan
6. the capital of Iceland
7. the oldest land animal
8. the Celtic language of Scotland
9. the author of the Declaration of Independence
10. an Academy Award winner

Subtest 5 (infinitive; part of speech)
1. to complete; adj.
2. to forget; adv.
3. To finish; n.
4. To remain; n.
5. To avoid; n.
6. to invest; adj.
7. to join; n.
8. to play; n.
9. to fight; n.
10. to remember; adv.

Subtest 6
1. gerund
2. gerund
3. appositive
4. participial
5. gerund
6. appositive

7. appositive
8. participial
9. appositive
10. gerund
11. participial

12. participial
13. appositive
14. participial
15. gerund

Subtest 7

1. infinitive
2. infinitive
3. prepositional
4. infinitive
5. prepositional
6. prepositional
7. prepositional
8. infinitive

9. infinitive
10. prepositional
11. infinitive
12. prepositional
13. prepositional
14. infinitive
15. prepositional

Unit 4 Test: Clauses and Sentence Structure

Subtest 1

1. dec.
2. int.
3. exc.
4. dec.
5. imp.

6. exc.
7. dec.
8. imp.
9. int.
10. dec.

11. imp.
12. int.
13. imp.
14. dec.
15. exc.

Subtest 2 (Answers may vary.)

1. v.
2. subj.
3. main
4. main
5. subj.

6. subj.
7. v.
8. main
9. v.
10. main

11. subj.
12. v.
13. subj.
14. v.
15. v.

Subtest 3

1. are. Most *or* are; most
2. lives,
3. singing. There *or* singing; there
4. powerful,
5. Lithuania. He *or* Lithuania; he
6. pests. Most *or* pests; most
7. weeks. He *or* weeks; he
8. years. Duck *or* years; duck
9. wagon, restaurant. We *or* restaurant; we
10. humorous. Many *or*; humorous; many
11. gymnasium,
12. swimming. She *or* swimming; she
13. unclear, but
14. dependable, and
15. Lafayette. Her *or* Lafayette; her

Unit 5 Test: Diagraming Sentences

Subtest 1

11.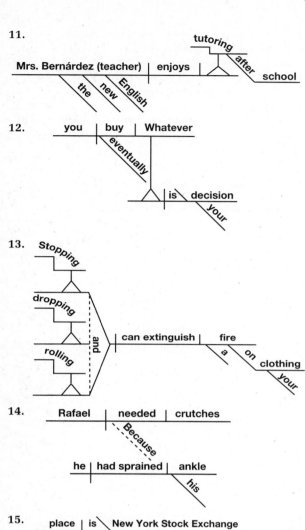

Mrs. Bernárdez (teacher) | enjoys ... tutoring ... after ... school
the / new / English

12. you | buy | Whatever
eventually ... is \ decision ... your

13. Stopping / dropping / rolling ... and ... can extinguish | fire
a ... on ... clothing ... your

14. Rafael | needed | crutches
Because ... he | had sprained | ankle ... his

15.

place | is \ New York Stock Exchange ... the
to \ work ... where
I | would like

16. night | is etched
The ... indelibly ... in ... mind ... my
we | met | that

Unit 6 Test: Verb Tenses and Voice

Subtest 1
1. jumped
2. known
3. flew
4. catch
5. win
6. done
7. wrote
8. go
9. came
10. sung
11. grown
12. lost
13. rung
14. put
15. frozen

Subtest 2
1. past
2. future
3. past perfect
4. present perfect
5. present
6. future perfect
7. past progressive
8. past
9. present progressive
10. present emphatic
11. future perfect
12. future
13. past perfect
14. future progressive
15. past emphatic
16. future
17. past
18. present perfect
19. future progressive
20. past perfect progressive

Subtest 3
1. lost
2. has flown
3. tried
4. surprised
5. tore *or* have torn
6. drunk
7. will defeat
8. given
9. had
10. rung

Subtest 4
1. will make
2. had hoped
3. has given
4. will be freezing
5. will have eaten
6. did like
7. has found
8. are searching
9. drew
10. do like
11. climbed
12. has been appearing

Subtest 5
1. watched, have thrown; threw
2. heard, rushed; C
3. blew, ride; rode
4. put, had set; set
5. will be, will be; C
6. was, fell; had fallen
7. do, had wanted; want
8. receive, had talked; will have talked
9. have learned, plays; C
10. used, learns; had learned *or* learned

Subtest 6
1. cuts; A
2. are making; A
3. have been made; P
4. were knocked; P
5. rode; A
6. will be donated; P
7. imitated; A
8. is being planned; P
9. report; A
10. will store; A

Unit 7 Test: Subject-Verb Agreement

Subtest 1
1. joins
2. stimulate
3. were
4. change
5. were walking
6. snaps
7. burn
8. was
9. has broken
10. appear
11. bring
12. use
13. tastes
14. have encountered
15. sleeps
16. seems
17. was chasing
18. are
19. destroys
20. relieve
21. filibuster
22. scream
23. are
24. has
25. was
26. pick
27. knows
28. kicks
29. have
30. keep

Subtest 2 (verb, subject)
1. is; rain
2. dump; Raccoons
3. was; marathon
4. loves; Peggy
5. are; games
6. is; pastime
7. looms; school
8. is; sun
9. comprises; sport
10. is; constellation
11. is visiting; teacher
12. see; hens
13. sings; Peter Gabriel
14. tower; Great Pyramids
15. was; last
16. was; flight
17. are; termites
18. moseys; sheriff
19. appear; Butterflies
20. Does; president
21. attend; Producers
22. make; All
23. Do; Boris, Igal
24. Does; press
25. believes; school
26. constitutes; branch
27. endangers; minute
28. is; cabin
29. runs; rabbit
30. remain; relatives

Subtest 3

1. is	8. decorate	15. asks
2. make	9. are	16. Do
3. have	10. produces	17. float
4. roars	11. are	18. are
5. beats	12. crosses	19. ripen
6. balance	13. perform	20. shouts
7. contribute	14. understands	

Unit 8 Test: Using Pronouns Correctly

Subtest 1

1. their	6. me	11. whom
2. I	7. her	12. them
3. my	8. we	13. I
4. who	9. him	14. them
5. whom	10. Who	15. who

Subtest 2 (pronoun, antecedent)

1. his or her; everyone
2. her; Yvonne
3. their; cast
4. their; students
5. their; Many
6. he; Louis
7. they; Glenn, Lisa
8. he or she; No one
9. they; relatives
10. our; we

Subtest 3

1. pos.	4. pos.	7. pos.	10. pos.
2. nom.	5. nom.	8. obj.	
3. obj.	6. nom.	9. pos.	

Subtest 4 (Answers may vary.)

1. Omar's family likes to visit exotic locations because those places are exciting.
2. This dictionary says that *fax* comes from *facsimile.*
3. Some people claim that lightning never strikes the same place twice.
4. In 1946 ENIAC, the first all-purpose, all-electronic, digital computer, was activated.

Unit 9 Test: Using Modifiers Correctly

Subtest 1

1. more unhappy	5. well	9. less
2. better	6. prettiest	10. calmer
3. worse	7. quickest	
4. faster	8. well	

Subtest 2

1. farthest	5. icier	9. worse
2. rougher	6. scariest	10. slower
3. more easily	7. smaller	
4. best	8. most successful	

Subtest 3 (Answers may vary.)

1. From our visiting cousins we learned about Grandma Jenny's escape.
2. Mr. Kim taught his son, when he was six years old, to ride a bicycle.
3. The audience listened attentively to the chorus singing enthusiastically.
4. Shami plays on only the varsity volleyball team.
5. With great reluctance I accepted the gift.
6. A huge whale in the ocean caught the eye of the jogger.
7. Kasem bought only one audiocassette because he hadn't saved enough money for two.

8. Beth rode on the bus to her part-time job.
9. The couch collapsed from the weight of the family watching television.
10. Balancing on a high curb, we were able to photograph the politician.

Subtest 4

1. most nicest	3. more warmer	5. a muffin
2. C	4. Tanya	

Subtest 5 (double negative, correction)

1. don't have no; don't have any, have no
2. don't need no; don't need any, need no
3. didn't tell nobody; didn't tell anybody, told nobody
4. hasn't built no; hasn't built any, has built no
5. wasn't getting nowhere; wasn't getting anywhere, was getting nowhere

Unit 10 Test: Usage

Subtest 1

1. emigrated	8. affect	15. into
2. teach	9. set	16. between
3. except	10. leave	17. lend
4. said	11. hung	18. preceded
5. These kinds	12. besides	19. May
6. well	13. than	20. lose
7. number	14. lie	

Subtest 2

1. respectfully	14. a lot	
2. that	15. C	
3. as	16. rise	
4. C	17. C	
5. from	18. C	
6. have	19. a while	
7. C	20. fewer	
8. C	21. can hardly	
9. an	22. all right	
10. that	23. C	
11. passed	24. had	
12. C	25. as fast as	
13. Because		

Unit 11 Test: Capitalization

Subtest 1 (words to be capped; *words to be lowercased*)

1. **Mount, River**
2. **July, Lindale, Texas,** *oak, runway*
3. *biology,* **French**
4. **Uncle, Middle School, St., Elementary School**
5. **Judge**
6. **Shakespearean,** *motion pictures*
7. *videotape,* **Scotland**
8. *baseball,* **Coach, League**
9. **Boys' Club, Medical Center**
10. *nursing, high school*
11. *pokeweed, poke salad*
12. **R., Basketball Hall, Fame,** *player, coach*
13. **Somalis,** *a,* **Ocean**
14. **Swiss,** *bacteria, carbon*
15. *north,* **Arctic Circle**
16. *rhinos,* **Zimbabwe, Wildlife Center, Texas**
17. **Shasta,** *northern, eighteenth century*
18. *spacecraft, lightning,* **Jupiter's**

19. *port,* **Sea**
20. **Light, Antarctica**
21. **During, April,** *sandhill cranes,* **River, Nebraska**
22. **World War, S., S.S., Cold War**
23. **The, Manual, Style, University, Press**
24. **Conference,** *universities,* **South**
25. **German, Department, Agriculture, Friday**
26. **Milky Way**
27. **Memorial Day, Labor Day**
28. **Nile River, Toyota Land Rover**
29. **Canon, Nikon, Christmas**
30. **Corporation,** *automobiles,* **Tennessee**
31. **Spanish,** *afternoon*
32. **From, America, President, Vice President**
33. **For, Yankees,** *major league,* **The, World Series**
34. **Bulls,** *retirement,* **team**
35. **European,** *tourist attractions*

Unit 12 Test: Punctuation, Abbreviations, and Numbers

Subtest 1

1. .
2. ?
3. !
4. ?
5. .
6. !
7. ?
8. .
9. !
10. .

Subtest 2

1. following:
2. exhausted;
3. construction;
4. 1974 to 1977:
5. 8:8–12; 31:31–34
6. 12:10
7. games;
8. Botswana;
9. flowers:
10. librarian; florist;

Subtest 3

1. Wilbur was both determined and committed to becoming a veterinarian.
2. The next goal for the golf team is to perform well in the district competition, and a good performance at the district level will give the team an opportunity to win a state championship.
3. Ignoring Roscoe's outburst, Jeannie reported her solution to the algebra exercise.
4. The Witwatersrand complex, a mineral deposit containing gold, lies beneath the Transvaal and the Orange Free State in the Republic of South Africa, making South Africa the world's largest producer of gold.
5. The community was sufficiently large to include a recreation center, three swimming pools, and three urban parks.
6. Much of eastern Brazil is covered by dense, lush tropical rain forest.
7. The Red Sea, unlike the Mediterranean Sea, touches both Egypt and the Sudan.
8. Josephine's mother, Rachel, after she learned of Josephine's scholarship, was ecstatic.
9. On September 11, 1983, Dr. Avery Miles, D.V.M., addressed a group of horse trainers gathered at the River Inn at 3850 East Montague Avenue.
10. Before entering the city limits of Nashville, Tennessee, Regina looked at her watch.
11. Never neglect to finish a project, Sherman.
12. Abe sold everything that he owned, counted his profit, and departed for Tallahassee, Florida.
13. Harold, can you remember an enjoyable educational program on television last week?
14. The choir, if it is to be ready for the performance next weekend, must add an extra practice Wednesday night.
15. All of the staff, with the exception of Dr. Gloria Knight, Ph.D., discussed the matter on Tuesday, May 7.

Subtest 4 (Answers may vary somewhat.)

1. Born in 1942 in Liverpool—a British port and center of international commerce—Paul McCartney was the son of a cotton trader and a midwife.
2. The World Cup match between Brazil and Canada begins at precisely 3:00 P.M. Pacific Standard Time (6:00 P.M. Eastern Standard Time).
3. Miguel's poems about birds (the one about geese is wonderful) were written last year.
4. Due to the success of the UCLA basketball team, Coach John R. Wooden became known as the "Wizard of Westwood."
5. Mr. Nash exclaimed, "Your spotted mutt tried to bite my leg!" when Ernie arrived at the apartment.
6. The Gleasons—like many other families in East Orange, New Jersey—were hospitable to strangers.
7. The splitting of atomic nuclei (fission) is used to generate electricity in nuclear power plants.
8. George Herman "Babe" Ruth hit 714 home runs during his baseball career.
9. The price of gasoline in certain African countries can be $.50 per liter ($1.89 per gallon) more than the price of gasoline in the United States.
10. Gena and I enjoyed the documentary film on Canadian railroads (Gordan Lightfoot's music was very appropriate) that aired on Channel 18 last week.
11. Omar did not say that the plane would be on time.
12. Glancing at the newsstand, her eyes focused on the headline, "Many Still Missing After Bridge Collapses."
13. "People can learn everything about me through my songs, if they know where to look," Bob Dylan stated in a 1990 interview.
14. Research grants from the American Cancer Society have led to significant progress in understanding and treating cancer.
15. With the assistance of the mayor—to whom the staff of Channel 21 had written for permission—television cameras were allowed at the ceremony.

Subtest 5 (Answers may vary somewhat.)

1. In order to prevent canine distemper from infecting lions—which are a big tourist attraction in Tanzania's Serengeti National Park—the Veterinary Investigation Centre is planning to vaccinate some thirty thousand domestic dogs living near the park.
2. During a long and productive life of ninety-three years, Linus C. Pauling, Ph.D., worked to advance the human condition; two Nobel Prizes are a testimony to Dr. Pauling's tireless efforts to improve human life.

3. One of two U.S. presidents born in Vermont—Chester A. Arthur is the other—Calvin Coolidge assumed the presidency after Warren G. Harding's death in 1923.
4. Referring to the effect of acid rain on forest songbirds in the Netherlands, ecologist Japp Graveland stated, "Right now the number of young per pair is half what it is in a normal forest."
5. Peter Jenkins's book *A Walk Across America* first appeared in the April 1977 issue of *National Geographic* magazine as an article titled "A Walk Across America."
6. Sir Isaac Newton's discoveries from his investigations with gravity and motion were published in the book *Philosophae Naturalis Principia Mathematica* in 1687.
7. The 1992–93 Dallas Cowboys made the franchise's thirty-third season a memorable one by winning Super Bowl XXVII.
8. The school day for Carr Middle School begins precisely at 8:10 A.M.
9. The manufacturing plant near Lois's home estimated financial losses totaling ten thousand dollars resulting from the four-hour power outage.
10. Two films made from John Steinbeck's novels, *The Grapes of Wrath* starring Henry Fonda and *East of Eden* starring James Dean, greatly boosted Mr. Fonda's and Mr. Dean's acting careers.

Unit 13 Test: Vocabulary and Spelling

Subtest 1
1. vague
2. sorrowful
3. believable
4. peaceful
5. sign
6. something detested
7. rambling
8. rowdy
9. predicament
10. clear

Subtest 2
1. life, r
2. within, p
3. without, s
4. together, p
5. raise, r
6. person who, s
7. little, s
8. from, p
9. teach, r
10. not, p

Subtest 3
1. believe
2. neighbor
3. achieve
4. precede
5. friend
6. succeed
7. definition
8. exceed
9. combination
10. discipline
11. lamppost
12. courageous

Subtest 4
1. thinness
2. acquiring
3. responsible
4. believable
5. hummed
6. practically
7. enforcing
8. advertisement
9. forgetting
10. danceable

Subtest 5
1. monkeys
2. potatoes
3. skies
4. couches
5. leaves
6. sheep
7. Williamses
8. sisters-in-law
9. vice presidents
10. checkbooks

Unit 14 Test: Composition

Subtest 1 (Answers will vary.)
Last fall my sister and I saw the Pacific Ocean for the first time. Our cousins Billy, Evelyn, and Dusty had invited us to stay with them in Florence, Oregon, near the ocean.

Early on a Monday morning we all left the house after breakfast for a walk to the beach. With my view obstructed by a few trees, I could hear the ocean for nearly fifteen minutes before I could see it. As everyone walked barefoot along the beach, Evelyn spotted tracks in the sand leading into the water. Billy suggested that the tracks were made by a bear attempting to catch fish.

Subtest 2 (Answers will vary.)
1. The wailings of the newborn baby sounded like the cries of a little goat.
2. Their minds were filled with memories and images of the past.
3. Smoke billowed from the boxcar closest to the locomotive.
4. The snarling huskies formed a line between me and the front door.
5. A narrow beam of light from the rising sun bypassed the window blind at 6:00 A.M.
6. Just watching Bruce empty the packages from the truck could make me feel tired.
7. Within twenty minutes Carolyn's backyard was transformed into a lake by the deluge.
8. Having Arthur in the lineup this year has made the Cats practically unbeatable.
9. With the tent anchored and the hickory logs blazing, Mom realized that everyone had neglected to bring a can opener.
10. When Mary Lou finally arrived in Brugge, she discovered that the steeple, which had served as her lighthouse, belonged to the Notre Dame Cathedral.

Subtest 3 (Answers will vary.)
At the science fair held at Schmidt Middle School last March, only three participants received a rating of superior. One superior rating went to Connie Robinson from Mrs. Jenning's class. Connie's project studied weather balloons. Another superior rating was awarded to Tony Herrera from Mrs. Ayala's class for his project on the effects of a magnetic field on plant growth. My good friend, Doug Liddell, from Mr. Middleton's class received the third superior rating. Doug's project on the use of vegetable oils in fuels for automobiles was my favorite.

Subtest 4 (Answers will vary.)
Opinion: 1. Class field trips have educational value that other exercises or activities cannot supply.
2. Class field trips have little value.
Audience: Either the faculty and administration of the school or the readers of the school newspaper
Attitude of audience: The administration may view class field trips as too expensive and disruptive; the students may view them as an enjoyable change from the routine of the classroom.
What audience needs to know: Audience members may not know how individual students have benefited from past field trips.
Supporting evidence: Any information relating a class field trip to an improvement in a student's attitude and performance could be persuasive.